The Yellow Dwarf

Max

THE YELLOW BOOK

a selection

The Yellow Book

a selection

Compiled by Norman Denny

SPRING BOOKS • LONDON

Published by
SPRING BOOKS
SPRING HOUSE • SPRING PLACE • LONDON NW5
Printed in Czechoslovakia

Contents

Literature

Literature

Art

"The Yellow Dwarf." *Max Beerbohm.* (*Frontispiece.*)

(*At end of book*)

Art

19. Mr. John Davidson. *Will Rothenstein.*

20. The Mysterious Rose Garden. *Aubrey Beardsley.*

21. Study of Durham. *F. G. Cotman.*

22. The Mirror. *P. Wilson Steer.*

23. Portrait of a Girl. *Robert Halls.*

24. A Sketch. *Constantin Guys.*

25. The Yellow Book. *Gertrude D. Hammond.*

26. Souvenir de Paris. *Charles Conder.*

27. Portrait of Kenneth Grahame. *E. A. Walton*

28. A Barb. *John Lavery.*

29. " Come unto these Yellow Sands." *H. Isabel Adams.*

30. The Dew. *J. Herbert McNair.*

31. The Butterflies. *D. Y. Cameron.*

32. " So the wind drove us on to the cavern of gloom,
Where we fell in the toils of the foul sea-snake;
Their scaly folds drew us on to our doom,
Pray for us, stranger, for Christ's sweet sake."
Patten Wilson.

33. Portrait of Miss Evelyn Sharp. *E. A. Walton.*

34. Grief. *A. Szold.*

35. Old Houses off the Dry Gate, Glasgow. *Muirhead Bone.*

36. A Shepherd Boy. *E. Philip Pimlott.*

Selector's Note

THE dust died down long ago. Only the longest memories among those to whom the *Yellow Book* is something more than a name are likely to recall the fury aroused by the first volume, which moved a young gentleman at Oxford, a Mr. Beerbohm, to record with evident satisfaction: " . . . so far as anyone in literature can be lynched, I was." *

The crisis a year later, as a result of which Aubrey Beardsley ceased to be Art Editor, was a tragic misfortune arising out of quite other matters. The *Yellow Book* stirred up its own commotion, whose violence is hard to believe in as in these days one looks through the pages. What is scarcely less astonishing is that the name should have become so largely associated with the terms " decadence " and " fin de siècle ". In fact, it was neither decadent nor the end of anything. It was a youthful and vigorous attempt to make a beginning, to break new ground, to clear the air—and, of course, (in the phrase its editor would have preferred), to *épater le bourgeois*. The very colour chosen was that of the notoriously immoral French novel. But this attitudinising could only have produced such spectacular results in the climate of that particular time. The solemn century was outraged at being treated as though it were already over. The *Yellow Book* could

* The attack on him was provoked by "A Defence of Cosmetics ", included in this volume. The *Westminster Gazette*, referring also to Beardsley's drawings, talked about " an Act of Parliament to make this kind of thing illegal ".

Selector's Note

not be forgiven for daring to be Edwardian with Victoria still on the throne.

To make some kind of a *Yellow Book* anthology by simply picking out the plums—the Jameses, Beerbohms, Kenneth Grahames, le Galliennes and so on—would have been a simple but dull task. We have tried to do better. Following precisely the original format, we have tried to make a representative *Yellow Book*, a single volume which may be considered a fair summary of all its thirteen volumes, showing what it was really like and what it was about. Although something has been included of nearly all the contributors whose names are still remembered, the more or less forgotten figure equally largely. Pieces have as a rule been selected both for their intrinsic merits and for what may be called their *Yellow Book* virtues. Only in one or two cases (for example, that of the last item) have other considerations, perhaps " period interest ", been allowed to prevail.

Undoubtedly injustice has been done. Not every contributor has been given his fair share of space, and on the score of length some of the best has been left out. But if, for example, " The Happy Hypocrite " is missing, it can fairly be claimed that this is so well-known and easy of access that there was no need to reprint it here. Another omission is H. G. Wells' " A Slip Under the Microscope ". But it was his only contribution: he was not really a *Yellow Book* man: and with all respect we have ruled that it does not quite fit. The unremembered have been worse treated. There were many more who deserved a place, and some of those who have been included—Ella D'Arcy, Harland's assistant-editor, for one—have had less than their due. And there were contributions which now appear so funnily bad that it was hard to keep them out. Yet it would have been unjust to do otherwise. If so much of the best had to be discarded, in order to get a cross-section, it was only fair to overlook the worst.

Selector's Note

The remarkable thing about the *Yellow Book* is not that it had its lapses, but that the general standard, of the prose at least, was so high.

The same general principles have governed the selection of the drawings: but here we have tended to prefer the better to the worse, not only because so much of the latter was simply dull, but because much was badly and unworthily reproduced. No attempt could be made to arrange the contents in chronological order, although this might have afforded the reader some indication of the change in tone—a decided lessening of exuberance—which followed the crisis and the departure of Beardsley. Everything has been shuffled together on the original plan of interspersing prose and verse, fiction and *belles lettres*. Certain precedents have, however, been followed. "The Death of the Lion", for example, goes to the head of the list because that is the place it occupied in the first volume ; and Henry Harland has been placed high up because that is where he generally put himself.

A word must be said about Henry Harland, the editor. He figures in each of the thirteen volumes, and is the only one of his contributors to do so. Indeed, he sometimes appears twice, since he wrote several open letters, criticising the contents of the *Yellow Book* and discoursing upon literature at large, under the pseudonym of "The Yellow Dwarf" : a secret that seems to have been remarkably well kept. His exotic appearance—dark moustache, long hair and little wisp of beard—lent substance to the rumours, which he fostered, of a mysterious and romantic Russian origin: although the fact is that he was born in America, of English descent. It was undoubtedly he who brought to the *Yellow Book* that especial nostalgia which constantly pervaded it, and which he himself might have termed *la nostalgie du Boul' Miche*—a fervour as consuming as that which a later generation of writers, mostly American, came to feel for Montparnasse. But whatever one may make of all this, it is on record that he was the most charming

Selector's Note

of companions, and he was certainly a good and courageous editor.

It is pleasant to think of him as with Beardsley and John Lane he nursed their project through those first months of 1894. Beardsley, the chief instigator of its naughtiness, then only twenty-two and a good deal of an urchin as well as a genius, may have been of sterner stuff: but one can imagine those other two in a mounting fever of trepidation as the day drew near for their bombshell to be released. They were going to war, when all is said; they were planning an assault on a citadel that was still formidable. Henry Vizetelly died in that same year, largely of the persecution to which he was subjected for the offence of having published translations of Zola. If there were high spirits at the office in Vigo Street, there must have been heart-searchings as well, misgivings, apprehensions—perhaps even moments of wishing they had never started it. And they can never have thought how lucky they were to be living in a world in which such explosions could be heard.

NORMAN DENNY.

Bibliographic Note

THE first quarterly volume of *The Yellow Book*, priced five shillings, appeared in April, 1894, under the joint imprint of Elkin Mathews and John Lane; but from the third volume onwards it was published by John Lane alone. The editor throughout was Henry Harland. Aubrey Beardsley was art editor of the first four volumes, being succeeded by John Lane. The thirteenth and last volume appeared in April, 1897.

All the volumes were reprinted. They were, however, not sold to the trade in the ordinary way, but were circulated by what can only be described as irregular methods and passed off as first editions. A later generation at the Bodley Head makes this painful avowal in the interests of truth.

THE YELLOW BOOK
a selection

The Death of the Lion

By Henry James

I

I HAD simply, I suppose, a change of heart, and it must have
begun when I received my manuscript back from Mr. Pinhorn.
Mr. Pinhorn was my " chief," as he was called in the office : he
had accepted the high mission of bringing the paper up. This
was a weekly periodical, and had been supposed to be almost past
redemption when he took hold of it. It was Mr. Deedy who had
let it down so dreadfully—he was never mentioned in the office
now save in connection with that misdemeanour. Young as I
was I had been in a manner taken over from Mr. Deedy, who
had been owner as well as editor ; forming part of a promiscuous
lot, mainly plant and office-furniture, which poor Mrs. Deedy, in
her bereavement and depression, parted with at a rough valuation.
I could account for my continuity only on the supposition that
I had been cheap. I rather resented the practice of fathering
all flatness on my late protector, who was in his unhonoured
grave ; but as I had my way to make I found matter enough for
complacency in being on a " staff." At the same time I was
aware that I was exposed to suspicion as a product of the old
lowering system. This made me feel that I was doubly bound to
have

17

have ideas, and had doubtless been at the bottom of my proposing
to Mr. Pinhorn that I should lay my lean hands on Neil Paraday.
I remember that he looked at me first as if he had never heard of
this celebrity, who indeed at that moment was by no means in the
middle of the heavens; and even when I had knowingly explained
he expressed but little confidence in the demand for any such
matter. When I had reminded him that the great principle on
which we were supposed to work was just to create the demand
we required, he considered a moment and then rejoined: "I see;
you want to write him up."

" Call it that if you like."

" And what's your inducement ? "

" Bless my soul—my admiration ! "

Mr. Pinhorn pursed up his mouth.   " Is there much to be done
with him ? "

" Whatever there is, we should have it all to ourselves, for he
hasn't been touched."

This argument was effective, and Mr. Pinhorn responded:
" Very well, touch him."   Then he added : " But where can you
do it ? "

" Under the fifth rib ! " I laughed.

Mr. Pinhorn stared.   " Where's that ? "

" You want me to go down and see him ? " I inquired, when I
had enjoyed his visible search for this obscure suburb.

"I don't ' want ' anything—the proposal's your own.   But you
must remember that that's the way we do things *now*," said Mr.
Pinhorn, with another dig at Mr. Deedy.

Unregenerate as I was, I could read the queer implications of
this speech.   The present owner's superior virtue as well as his
deeper craft spoke in his reference to the late editor as one of
that baser sort who deal in false representations.   Mr. Deedy
would

would as soon have sent me to call on Neil Paraday as he would
have published a " holiday-number; " but such scruples presented
themselves as mere ignoble thrift to his successor, whose own
sincerity took the form of ringing door-bells and whose definition
of genius was the art of finding people at home.   It was as if Mr.
Deedy had published reports without his young men's having, as
Mr. Pinhorn would have said, really been there.   I was unregenerate, as I have hinted, and I was not concerned to straighten
out the journalistic morals of my chief, feeling them indeed to be
an abyss over the edge of which it was better not to peer.   Really
to be there this time moreover was a vision that made the idea of
writing something subtle about Neil Paraday only the more
inspiring.   I would be as considerate as even Mr. Deedy could
have wished, and yet I should be as present as only Mr. Pinhorn
could conceive.   My allusion to the sequestered manner in which
Mr. Paraday lived (which had formed part of my explanation,
though I knew of it only by hearsay) was, I could divine, very
much what had made Mr. Pinhorn bite.   It struck him as in-
consistent with the success of his paper that any one should be so
sequestered as that.   Moreover, was not an immediate exposure of
everything just what the public wanted ?   Mr. Pinhorn effectually
called me to order by reminding me of the promptness with which
I had met Miss Braby at Liverpool, on her return from her fiasco in
the States.   Hadn't we published, while its freshness and flavour
were unimpaired, Miss Braby's own version of that great inter-
national episode ?   I felt somewhat uneasy at this coupling of the
actress and the author, and I confess that after having enlisted Mr.
Pinhorn's sympathies I procrastinated a little.   I had succeeded
better than I wished, and I had, as it happened, work nearer at
hand.   A few days later I called on Lord Crouchley and carried
off in triumph the most unintelligible statement that had yet
                                                    appeared

appeared of his lordship's reasons for his change of front. I thus
set in motion in the daily papers columns of virtuous verbiage.
The following week I ran down to Brighton for a chat, as Mr.
Pinhorn called it, with Mrs. Bounder, who gave me, on the
subject of her divorce, many curious particulars that had not been
articulated in court. If ever an article flowed from the primal
fount it was that article on Mrs. Bounder. By this time, however,
I became aware that Neil Paraday's new book was on the point of
appearing, and that its approach had been the ground of my
original appeal to Mr. Pinhorn, who was now annoyed with me
for having lost so many days. He bundled me off—we would at
least not lose another. I have always thought his sudden alertness a
remarkable example of the journalistic instinct. Nothing had
occurred, since I first spoke to him, to create a visible urgency,
and no enlightenment could possibly have reached him. It was a
pure case of professional *flair*—he had smelt the coming glory as
an animal smells its distant prey.

II

I may as well say at once that this little record pretends in no
degree to be a picture either of my introduction to Mr. Paraday
or of certain proximate steps and stages. The scheme of my
narrative allows no space for these things and in any case a pro-
hibitory sentiment would be attached to my recollection of so rare
an hour. These meagre notes are essentially private, and if they
see the light the insidious forces that, as my story itself shows,
make at present for publicity will simply have overmastered my
precautions. The curtain fell lately enough on the lamentable
drama.

drama. My memory of the day I alighted at Mr. Paraday's door is a fresh memory of kindness, hospitality, compassion, and of the wonderful illuminating talk in which the welcome was conveyed. Some voice of the air had taught me the right moment, the moment of his life at which an act of unexpected young allegiance might most come home. He had recently recovered from a long, grave illness. I had gone to the neighbouring inn for the night, but I spent the evening in his company, and he insisted the next day on my sleeping under his roof. I had not an indefinite leave: Mr. Pinhorn supposed us to put our victims through on the gallop. It was later, in the office, that the step was elaborated and regulated. I fortified myself however, as my training had taught me to do, by the conviction that nothing could be more advantageous for my article than to be written in the very atmosphere. I said nothing to Mr. Paraday about it, but in the morning, after my removal from the inn, while he was occupied in his study, as he had notified me that he should need to be, I committed to paper the quintessence of my impressions. Then thinking to commend myself to Mr. Pinhorn by my celerity, I walked out and posted my little packet before luncheon. Once my paper was written I was free to stay on, and if it was designed to divert attention from my frivolity in so doing I could reflect with satisfaction that I had never been so clever. I don't mean to deny of course that I was aware it was much too good for Mr. Pinhorn; but I was equally conscious that Mr. Pinhorn had the supreme shrewdness of recognising from time to time the cases in which an article was not too bad only because it was too good. There was nothing he loved so much as to print on the right occasion a thing he hated. I had begun my visit to Mr. Paraday on a Monday, and on the Wednesday his book came out. A copy of it arrived by the first post, and he let me go out into the garden
with

with it immediately after breakfast.   I read it from beginning to end that day, and in the evening he asked me to remain with him the rest of the week and over the Sunday.

That night my manuscript came back from Mr. Pinhorn, accompanied with a letter, of which the gist was the desire to know what I meant by sending him such stuff.   That was the meaning of the question, if not exactly its form, and it made my mistake immense to me.   Such as this mistake was I could now only look it in the face and accept it.   I knew where I had failed, but it was exactly where I couldn't have succeeded.   I had been sent down there to be personal, and in point of fact I hadn't been personal at all; what I had sent up to London was merely a little finicking, feverish study of my author's talent.   Anything less relevant to Mr. Pinhorn's purpose couldn't well be imagined, and he was visibly angry at my having (at his expense, with a second-class ticket) approached the object of our arrangement only to be so deucedly distant.   For myself, I knew but too well what had happened, and how a miracle—as pretty as some old miracle of legend—had been wrought on the spot to save me.   There had been a big brush of wings, the flash of an opaline robe, and then, with a great cool stir of the air, the sense of an angel's having swooped down and caught me to his bosom.   He held me only till the danger was over, and it all took place in a minute.   With my manuscript back on my hands I understood the phenomenon better, and the reflections I made on it are what I meant, at the beginning of this anecdote, by my change of heart.   Mr. Pinhorn's note was not only a rebuke decidedly stern, but an invitation immediately to send him (it was the case to say so) the genuine article, the revealing and reverberating sketch to the promise of which—and of which alone—I owed my squandered privilege.   A week or two later I recast my peccant paper, and giving it a
particular

particular application to Mr. Paraday's new book, obtained for it the hospitality of another journal, where, I must admit, Mr. Pinhorn was so far justified that it attracted not the least attention.

III

I was frankly, at the end of three days, a very prejudiced critic, so that one morning when, in the garden, Neil Paraday had offered to read me something I quite held my breath as I listened. It was the written scheme of another book—something he had put aside long ago, before his illness, and lately taken out again to reconsider. He had been turning it round when I came down upon him, and it had grown magnificently under this second hand. Loose, liberal, confident, it might have passed for a great gossiping eloquent letter—the overflow into talk of an artist's amorous plan. The subject I thought singularly rich, quite the strongest he had yet treated; and this familiar statement of it, full too of fine maturities, was really, in summarised splendour, a mine of gold, a precious, independent work. I remember rather profanely wondering whether the ultimate production could possibly be so happy. His reading of the epistle, at any rate, made me feel as if I were, for the advantage of posterity, in close correspondence with him—were the distinguished person to whom it had been affectionately addressed. It was high distinction simply to be told such things. The idea he now communicated had all the freshness, the flushed fairness of the conception untouched and untried: it was Venus rising from the sea, before the airs had blown upon her. I had never been so throbbingly present at such an unveiling. But when he had tossed the last bright word after

the

the others, as I had seen cashiers in banks, weighing mounds of coin, drop a final sovereign into the tray, I became conscious of a sudden prudent alarm.

" My dear master, how, after all, are you going to do it ? " I asked. " It's infinitely noble, but what time it will take, what patience and independence, what assured, what perfect conditions it will demand! Oh for a lone isle in a tepid sea ! "

" Isn't this practically a lone isle, and aren't you, as an encircling medium, tepid enough ? " he replied; alluding with a laugh to the wonder of my young admiration and the narrow limits of his little provincial home. " Time isn't what I've lacked hitherto: the question hasn't been to find it, but to use it. Of course my illness made a great hole, but I daresay there would have been a hole at any rate. The earth we tread has more pockets than a billiard-table. The great thing is now to keep on my feet."

"That's exactly what I mean."

Neil Paraday looked at me with eyes—such pleasant eyes as he had—in which, as I now recall their expression, I seem to have seen a dim imagination of his fate. He was fifty years old, and his illness had been cruel, his convalescence slow. "It isn't as if I weren't all right."

" Oh, if you weren't all right I wouldn't look at you ! " I tenderly said.

We had both got up, quickened by the full sound of it all, and he had lighted a cigarette. I had taken a fresh one, and, with an intenser smile, by way of answer to my exclamation, he touched it with the flame of his match. " If I weren't better I shouldn't have thought of *that* ! " He flourished his epistle in his hand.

" I don't want to be discouraging, but that's not true," I returned. " I'm sure that during the months you lay here in pain you had visitations sublime. You thought of a thousand things.
You

You think of more and more all the while. That's what makes you, if you will pardon my familiarity, so respectable. At a time when so many people are spent you come into your second wind. But, thank God, all the same, you're better! Thank God, too, you're not, as you were telling me yesterday, 'successful.' If *you* weren't a failure, what would be the use of trying? That's my one reserve on the subject of your recovery—that it makes you 'score,' as the newspapers say. It looks well in the newspapers, and almost anything that does that is horrible. 'We are happy to announce that Mr. Paraday, the celebrated author, is again in the enjoyment of excellent health.' Somehow I shouldn't like to see it."

"You won't see it; I'm not in the least celebrated—my obscurity protects me. But couldn't you bear even to see I was dying or dead?" my companion asked.

"Dead—*passe encore*; there's nothing so safe. One never knows what a living artist may do—one has mourned so many. However, one must make the worst of it; you must be as dead as you can."

"Don't I meet that condition in having just published a book?"

"Adequately, let us hope; for the book is verily a master-piece."

At this moment the parlour-maid appeared in the door that opened into the garden: Paraday lived at no great cost, and the frisk of petticoats, with a timorous "Sherry, sir?" was about his modest mahogany. He allowed half his income to his wife, from whom he had succeeded in separating without redundancy of legend. I had a general faith in his having behaved well, and I had once, in London, taken Mrs. Paraday down to dinner. He now turned to speak to the maid, who offered him, on a tray, some card or note,

while

while agitated, excited, I wandered to the end of the garden. The idea of his security became supremely dear to me, and I asked myself if I were the same young man who had come down a few days before to scatter him to the four winds. When I retraced my steps he had gone into the house and the woman (the second London post had come in) had placed my letters and a newspaper on a bench. I sat down there to the letters, which were a brief business, and then, without heeding the address, took the paper from its envelope. It was the journal of highest renown, *The Empire* of that morning. It regularly came to Paraday, but I remembered that neither of us had yet looked at the copy already delivered. This one had a great mark on the " editorial " page, and, uncrumpling the wrapper, I saw it to be directed to my host and stamped with the name of his publishers. I instantly divined that *The Empire* had spoken of him, and I have not forgotten the odd little shock of the circumstance. It checked all eagerness and made me drop the paper a moment. As I sat there, conscious of a palpitation, I think I had a vision of what was to be. I had also a vision of the letter I would presently address to Mr. Pinhorn, breaking as it were with Mr. Pinhorn. Of course, however, the next minute the voice of *The Empire* was in my ears.

The article was not, I thanked Heaven, a review; it was a " leader," the last of three, presenting Neil Faraday to the human race. His new book, the fifth from his hand, had been but a day or two out, and *The Empire*, already aware of it, fired, as if on the birth of a prince, a salute of a whole column. The guns had been booming these three hours in the house without our suspecting them. The big blundering newspaper had discovered him, and now he was proclaimed and anointed and crowned. His place was assigned him as publicly as if a fat usher with a wand had pointed to the topmost chair; he was to pass up and still up, higher and
higher,

higher, between the watching faces and the envious sounds—away up to the daïs and the throne. The article was a date; he had taken rank at a bound—waked up a national glory. A national glory was needed, and it was an immense convenience he was there. What all this meant rolled over me, and I fear I grew a little faint —it meant so much more than I could say " yea " to on the spot. In a flash, somehow, all was different; the tremendous wave I speak of had swept something away. It had knocked down, I suppose, my little customary altar, my twinkling tapers and my flowers, and had reared itself into the likeness of a temple vast and bare. When Neil Paraday should come out of the house he would come out a contemporary. That was what had happened—the poor man was to be squeezed into his horrible age. I felt as if he had been overtaken on the crest of the hill and brought back to the city. A little more and he would have dipped down to posterity and escaped.

IV

When he came out it was exactly as if he had been in custody, for beside him walked a stout man with a big black beard, who, save that he wore spectacles, might have been a policeman, and in whom at a second glance I recognised the highest contemporary enterprise.

" This is Mr. Morrow," said Paraday, looking, I thought, rather white; " he wants to publish heaven knows what about me."

I winced as I remembered that this was exactly what I myself had wanted. " Already ? " I exclaimed, with a sort of sense that my friend had fled to me for protection.

Mr. Morrow

Mr. Morrow glared, agreeably, through his glasses: they suggested the electric headlights of some monstrous modern ship, and I felt as if Paraday and I were tossing terrified under his bows. I saw that his momentum was irresistible. " I was confident that I should be the first in the field," he declared. " A great interest is naturally felt in Mr. Paraday's surroundings."

" I hadn't the least idea of it," said Paraday, as if he had been told he had been snoring.

" I find he has not read the article in *The Empire*," Mr. Morrow remarked to me. " That's so very interesting—it's something to start with," he smiled. He had begun to pull off his gloves, which were violently new, and to look encouragingly round the little garden. As a " surrounding " I felt that I myself had already been taken in; I was a little fish in the stomach of a bigger one. " I represent," our visitor continued, " a syndicate of influential journals, no less than thirty-seven, whose public— whose publics, I may say—are in peculiar sympathy with Mr. Paraday's line of thought. They would greatly appreciate any expression of his views on the subject of the art he so brilliantly practises. Besides any connection with the syndicate just mentioned, I hold a particular commission from *The Tatler*, whose most prominent department, ' Smatter and Chatter '—I daresay you've often enjoyed it—attracts such attention. I was honoured only last week, as a representative of *The Tatler*, with the confidence of Guy Walsingham, the author of ' Obsessions.' She expressed herself thoroughly pleased with my sketch of her method; she went so far as to say that I had made her genius more comprehensible even to herself."

Neil Paraday had dropped upon the garden-bench and sat there, at once detached and confused; he looked hard at a bare spot in the lawn, as if with an anxiety that had suddenly made him grave.

His

His movement had been interpreted by his visitor as an invitation to sink sympathetically into a wicker chair that stood hard by, and as Mr. Morrow so settled himself I felt that he had taken official possession and that there was no undoing it. One had heard of unfortunate people's having "a man in the house," and this was just what we had. There was a silence of a moment, during which we seemed to acknowledge in the only way that was possible the presence of universal fate; the sunny stillness took no pity, and my thought, as I was sure Paraday's was doing, performed within the minute a great distant revolution. I saw just how emphatic I should make my rejoinder to Mr. Pinhorn, and that having come, like Mr. Morrow, to betray, I must remain as long as possible to save. Not because I had brought my mind back, but because our visitor's last words were in my ear, I presently inquired with gloomy irrelevance if Guy Walsingham were a woman.

"Oh yes, a mere pseudonym; but convenient, you know, for a lady who goes in for the larger latitude. 'Obesssions, by Miss So-and-So,' would look a little odd, but men are more naturally indelicate. Have you peeped into 'Obsessions'?" Mr. Morrow continued sociably to our companion.

Paraday, still absent, remote, made no answer, as if he had not heard the question: a manifestation that appeared to suit the cheerful Mr. Morrow as well as any other. Imperturbably bland, he was a man of resources—he only needed to be on the spot. He had pocketed the whole poor place while Paraday and I were woolgathering, and I could imagine that he had already got his "heads." His system, at any rate, was justified by the inevitability with which I replied, to save my friend the trouble: "Dear, no; he hasn't read it. He doesn't read such things!" I unwarily added.

"Things

"Things that are *too* far over the fence, eh?" I was indeed a godsend to Mr. Morrow. It was the psychological moment; it determined the appearance of his notebook, which, however, he at first kept slightly behind him, as the dentist, approaching his victim, keeps his horrible forceps. "Mr. Paraday holds with the good old proprieties—I see!" And, thinking of the thirty-seven influential journals, I found myself, as I found poor Paraday, helplessly gazing at the promulgation of this ineptitude. "There's no point on which distinguished views are so acceptable as on this question—raised perhaps more strikingly than ever by Guy Walsingham—of the permissibility of the larger latitude. I have an appointment, precisely in connection with it, next week, with Dora Forbes, the author of 'The Other Way Round,' which everybody is talking about. Has Mr. Paraday glanced at 'The Other Way Round'?" Mr. Morrow now frankly appealed to me. I took upon myself to repudiate the supposition, while our companion, still silent, got up nervously and walked away. His visitor paid no heed to his withdrawal; he only opened out the notebook with a more motherly pat. "Dora Forbes, I gather, takes the ground, the same as Guy Walsingham's, that the larger latitude has simply got to come. He holds that it has got to be squarely faced. Of course his sex makes him a less prejudiced witness. But an authoritative word from Mr. Paraday—from the point of view of *his* sex, you know—would go right round the globe. He takes the line that we *haven't* got to face it?"

I was bewildered; it sounded somehow as if there were three sexes. My interlocutor's pencil was poised, my private responsibility great. I simply sat staring, however, and only found presence of mind to say: "Is this Miss Forbes a gentleman?"

Mr. Morrow hesitated an instant, smiling: "It wouldn't be 'Miss'—there's a wife!"

"I

" I mean is she a man ? "

" The wife ? "—Mr. Morrow, for a moment, was as confused as myself. But when I explained that I alluded to Dora Forbes in person he informed me, with visible amusement at my being so out of it, that this was the " pen-name " of an indubitable male —he had a big red moustache. " He only assumes a feminine personality because the ladies are such popular favourites. A great deal of interest is felt in this assumption, and there's every pro-spect of its being widely imitated." Our host at this moment joined us again, and Mr. Morrow remarked invitingly that he should be happy to make a note of any observation the movement in question, the bid for success under a lady's name, might suggest to Mr. Paraday. But the poor man, without catching the allu-sion, excused himself, pleading that, though he was greatly honoured by his visitor's interest, he suddenly felt unwell and should have to take leave of him—have to go and lie down and keep quiet. His young friend might be trusted to answer for him, but he hoped Mr. Morrow didn't expect great things even of his young friend. His young friend, at this moment, looked at Neil Paraday with an anxious eye, greatly wondering if he were doomed to be ill again; but Paraday's own kind face met his ques-tion reassuringly, seemed to say in a glance intelligible enough: " Oh, I'm not ill, but I'm scared: get him out of the house as quietly as possible." Getting newspaper men out of the house was odd business for an emissary of Mr. Pinhorn, and I was so exhila-rated by the idea of it that I called after him as he left us:

" Read the article in *The Empire*, and you'll soon be all right ! "

" Delicious

V

" Delicious my having come down to tell him of it ! " Mr. Morrow ejaculated. " My cab was at the door twenty minutes after *The Empire* had been laid upon my breakfast-table. Now what have you got for me ? " he continued, dropping again into his chair, from which, however, the next moment he quickly rose. " I was shown into the drawing-room, but there must be more to see—his study, his literary sanctum, the little things he has about, or other domestic objects or features. He wouldn't be lying down on his study-table ? There's a great interest always felt in the scene of an author's labours. Sometimes we're favoured with very delightful peeps. Dora Forbes showed me all his table-drawers, and almost jammed my hand into one into which I made a dash ! I don't ask that of you, but if we could talk things over right there where he sits I feel as if I should get the keynote."

I had no wish whatever to be rude to Mr. Morrow, I was much too initiated not to prefer the safety of other ways; but I had a quick inspiration and I entertained an insurmountable, an almost superstitious objection to his crossing the threshold of my friend's little lonely, shabby, consecrated workshop. " No, no— we sha'n't get at his life that way," I said. " The way to get at his life is to—But wait a moment ! " I broke off and went quickly into the house; then, in three minutes, I reappeared before Mr. Morrow with the two volumes of Paraday's new book. " His life's here," I went on, " and I'm so full of this admirable thing that I can't talk of anything else. The artist's life's his work, and this is the place to observe him. What he has to tell

us

us he tells us with *this* perfection. My dear sir, the best interviewer's the best reader."

Mr. Morrow good-humouredly protested. "Do you mean to say that no other source of information should be opened to us?"

"None other till this particular one—by far the most copious—has been quite exhausted. Have you exhausted it, my dear sir? Had you exhausted it when you came down here? It seems to me in our time almost wholly neglected, and something should surely be done to restore its ruined credit. It's the course to which the artist himself at every step, and with such pathetic confidence, refers us. This last book of Mr. Paraday's is full of revelations."

"Revelations?" panted Mr. Morrow, whom I had forced again into his chair.

"The only kind that count. It tells you with a perfection that seems to me quite final all the author thinks, for instance, about the advent of the 'larger latitude.'"

"Where does it do that?" asked Mr. Morrow, who had picked up the second volume and was insincerely thumbing it.

"Everywhere—in the whole treatment of his case. Extract the opinion, disengage the answer—those are the real acts of homage."

Mr. Morrow, after a minute, tossed the book away. "Ah, but you mustn't take me for a reviewer."

"Heaven forbid I should take you for anything so dreadful! You came down to perform a little act of sympathy, and so, I may confide to you, did I. Let us perform our little act together. These pages overflow with the testimony we want: let us read them and taste them and interpret them. You will of course have perceived for yourself that one scarcely does read Neil Paraday till one reads him aloud; he gives out to the ear an extraordinary quality, and it's only when you expose it confidently to

that

that test that you really get near his style. Take up your book again and let me listen, while you pay it out, to that wonderful fifteenth chapter. If you feel that you can't do it justice, compose yourself to attention while I produce for you—I think I can!—this scarcely less admirable ninth."

Mr. Morrow gave me a straight glance which was as hard as a blow between the eyes; he had turned rather red and a question had formed itself in his mind which reached my sense as distinctly as if he had uttered it: "What sort of a damned fool are *you*?" Then he got up, gathering together his hat and gloves, buttoning his coat, projecting hungrily all over the place the big transparency of his mask. It seemed to flare over Fleet Street and somehow made the actual spot distressingly humble: there was so little for it to feed on unless he counted the blisters of our stucco or saw his way to do something with the roses. Even the poor roses were common kinds. Presently his eyes fell upon the manuscript from which Paraday had been reading to me and which still lay on the bench. As my own followed them I saw that it looked promising, looked pregnant, as if it gently throbbed with the life the reader had given it. Mr. Morrow indulged in a nod toward it and a vague thrust of his umbrella. "What's that?"

"Oh, it's a plan—a secret."

"A secret!" There was an instant's silence, and then Mr. Morrow made another movement. I may have been mistaken, but it affected me as the translated impulse of the desire to lay hands on the manuscript, and this led me to indulge in a quick anticipatory grab which may very well have seemed ungraceful, or even impertinent, and which at any rate left Mr. Paraday's two admirers very erect, glaring at each other while one of them held a bundle of papers well behind him. An instant later Mr. Morrow quitted me abruptly, as if he had really carried something

thing away. To reassure myself, watching his broad back recede, I only grasped my manuscript the tighter. He went to the back-door of the house, the one he had come out from, but on trying the handle he appeared to find it fastened. So he passed round into the front garden, and, by listening intently enough, I could presently hear the outer gate close behind him with a bang. I thought again of the thirty-seven influential journals and wondered what would be his revenge. I hasten to add that he was magnanimous: which was just the most dreadful thing he could have been. *The Tatler* published a charming, chatty, familiar account of Mr. Paraday's " Home-life," and on the wings of the thirty-seven influential journals it went, to use Mr. Morrow's own expression, right round the globe.

VI

A week later, early in May, my glorified friend came up to town, where, it may be veraciously recorded, he was the king of the beasts of the year. No advancement was ever more rapid, no exaltation more complete, no bewilderment more teachable. His book sold but moderately, though the article in *The Empire* had done unwonted wonders for it; but he circulated in person in a manner that the libraries might well have envied. His formula had been found—he was a " revelation." His momentary terror had been real, just as mine had been—the overclouding of his passionate desire to be left to finish his work. He was far from unsociable, but he had the finest conception of being let alone that I have ever met. For the time, however, he took his profit where it seemed most to crowd upon him, having in his pocket
                                                                    the

the portable sophistries about the nature of the artist's task. Observation too was a kind of work and experience a kind of success; London dinners were all material and London ladies were fruitful toil. " No one has the faintest conception of what I'm trying for," he said to me, " and not many have read three pages that I've written; but they're all enthusiastic, enchanted, devoted." He found himself in truth equally amused and fatigued; but the fatigue had the merit of being a new sort, and the phantasmagoric town was perhaps after all less of a battlefield than the haunted study. He once told me that he had had no personal life to speak of since his fortieth year, but had had more than was good for him before. London closed the parenthesis and exhibited him in relations; one of the most inevitable of these being that in which he found himself to Mrs. Weeks Wimbush, wife of the boundless brewer and proprietress of the universal menagerie. In this establishment, as everybody knows, on occasions when the crush is great, the animals rub shoulders freely with the spectators and the lions sit down for whole evenings with the lambs.

It had been ominously clear to me from the first that in Neil Paraday this lady, who, as all the world agreed, was tremendous fun, considered that she had secured a prime attraction, a creature of almost heraldic oddity. Nothing could exceed her enthusiasm over her capture, and nothing could exceed the confused apprehensions it excited in me. I had an instinctive fear of her which I tried without effect to conceal from her victim, but which I let her perceive with perfect impunity. Paraday heeded it, but she never did, for her conscience was that of a romping child. She was a blind, violent force, to which I could attach no more idea of responsibility than to the hum of a spinning-top. It was difficult to say what she conduced to but to circulation. She was constructed of steel and leather, and all I asked of her for our tractable friend was

was not to do him to death. He had consented for a time to be
of indiarubber, but my thoughts were fixed on the day he should
resume his shape or at least get back into his box. It was evidently all right, but I should be glad when it was well over. I
was simply nervous—the impression was ineffaceable of the hour
when, after Mr. Morrow's departure, I had found him on the sofa
in his study. That pretext of indisposition had not in the least
been meant as a snub to the envoy of *The Tatler*—he had gone
to lie down in very truth. He had felt a pang of his old pain, the
result of the agitation wrought in him by this forcing open of a
new period. His old programme, his old ideal even had to be
changed. Say what one would, success was a complication and
recognition had to be reciprocal. The monastic life, the pious
illumination of the missal in the convent cell were things of the
gathered past. It didn't engender despair, but it at least required
adjustment. Before I left him on that occasion we had passed a
bargain, my part of which was that I should make it my business
to take care of him. Let whoever would represent the interest in
his presence (I had a mystical prevision of Mrs. Weeks Wimbush),
I should represent the interest in his work—in other words, in his
absence. These two interests were in their essence opposed; and
I doubt, as youth is fleeting, if I shall ever again know the
intensity of joy with which I felt that in so good a cause I was
willing to make myself odious.

One day, in Sloane Street, I found myself questioning Paraday's
landlord, who had come to the door in answer to my knock. Two
vehicles, a barouche and a smart hansom, were drawn up before
the house.

" In the drawing-room, sir ?   Mrs. Weeks Wimbush."

" And in the dining-room ? "

" A young lady, sir—waiting: I think a foreigner."

It

It was three o'clock, and on days when Paraday didn't lunch out he attached a value to these subjugated hours. On which days, however, didn't the dear man lunch out? Mrs. Wimbush, at such a crisis, would have rushed round immediately after her own repast. I went into the dining-room first, postponing the pleasure of seeing how, upstairs, the lady of the barouche would, on my arrival, point the moral of my sweet solicitude. No one took such an interest as herself in his doing only what was good for him, and she was always on the spot to see that he did it. She made appointments with him to discuss the best means of economising his time and protecting his privacy. She further made his health her special business, and had so much sympathy with my own zeal for it that she was the author of pleasing fictions on the subject of what my devotion had led me to give up. I gave up nothing (I don't count Mr. Pinhorn) because I had nothing, and all I had as yet achieved was to find myself also in the menagerie. I had dashed in to save my friend, but I had only got domesticated and wedged; so that I could do nothing for him but exchange with him over people's heads looks of intense but futile intelligence.

VII

The young lady in the dining-room had a brave face, black hair, blue eyes, and in her lap a big volume. " I've come for his autograph," she said, when I had explained to her that I was under bonds to see people for him when he was occupied. " I've been waiting half an hour, but I'm prepared to wait all day." I don't know whether it was this that told me she was American, for

for the propensity to wait all day is not in general characteristic
of her race. I was enlightened probably not so much by the
spirit of the utterance as by some quality of its sound. At any
rate I saw she had an individual patience and a lovely frock, together with an expression that played among her pretty features
as a breeze among flowers. Putting her book upon the table, she
showed me a massive album, showily bound and full of autographs
of price. The collection of faded notes, of still more faded
" thoughts," of quotations, platitudes, signatures, represented a
formidable purpose.

" Most people apply to Mr. Paraday by letter, you know," I said.

" Yes, but he doesn't answer. I've written three times."

" Very true," I reflected; " the sort of letter you mean goes
straight into the fire."

" How do you know the sort I mean ? " my interlocutress
asked. She had blushed and smiled and in a moment she added:
" I don't believe he gets many like them ! "

" I'm sure they're beautiful, but he burns without reading." I
didn't add that I had told him he ought to.

" Isn't he then in danger of burning things of importance ? "

" He would be, if distinguished men hadn't an infallible nose for
a petition."

She looked at me a moment—her face was sweet and gay.
" Do *you* burn without reading, too ? " she asked; in answer to
which I assured her that if she would trust me with her repository
I would see that Mr. Paraday should write his name in it.

She considered a little. " That's very well, but it wouldn't
make me see him."

" Do you want very much to see him ? " It seemed ungracious
to catechise so charming a creature, but somehow I had never yet
taken my duty to the great author so seriously.

" Enough

" Enough to have come from America for the purpose."

I stared. " All alone ? "

" I don't see that that's exactly your business; but if it will make me more appealing I will confess that I am quite by myself. I had to come alone or not at all."

She was interesting; I could imagine that she had lost parents, natural protectors—could conceive even that she had inherited money. I was in a phase of my own fortunes when keeping hansoms at doors seemed to me pure swagger. As a trick of this frank and delicate girl, however, it became romantic—a part of the general romance of her freedom, her errand, her innocence. The confidence of young Americans was notorious, and I speedily arrived at a conviction that no impulse could have been more generous than the impulse that had operated here. I foresaw at that moment that it would make her my peculiar charge, just as circumstances had made Neil Paraday. She would be another person to look after, and one's honour would be concerned in guiding her straight. These things became clearer to me later; at the instant I had scepticism enough to observe to her, as I turned the pages of her volume, that her net had, all the same, caught many a big fish. She appeared to have had fruitful access to the great ones of the earth; there were people moreover whose signatures she had presumably secured without a personal interview. She couldn't have waylaid George Washington and Friedrich Schiller and Hannah More. She met this argument, to my surprise, by throwing up the album without a pang. It wasn't even her own; she was responsible for none of its treasures. It belonged to a girl-friend in America, a young lady in a western city. This young lady had insisted on her bringing it, to pick up more autographs: she thought they might like to see, in Europe, in what company they would be. The " girl-friend," the western city,

the

the immortal names, the curious errand, the idyllic faith, all made a story as strange to me, and as beguiling, as some tale in the Arabian Nights. Thus it was that my informant had encumbered herself with the ponderous tome; but she hastened to assure me that this was the first time she had brought it out. For her visit to Mr. Paraday it had simply been a pretext. She didn't really care a straw that he should write his name ; what she did want was to look straight into his face.

I demurred a little. " And why do you require to do that ? "

" Because I just love him! " Before I could recover from the agitating effect of this crystal ring my companion had continued: " Hasn't there ever been any face that you've wanted to look into ? "

How could I tell her so soon how much I appreciated the opportunity of looking into hers ? I could only assent in general to the proposition that there were certainly for every one such faces; and I felt that the crisis demanded all my lucidity, all my wisdom. " Oh, yes, I'm a student of physiognomy. Do you mean," I pursued, " that you've a passion for Mr. Paraday's books ? "

" They've been everything to me—I know them by heart. They've completely taken hold of me. There's no author about whom I feel as I do about Neil Paraday."

" Permit me to remark then," I presently rejoined, " that you're one of the right sort."

" One of the enthusiasts ? Of course I am ! "

" Oh, there are enthusiasts who are quite of the wrong. I mean you're one of those to whom an appeal can be made."

" An appeal ? " Her face lighted as if with the chance of some great sacrifice.

If she was ready for one it was only waiting for her, and in a
moment

moment I mentioned it. " Give up this rigid purpose of seeing him. Go away without it. That will be far better."

She looked mystified; then she turned visibly pale. " Why, hasn't he any personal charm ? " The girl was terrible and laughable in her bright directness.

" Ah, that dreadful word ' personal '! " I exclaimed; " we're dying of it, and you women bring it out with murderous effect. When you encounter a genius as fine as this idol of ours, let him off the dreary duty of being a personality as well. Know him only by what's best in him, and spare him for the same sweet sake."

My young lady continued to look at me in confusion and mistrust, and the result of her reflection on what I had just said was to make her suddenly break out: " Look here, sir—what's the matter with him ? "

" The matter with him is that, if he doesn't look out, people will eat a great hole in his life."

She considered a moment. " He hasn't any disfigurement ? "

" Nothing to speak of! "

" Do you mean that social engagements interfere with his occupations ? "

" That but feebly expresses it."

" So that he can't give himself up to his beautiful imagination ? "

" He's badgered, bothered, overwhelmed, on the pretext of being applauded. People expect him to give them his time, his golden time, who wouldn't themselves give five shillings for one of his books."

" Five ? I'd give five thousand! "

" Give your sympathy—give your forbearance. Two-thirds of those who approach him only do it to advertise themselves."

" Why,

"Why, it's too bad!" the girl exclaimed, with the face of an angel.

I followed up my advantage. "There's a lady with him now who's a terrible complication, and who yet hasn't read, I am sure, ten pages that he ever wrote."

My visitor's wide eyes grew tenderer. "Then how does she talk——?"

"Without ceasing. I only mention her as a single case. Do you want to know how to show a superlative consideration? Simply avoid him."

"Avoid him?" she softly wailed.

"Don't force him to have to take account of you; admire him in silence, cultivate him at a distance and secretly appropriate his message. Do you want to know," I continued, warming to my idea, "how to perform an act of homage really sublime?" Then as she hung on my words: "Succeed in never seeing him!"

"Never?" she pathetically gasped.

"The more you get into his writings the less you'll want to; and you'll be immensely sustained by the thought of the good you're doing him."

She looked at me without resentment or spite, and at the truth I had put before her with candour, credulity and pity. I was afterwards happy to remember that she must have recognised in my face the liveliness of my interest in herself. "I think I see what you mean."

"Oh, I express it badly; but I should be delighted if you would let me come to see you—to explain it better."

She made no response to this, and her thoughtful eyes fell on the big album, on which she presently laid her hands as if to take it away. "I did use to say out West that they might write a little

less

less for autographs (to all the great poets, you know) and study the thoughts and style a little more."

"What do they care for the thoughts and style? They didn't even understand you. I'm not sure," I added, "that I do myself, and I daresay that you by no means make me out." She had got up to go, and though I wanted her to succeed in not seeing Neil Paraday I wanted her also, inconsequently, to remain in the house. I was at any rate far from desiring to hustle her off. As Mrs. Weeks Wimbush, upstairs, was still saving our friend in her own way, I asked my young lady to let me briefly relate, in illustration of my point, the little incident of my having gone down into the country for a profane purpose and been converted on the spot to holiness. Sinking again into her chair to listen, she showed a deep interest in the anecdote. Then, thinking it over gravely, she exclaimed with her odd intonation:

"Yes, but you do see him!" I had to admit that this was the case; and I was not so prepared with an effective attenuation as I could have wished. She eased the situation off, however, by the charming quaintness with which she finally said: "Well, I wouldn't want him to be lonely!" This time she rose in earnest, but I persuaded her to let me keep the album to show to Mr. Paraday. I assured her I would bring it back to her myself. "Well, you'll find my address somewhere in it, on a paper!" she sighed resignedly, as she took leave.

VIII

I blush to confess it, but I invited Mr. Paraday that very day to transcribe into the album one of his most characteristic passages.

I

I told him how I had got rid of the strange girl who had brought it—her ominous name was Miss Hurter and she lived at an hotel; quite agreeing with him moreover as to the wisdom of getting rid with equal promptitude of the book itself. This was why I carried it to Albemarle Street no later than on the morrow. I failed to find her at home, but she wrote to me and I went again: she wanted so much to hear more about Neil Paraday. I returned repeatedly, I may briefly declare, to supply her with this information. She had been immensely taken, the more she thought of it, with that idea of mine about the act of homage: it had ended by filling her with a generous rapture. She positively desired to do something sublime for him, though indeed I could see that, as this particular flight was difficult, she appreciated the fact that my visits kept her up. I had it on my conscience to keep her up; I neglected nothing that would contribute to it, and her conception of our cherished author's independence became at last as fine as his own conception. "Read him, read him," I constantly repeated; while, seeking him in his works, she represented herself as convinced that, according to my assurance, this was the system that had, as she expressed it, weaned her. We read him together when I could find time, and the generous creature's sacrifice was fed by our conversation. There were twenty selfish women, about whom I told her, who stirred her with a beautiful rage. Immediately after my first visit her sister, Mrs. Milsom, came over from Paris, and the two ladies began to present, as they called it, their letters. I thanked our stars that none had been presented to Mr. Paraday. They received invitations and dined out, and some of these occasions enabled Fanny Hurter to perform, for consistency's sake, touching feats of submission. Nothing indeed would now have induced her even to look at the object of her admiration. Once, hearing his name announced at a party, she instantly left the room

by

by another door and then straightway quitted the house.   At
another time, when I was at the opera with them (Mrs. Milsom
had invited me to their box) I attempted to point Mr. Paraday
out to her in the stalls.   On this she asked her sister to change
places with her, and, while that lady devoured the great man
through a powerful glass, presented, all the rest of the evening,
her inspired back to the house.   To torment her tenderly I pressed
the glass upon her, telling her how wonderfully near it brought our
friend's handsome head.   By way of answer she simply looked at me
in grave silence;   on which I saw that tears had gathered in her eyes.
These tears, I may remark, produced an effect on me of which
the end is not yet.   There was a moment when I felt it my
duty to mention them to Neil Paraday;   but I was deterred
by the reflection that there were questions more relevant to his
happiness.

These questions indeed, by the end of the season, were reduced
to a single one——the question of reconstituting, so far as might be
possible, the conditions under which he had produced his best
work.   Such conditions could never all come back, for there was
a new one that took up too much place;   but some perhaps were
not beyond recall.   I wanted above all things to see him sit down
to the subject of which, on my making his acquaintance, he had
read me that admirable sketch.   Something told me there was no
security but in his doing so before the new factor, as we used to say
at Mr. Pinhorn's, should render the problem incalculable.   It only
half reassured me that the sketch itself was so copious and so eloquent
that even at the worst there would be the making of a small but complete book, a tiny volume which, for the faithful, might well become
an object of adoration.   There would even not be wanting critics
to declare, I foresaw, that the plan was a thing to be more thankful
for than the structure to have been reared on it.   My impatience
for

for the structure, none the less, grew and grew with the interruptions. He had, on coming up to town, begun to sit for his portrait to a young painter, Mr. Rumble, whose little game, as we used to say at Mr. Pinhorn's, was to be the first to perch on the shoulders of renown. Mr. Rumble's studio was a circus in which the man of the hour, and still more the woman, leaped through the hoops of his showy frames almost as electrically as they burst into telegrams and "specials." He pranced into the exhibitions on their back; he was the reporter on canvas, the Vandyke up to date, and there was one roaring year in which Mrs. Bounder and Miss Braby, Guy Walsingham and Dora Forbes proclaimed in chorus from the same pictured walls that no one had yet got ahead of him.

Paraday had been promptly caught and saddled, accepting with characteristic good-humour his confidential hint that to figure in his show was not so much a consequence as a cause of immortality. From Mrs. Wimbush to the last " representative " who called to ascertain his twelve favourite dishes, it was the same ingenuous assumption that he would rejoice in the repercussion. There were moments when I fancied I might have had more patience with them if they had not been so fatally benevolent. I hated, at all events, Mr. Rumble's picture, and had my bottled resentment ready when, later on, I found my distracted friend had been stuffed by Mrs. Wimbush into the mouth of another cannon. A young artist in whom she was intensely interested, and who had no connection with Mr. Rumble, was to show how far he could shoot him. Poor Paraday, in return, was naturally to write something somewhere about the young artist. She played her victims against each other with admirable ingenuity, and her establishment was a huge machine in which the tiniest and the biggest wheels went round to the same treadle. I had a scene
with

with her in which I tried to express that the function of such a man was to exercise his genius—not to serve as a hoarding for pictorial posters. The people I was perhaps angriest with were the editors of magazines who had introduced what they called new features, so aware were they that the newest feature of all would be to make him grind their axes by contributing his views on vital topics and taking part in the periodical prattle about the future of fiction. I made sure that before I should have done with him there would scarcely be a current form of words left me to be sick of; but meanwhile I could make surer still of my animosity to bustling ladies for whom he drew the water that irrigated their social flower-beds.

I had a battle with Mrs. Wimbush over the artist she protected, and another over the question of a certain week, at the end of July, that Mr. Paraday appeared to have contracted to spend with her in the country. I protested against this visit; I intimated that he was too unwell for hospitality without a *nuance*, for caresses without imagination; I begged he might rather take the time in some restorative way. A sultry air of promises, of reminders hung over his August, and he would greatly profit by the interval of rest. He had not told me he was ill again—that he had had a warning; but I had not needed this, and I found his reticence his worst symptom. The only thing he said to me was that he believed a comfortable attack of something or other would set him up: it would put out of the question everything but the exemptions he prized. I am afraid I shall have presented him as a martyr in a very small cause if I fail to explain that he surrendered himself much more liberally than I surrendered him. He filled his lungs, for the most part, with the comedy of his queer fate: the tragedy was in the spectacles through which I chose to look. He was conscious of inconvenience, and above all of a great

great renouncement; but how could he have heard a mere dirge in the bells of his accession ? The sagacity and the jealousy were mine, and his the impressions and the anecdotes. Of course, as regards Mrs. Wimbush, I was worsted in my encounters, for was not the state of his health the very reason for his coming to her at Prestidge ? Wasn't it precisely at Prestidge that he was to be coddled, and wasn't the dear Princess coming to help her to coddle him ? The dear Princess, now on a visit to England, was of a famous foreign house, and, in her gilded cage with her retinue of keepers and feeders, was the most expensive specimen in the good lady's collection. I don't think her august presence had had to do with Paraday's consenting to go, but it is not impossible that he had operated as a bait to the illustrious visitor. The party had been made up for him, Mrs. Wimbush averred, and every one was counting on it, the dear Princess most of all. If he was well enough he was to read them something absolutely fresh, and it was on that particular prospect the Princess had set her heart. She was so fond of genius, in *any* walk of life, and she was so used to it, and understood it so well; she was the greatest of Mr. Paraday's admirers, she devoured everything he wrote. And then he read like an angel. Mrs. Wimbush reminded me that he had again and again given her, Mrs. Wimbush, the privilege of listening to him.

I looked at her for a moment. " What has he read to you ? " I crudely inquired.

For a moment too she met my eyes, and for the fraction of a moment she hesitated and coloured. " Oh, all sorts of things ! "

I wondered whether this were a perfect fib or only an imperfect recollection, and she quite understood my unuttered comment on her perception of such things. But if she could forget Neil Paraday's beauties she could of course forget my rudeness, and

three

three days later she invited me, by telegraph, to join the party at Prestidge. This time she might indeed have had a story about what I had given up to be near the master. I addressed from that fine residence several communications to a young lady in London, a young lady whom, I confess, I quitted with reluctance and whom the reminder of what she herself could give up was required to make me quit at all. It adds to the gratitude I owe her on other grounds that she kindly allows me to transcribe from my letters a few of the passages in which that hateful sojourn is candidly commemorated.

IX

" I suppose I ought to enjoy the joke," I wrote, " of what's going on here, but somehow it doesn't amuse me. Pessimism on the contrary possesses me and cynicism solicits. I positively feel my own flesh sore from the brass nails in Neil Paraday's social harness. The house is full of people who like him, as they mention, awfully, and with whom his talent for talking nonsense has prodigious success. I delight in his nonsense myself; why is it therefore that I grudge these happy folk their artless satisfaction? Mystery of the human heart—abyss of the critical spirit! Mrs. Wimbush thinks she can answer that question, and as my want of gaiety has at last worn out her patience she has given me a glimpse of her shrewd guess. I am made restless by the selfishness of the insincere friend—I want to monopolise Paraday in order that he may push me on. To be intimate with him is a feather in my cap; it gives me an importance that I couldn't naturally pretend to, and I seek to deprive him of social refreshment because I fear that meeting more disinterested people may enlighten

enlighten him as to my real spirit. All the disinterested people here are his particular admirers and have been carefully selected as such. There is supposed to be a copy of his last book in the house, and in the hall I come upon ladies, in attitudes, bending gracefully over the first volume. I discreetly avert my eyes, and when I next look round the precarious joy has been superseded by the book of life. There is a sociable circle or a confidential couple, and the relinquished volume lies open on its face, as if it had been dropped under extreme coercion. Somebody else presently finds it and transfers it, with its air of momentary desolation, to another piece of furniture. Every one is asking every one about it all day, and every one is telling every one where they put it last. I'm sure it's rather smudgy about the twentieth page. I have a strong impression too that the second volume is lost— has been packed in the bag of some departing guest; and yet everybody has the impression that somebody else has read to the end. You see therefore that the beautiful book plays a great part in our conversation. Why should I take the occasion of such distinguished honours to say that I begin to see deeper into Gustave Flaubert's doleful refrain about the hatred of literature? I refer you again to the perverse constitution of man.

" The Princess is a massive lady with the organisation of an athlete and the confusion of tongues of a *valet de place*. She contrives to commit herself extraordinarily little in a great many languages, and is entertained and conversed with in detachments and relays, like an institution which goes on from generation to generation or a big building contracted for under a forfeit. She can't have a personal taste, any more than, when her husband succeeds, she can have a personal crown, and her opinion on any matter is rusty and heavy and plain—made, in the night of ages, to last and be transmitted. I feel as if I ought to pay some one a

fee

fee for my glimpse of it. She has been told everything in the
world and has never perceived anything, and the echoes of her
education respond awfully to the rash footfall—I mean the casual
remark—in the cold Valhalla of her memory. Mrs. Wimbush
delights in her wit and says there is nothing so charming as to
hear Mr. Paraday draw it out. He is perpetually detailed for this
job, and he tells me it has a peculiarly exhausting effect. Every
one is beginning—at the end of two days—to sidle obsequiously
away from her, and Mrs. Wimbush pushes him again and again into
the breach. None of the uses I have yet seen him put to irritate
me quite so much. He looks very fagged, and has at last confessed
to me that his condition makes him uneasy—has even promised
me that he will go straight home instead of returning to his final
engagements in town. Last night I had some talk with him
about going to-day, cutting his visit short; so sure am I that he
will be better as soon as he is shut up in his lighthouse. He told
me that this is what he would like to do; reminding me, however, that the first lesson of his greatness has been precisely that
he can't do what he likes. Mrs. Wimbush would never forgive
him if he should leave her before the Princess has received the
last hand. When I say that a violent rupture with our hostess
would be the best thing in the world for him he gives me to
understand that if his reason assents to the proposition his courage
hangs woefully back. He makes no secret of being mortally afraid
of her, and when I ask what harm she can do him that she hasn't
already done he simply repeats: 'I'm afraid, I'm afraid: Don't
inquire too closely,' he said last night; ' only believe that I feel
a sort of terror. It's strange, when she's so kind! At any rate,
I would as soon overturn that piece of priceless Sèvres as tell her
that I must go before my date.' It sounds dreadfully weak, but
he has some reason, and he pays for his imagination, which puts
him

him (I should hate it) in the place of others and makes him feel, even against himself, their feelings, their appetites, their motives. He's so beastly intelligent. Besides, the famous reading is still to come off, and it has been postponed a day, to allow Guy Walsingham to arrive. It appears that this eminent lady is staying at a house a few miles off, which means of course that Mrs. Wimbush has forcibly annexed her. She's to come over in a day or two—Mrs. Wimbush wants her to hear Mr. Paraday.

"To-day's wet and cold, and several of the company, at the invitation of the Duke, have driven over to luncheon at Bigwood. I saw poor Paraday wedge himself, by command, into the little supplementary seat of a brougham in which the Princess and our hostess were already ensconced. If the front glass isn't open on his dear old back perhaps he'll survive. Bigwood, I believe, is very grand and frigid, all marble and precedence, and I wish him well out of the adventure. I can't tell you how much more and more *your* attitude to him, in the midst of all this, shines out by contrast. I never willingly talk to these people about him, but see what a comfort I find it to scribble to you! I appreciate it; it keeps me warm ; there are no fires in the house. Mrs. Wimbush goes by the calendar, the temperature goes by the weather, the weather goes by God knows what, and the Princess is easily heated. I have nothing but my acrimony to warm me, and have been out under an umbrella to restore my circulation. Coming in an hour ago, I found Lady Augusta Minch rummaging about the hall. When I asked her what she was looking for she said she had mislaid something that Mr. Paraday had lent her. I ascertained in a moment that the article in question is a manuscript, and I have a foreboding that it's the noble morsel he read me six weeks ago. When I expressed my surprise that he should have passed about anything so precious (I happen to know it's his only copy—

in

in the most beautiful hand in all the world) Lady Augusta confessed to me that she had not had it from himself, but from Mrs. Wimbush, who had wished to give her a glimpse of it as a salve for her not being able to stay and hear it read.

"'Is that the piece he's to read,' I asked, 'when Guy Walsingham arrives?'

"'It's not for Guy Walsingham they're waiting now, it's for Dora Forbes,' Lady Augusta said. 'She's coming, I believe, early to-morrow. Meanwhile Mrs. Wimbush has found out about *him* and is actively wiring to him. She says he also must hear him.'

"'You bewilder me a little,' I replied; 'in the age we live in one gets lost among the genders and the pronouns. The clear thing is that Mrs. Wimbush doesn't guard such a treasure as jealously as she might.'

"'Poor dear, she has the Princess to guard! Mr. Paraday lent her the manuscript to look over.'

"'Did she speak as if it were the morning paper?'

"Lady Augusta stared—my irony was lost upon her. 'She didn't have time, so she gave me a chance first; because unfortunately I go to-morrow to Bigwood.'

"'And your chance has only proved a chance to lose it?'

"'I haven't lost it. I remember now—it was very stupid of me to have forgotten. I told my maid to give it to Lord Dorimont—or at least to his man.'

"'And Lord Dorimont went away directly after luncheon.'

"'Of course he gave it back to my maid—or else his man did,' said Lady Augusta. 'I daresay it's all right.'

"The conscience of these people is like a summer sea. They haven't time to 'look over' a priceless composition; they've only time to kick it about the house. I suggested that the 'man,' fired with a noble emulation, had perhaps kept the work for his own perusal;

perusal; and her ladyship wanted to know whether, if the thing didn't turn up again in time for the session appointed by our hostess, the author wouldn't have something else to read that would do just as well. Their questions are too delightful! I declared to Lady Augusta briefly that nothing in the world can ever do as well as the thing that does best; and at this she looked a little confused and scared. But I added that if the manuscript had gone astray our little circle would have the less of an effort of attention to make. The piece in question was very long—it would keep them three hours.

" ' Three hours! Oh, the Princess will get up!' said Lady Augusta.

" ' I thought she was Mr. Paraday's greatest admirer.'

" ' I daresay she is—she's so awfully clever. But what's the use of being a Princess——'

" ' If you can't dissemble your love?' I asked, as Lady Augusta was vague. She said, at any rate, that she would question her maid; and I am hoping that when I go down to dinner I shall find the manuscript has been recovered."

X

"It has not been recovered," I wrote early the next day, "and I am moreover much troubled about our friend. He came back from Bigwood with a chill and, being allowed to have a fire in his room, lay down a while before dinner. I tried to send him to bed and indeed thought I had put him in the way of it; but after I had gone to dress Mrs. Wimbush came up to see him, with the inevitable result that when I returned I found him under arms and
flushed

flushed and feverish, though decorated with the rare flower she
had brought him for his button-hole. He came down to dinner,
but Lady Augusta Minch was very shy of him. To-day he's in
great pain, and the advent of those ladies—I mean of Guy
Walsingham and Dora Forbes—doesn't at all console me. It
does Mrs. Wimbush, however, for she has consented to his remaining in bed, so that he may be all right to-morrow for the
séance. Guy Walsingham is already on the scene, and the doctor,
for Paraday, also arrived early. I haven't yet seen the author of
' Obsessions,' but of course I've had a moment by myself with
the doctor. I tried to get him to say that our invalid must go
straight home—I mean to-morrow or next day; but he quite
refuses to talk about the future. Absolute quiet and warmth and
the regular administration of an important remedy are the points
he mainly insists on. He returns this afternoon, and I'm to go
back to see the patient at one o'clock, when he next takes his
medicine. It consoles me a little that he certainly won't be able
to read—an exertion he was already more than unfit for. Lady
Augusta went off after breakfast, assuring me that her first care
would be to follow up the lost manuscript. I can see she thinks
me a shocking busybody and doesn't understand my alarm, but
she will do what she can, for she's a good-natured woman. ' So
are they all honourable men.' That was precisely what made her
give the thing to Lord Dorimont and made Lord Dorimont bag
it. What use *he* has for it God only knows. I have the worst
forebodings, but somehow I'm strangely without passion—desperately calm. As I consider the unconscious, the well-meaning
ravages of our appreciative circle I bow my head in submission to
some great natural, some universal accident; I'm rendered almost
indifferent, in fact quite gay (ha-ha!) by the sense of immitigable
fate. Lady Augusta promises me to trace the precious object and
let

let me have it, through the post, by the time Paraday is well enough to play his part with it. The last evidence is that her maid did give it to his lordship's valet. One would think it was some thrilling number of *The Family Budget.* Mrs. Wimbush, who is aware of the accident, is much less agitated by it than she would doubtless be were she not for the hour inevitably engrossed with Guy Walsingham."

Later in the day I informed my correspondent, for whom indeed I kept a sort of diary of the situation, that I had made the acquaintance of this celebrity and that she was a pretty little girl who wore her hair in what used to be called a crop. She looked so juvenile and so innocent that if, as Mr. Morrow had announced, she was resigned to the larger latitude, her fortitude must have come to her early. I spent most of the day hovering about Neil Paraday's room, but it was communicated to me from below that Guy Walsingham, at Prestidge, was a success. Towards evening I became conscious somehow that her resignation was contagious, and by the time the company separated for the night I was sure that the larger latitude had been generally accepted. I thought of Dora Forbes and felt that he had no time to lose. Before dinner I received a telegram from Lady Augusta Minch. " Lord Dorimont thinks he must have left bundle in train—inquire." How could I inquire—if I was to take the word as a command ? I was too worried and now too alarmed about Neil Paraday. The doctor came back, and it was an immense satisfaction to me to feel that he was wise and interested. He was proud of being called to so distinguished a patient, but he admitted to me that night that my friend was gravely ill. It was really a relapse, a recrudescence of his old malady. There could be no question of moving him: we must at any rate see first, on the spot, what turn his condition would take. Meanwhile, on the morrow, he

was

was to have a nurse. On the morrow the dear man was easier, and my spirits rose to such cheerfulness that I could almost laugh over Lady Augusta's second telegram: "Lord Dorimont's servant been to station—nothing found. Push inquiries." I did laugh, I am sure, as I remembered this was the mystic scroll I had scarcely allowed poor Mr. Morrow to point his umbrella at. Fool that I had been: the thirty-seven influential journals wouldn't have destroyed it, they would only have printed it. Of course I said nothing to Paraday.

When the nurse arrived she turned me out of the room, on which I went downstairs. I should premise that at breakfast the news that our brilliant friend was doing well excited universal complacency, and the Princess graciously remarked that he was only to be commiserated for missing the society of Miss Collop. Mrs. Wimbush, whose social gift never shone brighter than in the dry decorum with which she accepted this blemish on her perfection, mentioned to me that Guy Walsingham had made a very favourable impression on her Imperial Highness. Indeed I think every one did so and that, like the money-market or the national honour, her Imperial Highness was constitutionally sensitive. There was a certain gladness, a perceptible bustle in the air, however, which I thought slightly anomalous in a house where a great author lay critically ill. "*Le roy est mort—vive le roy*"! I was reminded that another great author had already stepped into his shoes. When I came down again after the nurse had taken possession I found a strange gentleman hanging about the hall and pacing to and fro by the closed door of the drawing-room. This personage was florid and bald, he had a big red moustache and wore showy knickerbockers—characteristics all that fitted into my conception of the identity of Dora Forbes. In a moment I saw what had happened: the author of "The Other Way Round"
had

had just alighted at the portals of Prestidge, but had suffered a
scruple to restrain him from penetrating further.   I recognised his
scruple when, pausing to listen at his gesture of caution, I heard a
shrill voice lifted in a prolonged monotonous quaver.   The famous
reading had begun, only it was the author of " Obsessions " who
now furnished the sacrifice.   The new visitor whispered to me
that he judged something was going on that he oughtn't to interrupt.

" Miss Collop arrived last night," I smiled, " and the Princess
has a thirst for the *inédit*."

Dora Forbes lifted his bushy brows.   "Miss Collop ? "

" Guy Walsingham, your distinguished *confrère*—or shall I say
your formidable rival ? "

" Oh ! " growled Dora Forbes.   Then he added : " Shall I
spoil it if I go in ? "

" I should think nothing could spoil it ! " I ambiguously
laughed.

Dora Forbes evidently felt the dilemma ;   he gave an irritated
crook to his moustache.   " *Shall* I go in ? " he presently asked.

We looked at each other hard a moment ;   then I expressed
something bitter that was in me, expressed it in an infernal
" Yes ! "   After this I got into the air, but not so quickly as
not to hear, as the door of the drawing-room opened, the dis-
concerted drop of Miss Collop's public manner :   she must have
been in the midst of the larger latitude.   Producing with extreme
rapidity, Guy Walsingham has just published a work in which
amiable people who are not initiated have been pained to see the
genius of a sister-novelist held up to unmistakable ridicule ;   so
fresh an exhibition does it seem to them of the dreadful way men
have always treated women.   Dora Forbes, it is true, at the
present hour, is immensely pushed by Mrs. Wimbush, and has sat

for

for his portrait to the young artists she protects, sat for it not only in oils but in monumental alabaster.

What happened at Prestidge later in the day is of course contemporary history. If the interruption I had whimsically sanctioned was almost a scandal, what is to be said of that general dispersal of the company which, under the doctor's rule, began to take place in the evening? His rule was soothing to behold, small comfort as I was to have at the end. He decreed in the interest of his patient an absolutely soundless house and a consequent break-up of the party. Little country practitioner as he was, he literally packed off the Princess. She departed as promptly as if a revolution had broken out, and Guy Walsingham emigrated with her. I was kindly permitted to remain, and this was not denied even to Mrs. Wimbush. The privilege was withheld indeed from Dora Forbes; so Mrs. Wimbush kept her latest capture temporarily concealed. This was so little, however, her usual way of dealing with her eminent friends that a couple of days of it exhausted her patience, and she went up to town with him in great publicity. The sudden turn for the worse her afflicted guest had, after a brief improvement, taken on the third night raised an obstacle to her seeing him before her retreat; a fortunate circumstance doubtless, for she was fundamentally disappointed in him. This was not the kind of performance for which she had invited him to Prestidge, or invited the Princess. Let me hasten to add that none of the generous acts which have characterised her patronage of intellectual and other merit have done so much for her reputation as her lending Neil Paraday the most beautiful of her numerous homes to die in. He took advantage to the utmost of the singular favour. Day by day I saw him sink, and I roamed alone about the empty terraces and gardens. His wife never came near him, but I scarcely noticed it: as I paced there with rage in

my

my heart I was too full of another wrong.   In the event of his
death it would fall to me perhaps to bring out in some charming
form, with notes, with the tenderest editorial care, that precious
heritage of his written project.   But where *was* that precious
heritage, and were both the author and the book to have been
snatched from us?   Lady Augusta wrote me that she had done
all she could and that poor Lord Dorimont, who had really been
worried to death, was extremely sorry.   I couldn't have the matter
out with Mrs. Wimbush, for I didn't want to be taunted by her
with desiring to aggrandise myself by a public connection with
Mr. Paraday's sweepings.   She had signified her willingness to
meet the expense of all advertising, as indeed she was always ready
to do.   The last night of the horrible series, the night before
he died, I put my ear closer to his pillow.

" That thing I read you that morning, you know."

" In your garden—that dreadful day?   Yes! "

" Won't it do as it is ? "

" It would have been a glorious book."

" It *is* a glorious book," Neil Paraday murmured.   " Print it as
it stands—beautifully."

" Beautifully! " I passionately promised.

It may be imagined whether, now that he has gone, the promise
seems to me less sacred.   I am convinced that if such pages had
appeared in his lifetime the Abbey would hold him to-day.   I
have kept the advertising in my own hands, but the manuscript
has not been recovered.   It's impossible, and at any rate intoler-
able, to suppose it can have been wantonly destroyed.   Perhaps
some chance blundering hand, some brutal ignorance has lighted
kitchen-fires with it.   Every stupid and hideous accident haunts
my meditations.   My undiscouragable search for the lost treasure
would make a long chapter.   Fortunately I have a devoted
associate

associate in the person of a young lady who has every day a fresh indignation and a fresh idea and who maintains with intensity that the prize will still turn up. Sometimes I believe her, but I have quite ceased to believe myself. The only thing for us, at all events, is to go on seeking and hoping together; and we should be closely united by this firm tie even were we not at present by another.

Two Sonnets

By William Watson

I—The Frontier

At the hushed brink of twilight,—when, as though
  Some solemn journeying phantom paused to lay
An ominous finger on the awestruck day,
Earth holds her breath till that great presence go,—
A moment comes of visionary glow,
Pendulous 'twixt the gold hour and the grey,
Lovelier than these, more eloquent than they
Of memory, foresight, and life's ebb and flow.

So have I known, in some fair woman's face,
While viewless yet was Time's more gross imprint,
The first, faint, hesitant, elusive hint
Of that invasion of the vandal years
Seem deeper beauty than youth's cloudless grace,
Wake subtler dreams, and touch me nigh to tears.

No

II—Night on Cubar Edge, Derbyshire

No echo of man's life pursues my ears;
　　Nothing disputes this Desolation's reign;
Change comes not, this dread temple to profane,
Where time by æons reckons, not by years.
Its patient form one crag, sole-stranded, rears,
Type of whate'er is destined to remain
While yon still host encamped on Night's waste plain
Keeps armèd watch, a million quivering spears.

Hushed are the wild and wing'd lives of the moor;
The sleeping sheep nestle 'neath ruined wall,
Or unhewn stones in random concourse hurled:
Solitude, sleepless, listens at Fate's door;
And there is built and 'stablisht over all
Tremendous Silence, older than the world.

The Invisible Prince

By Henry Harland

AT a masked ball given by the Countess Wohenhoffen, in Vienna, during carnival week, a year ago, a man draped in the embroidered silks of a Chinese mandarin, his features entirely concealed by an enormous Chinese head in cardboard, was standing in the Wintergarten, the big, dimly lighted conservatory, near the door of one of the gilt-and-white reception rooms, rather a stolid-seeming witness of the multicoloured romp within, when a voice behind him said, "How do you do, Mr. Field ? "—a woman's voice, an English voice.

The mandarin turned round.

From a black mask, a pair of blue-grey eyes looked into his broad, bland Chinese visage ; and a black domino dropped him an extravagant little courtesy.

"How do you do ? " he responded. "I'm afraid I'm not Mr. Field ; but I'll gladly pretend I am, if you'll stop and talk with me. I was dying for a little human conversation."

"Oh, you're afraid you're not Mr. Field, are you ? " the mask replied derisively. "Then why did you turn when I called his name ? "

"You mustn't hope to disconcert me with questions like that," said he. "I turned because I liked your voice."

He

He might quite reasonably have liked her voice, a delicate, clear, soft voice, somewhat high in register, with an accent, crisp, chiselled, concise, that suggested wit as well as distinction. She was rather tall, for a woman; one could divine her slender and graceful, under the voluminous folds of her domino.

She moved a little away from the door, deeper into the conservatory. The mandarin kept beside her. There, amongst the palms, a *fontaine lumineuse* was playing, rhythmically changing colour. Now it was a shower of rubies; now of emeralds or amethysts, of sapphires, topazes, or opals.

" How pretty," she said, " and how frightfully ingenious. I am wondering whether this wouldn't be a good place to sit down. What do *you* think ? " And she pointed with her fan to a rustic bench.

" I think it would be no more than fair to give it a trial," he assented.

So they sat down on the rustic bench, by the *fontaine lumineuse*.

" In view of your fear that you're not Mr. Field, it's rather a coincidence that at a masked ball in Vienna you should just happen to be English, isn't it ? " she asked.

" Oh, everybody's more or less English, in these days, you know," said he.

" There's some truth in that," she admitted, with a laugh. " What a diverting piece of artifice this Wintergarten is, to be sure. Fancy arranging the electric lights to shine through a dome of purple glass, and look like stars. They do look like stars, don't they ? Slightly over-dressed, showy stars, indeed ; stars in the German taste ; but stars, all the same. Then, by day, you know, the purple glass is removed, and you get the sun—the real sun. Do you notice the delicious fragrance of lilac ? If one
                                                                    hadn't

hadn't too exacting an imagination, one might almost persuade oneself that one was in a proper open-air garden, on a night in May. . . . Yes, everybody is more or less English, in these days. That's precisely the sort of thing I should have expected Victor Field to say."

"By-the-bye," questioned the mandarin, "if you don't mind increasing my stores of knowledge, who *is* this fellow Field ? "

"This fellow Field ? Ah, who indeed ? " said she. "That's just what I wish you'd tell me."

"I'll tell you with pleasure, after you've supplied me with the necessary data."

"Well, by some accounts, he's a little literary man in London."

"Oh, come ! You never imagined that I was a little literary man in London."

"You might be worse However, if the phrase offends you, I'll say a rising young literary man, instead. He writes things, you know."

"Poor chap, does he ? But then, that's a way they have, rising young literary persons ? "

"Doubtless. Poems and stories and things. And book reviews, I suspect. And even, perhaps, leading articles in the newspapers."

"*Toute la lyre enfin ?* What they call a penny-a-liner ? "

"I'm sure I don't know what he's paid. I should think he'd get rather more than a penny. He's fairly successful. The things he does aren't bad."

"I must look 'em up. But meantime, will you tell me how you came to mistake me for him ? Has he the Chinese type ? Besides, what on earth should a little London literary man be doing at the Countess Wohenhoffen's ? "

"He was standing near the door, over there, dying for a little
human

human conversation, till I took pity on him. No, he hasn't exactly the Chinese type, but he's wearing a Chinese costume, and I should suppose he'd feel uncommonly hot in that exasperatingly placid Chinese head. *I'm* nearly suffocated, and I'm only wearing a *loup*. For the rest, why *shouldn't* he be here ? "

" If your *loup* bothers you, pray take it off. Don't mind me."

" You're extremely good. But if I should take off my *loup*, you'd be sorry. Of course, manlike, you're hoping that I'm young and pretty."

" Well, and aren't you ? "

" I'm a perfect fright. I'm an old maid."

" Thank you. Manlike, I confess, I *was* hoping you'd be young and pretty. Now my hope has received the strongest confirmation. I'm sure you are."

" Your argument, with a meretricious air of subtlety, is facile and superficial. Don't pin your faith to it. Why *shouldn't* Victor Field be here ? "

" The Countess only receives tremendous swells. It's the most exclusive house in Europe."

" Are you a tremendous swell ? "

" Rather ! Aren't you ? "

She laughed a little, and stroked her fan, a big fan of fluffy black feathers.

" That's very jolly," said he.

" What ? " said she.

" That thing in your lap."

" My fan ? "

" I expect you'd call it a fan."

" For goodness' sake, what would *you* call it ? "

" I should call it a fan."

She

She gave another little laugh. "You have a nice **instinct** for the *mot juste,*" she informed him.

"Oh, no," he disclaimed, modestly. "But I can call a fan a fan, when I think it won't shock the sensibilities of my hearer."

"If the Countess only receives tremendous swells," said she, "you must remember that Victor Field belongs to the Aristocracy of Talent."

"Oh, *quant à ça,* so, from the Wohenhoffen's point of view, do the barber and the horse-leech. In this house, the Aristocracy of Talent dines with the butler."

"Is the Countess such a snob?"

"No; she's an Austrian. They draw the line so absurdly tight in Austria."

"Well, then, you leave me no alternative but to conclude that Victor Field is a tremendous swell. Didn't you notice, I bobbed him a courtesy?"

"I took the courtesy as a tribute to my Oriental magnificence. Field doesn't sound like an especially patrician name. I'd give anything to discover who you are. Can't you be induced to tell me? I'll bribe, entreat, threaten—I'll do anything you think might persuade you."

"I'll tell you at once, if you'll own up that you're Victor Field."

"Oh, I'll own up that I'm Queen Elizabeth if you'll tell me who you are. The end justifies the means."

"Then you *are* Victor Field?"

"If you don't mind suborning perjury, why should I mind committing it? Yes. And now, who are you?"

"No; I must have an unequivocal avowal. Are you or are you not Victor Field?"

"Let

" Let us put it at this, that I'm a good serviceable imitation ; an excellent substitute when the genuine article is not procurable."

" Of course, your real name isn't anything like Victor Field," she declared pensively.

" I never said it was.   But I admire the way in which you give with one hand and take back with the other."

" Your real name is . . . . Wait a moment . . . . Yes, now I have it.   Your real name . . . . It's rather long.   You don't think it will bore you ? "

" Oh, if it's really my real name, I daresay I'm hardened to it."

" Your real name is Louis Charles Ferdinand Stanislas John Joseph Emmanuel Maria Anna."

" Mercy upon me," he cried, " what a name !   You ought to have broken it to me in instalments.   And it's all Christian name at that.   Can't you spare me just a little rag of a surname, for decency's sake ? "

" The surnames of royalties don't matter, Monseigneur."

" Royalties ?   What ?   Dear me, here's rapid promotion !   I am royal now ?   And a moment ago I was a little penny-a-liner in London."

" *L'un n'empêche pas l'autre.*   Have you never heard the story of the Invisible Prince ? "

" I adore irrelevancy.   I seem to have read something about an invisible prince when I was young.   A fairy tale, wasn't it ? "

" The irrelevancy is only apparent.   The story I mean is a story of real life.   Have you ever heard of the Duke of Zeln ? "

" Zeln ?   Zeln ? " he repeated, reflectively.   " No, I don't think so."

She clapped her hands.   " Really, you do it admirably.   If I weren't perfectly sure of my facts, I believe I should be taken in.

Zeln,

Zeln, as any history would tell you, as any old atlas would show you, was a little independent duchy in the centre of Germany."

"Poor, dear thing! Like Jonah in the centre of the whale," he murmured, sympathetically.

"Hush. Don't interrupt. Zeln was a little independent German duchy, and the Duke of Zeln was its sovereign. After the war with France it was absorbed by Prussia. But the ducal family still rank as royal highnesses. Of course, you've heard of the Leczinskis ? "

"Lecz——what ? "

"Leczinski."

"How do you spell it ? "

"L—e—c—z—i—n—s—k—i."

"Good. Capital. You have a real gift for spelling."

"Will you be quiet," she said, severely, "and answer my question ? Are you familiar with the name ? "

"I should never venture to be familiar with a name I didn't know."

"Ah, you don't know it ? You have never heard of Stanislas Leczinski, who was king of Poland ? Of Marie Leczinska, who married Louis XV. ? "

"Oh, to be sure. I remember. The lady whose portrait one sees at Versailles."

"Quite so. Very well ; the last representative of the Leczinskis, in the elder line, was the Princess Anna Leczinska, who, in 1858, married the Duke of Zeln. She was the daughter of John Leczinski, Duke of Grodnia, and governor of Galicia, and of the Archduchess Henrietta d'Este, a cousin of the Emperor of Austria. She was also a great heiress, and an extremely handsome woman. But the Duke of Zeln was a bad lot, a viveur, a gambler, a spendthrift. His wife, like a fool, made her entire
                                                            fortune

fortune over to him, and he proceeded to play ducks and drakes with it. By the time their son was born he'd got rid of the last farthing. Their son wasn't born till '63, five years after their marriage. Well, and then, what did you suppose the duke did ? "

" Reformed, of course. The wicked husband always reforms when a child is born—and there's no more money."

" You know perfectly well what he did. He petitioned the German Diet to annul the marriage. You see, having exhausted the dowry of the Princess Anna, it occurred to him that if she could only be got out of the way, he might marry another heiress, and have the spending of another fortune."

" Clever dodge. Did it come off ? "

" It came off, all too well. He based his petition on the ground that the marriage had never been—I forget what the technical term is. Anyhow, he pretended that the princess had never been his wife except in name, and that the child couldn't possibly be his. The Emperor of Austria stood by his connection, like the loyal gentleman he is ; used every scrap of influence he possessed to help her. But the duke, who was a Protestant (the princess was of course a Catholic), persuaded all the Protestant States in the Diet to vote in his favour. The Emperor of Austria was powerless, the Pope was powerless. And the Diet annulled the marriage."

" Ah," said the mandarin.

" Yes. The marriage was annulled, and the child declared illegitimate. Ernest Augustus, as the duke was somewhat inconsequently named, married again, and had other children, the eldest of whom is the present bearer of the title—the same Duke of Zeln one hears of, quarrelling with the croupiers at Monte Carlo. The Princess Anna, with her baby, came to Austria. The Emperor gave her a pension, and lent her one of his country

houses

houses to live in—Schloss Sanct Andreas. Our hostess, by-the-bye, the Countess Wohenhoffen, was her intimate friend and her *première dame d'honneur*."

"Ah," said the mandarin.

"But the poor princess had suffered more than she could bear. She died when her child was four years old. The Countess Wohenhoffen took the infant, by the Emperor's desire, and brought him up with her own son Peter. He was called Prince Louis Leczinski. Of course, in all moral right, he was the Hereditary Prince of Zeln. His legitimacy, for the rest, and his mother's innocence, are perfectly well established, in every sense but a legal sense, by the fact that he has all the physical characteristics of the Zeln stock. He has the Zeln nose and the Zeln chin, which are as distinctive as the Hapsburgh lip."

"I hope, for the poor young man's sake, though, that they're not so unbecoming ? "

"They're not exactly pretty. The nose is a thought too long, the chin is a trifle short. However, I daresay the poor young man is satisfied. As I was about to tell you, the Countess Wohenhoffen brought him up, and the Emperor destined him for the Church. He even went to Rome and entered the Austrian College. He'd have been on the high road to a cardinalate by this time, if he'd stuck to the priesthood, for he had strong interest. But, lo and behold, when he was about twenty, he chucked the whole thing up."

"Ah ? *Histoire de femme ?* "

"Very likely, though I've never heard any one say so. At all events, he left Rome, and started upon his travels. He had no money of his own, but the Emperor made him an allowance. He started upon his travels, and he went to India, and he went to America, and he went to South Africa, and then, finally, in '87

or

or '88, he went—no one knows where. He totally disappeared, vanished into space. He's not been heard of since. Some people think he's dead. But the greater number suppose that he tired of his false position in the world, and one fine day determined to escape from it, by sinking his identity, changing his name, and going in for a new life under new conditions. They call him the Invisible Prince. His position *was* rather an ambiguous one, wasn't it ? You see, he was neither one thing nor the other. He had no *état-civil*. In the eyes of the law he was a bastard, yet he knew himself to be the legitimate son of the Duke of Zeln. He was a citizen of no country, yet he was the rightful heir to the throne. He was the last descendant of Stanislas Leczinski, yet it was without authority that he bore his name. And then, of course, the rights and wrongs of the matter were only known to a few. The majority of people simply remembered that there had been a scandal. And (as a wag once said of him) wherever he went, he left his mother's reputation behind him. No wonder he found the situation irksome. Well, there is the story of the Invisible Prince."

"And a very exciting, melodramatic little story, too. For my part, I suspect your Prince met a boojum. I love to listen to stories. Won't you tell me another ? Do, please."

"No, he didn't meet a boojum. He went to England, and set up for an author. The Invisible Prince and Victor Field are one and the same person."

"Oh, I say ! Not really ? "

"Yes, really."

"What makes you think so ? "

"I'm sure of it. To begin with, I must confide to you that Victor Field is a man I've never met."

"Never met . . . . ? But, by the blithe way in which you
                                                    were

were laying his sins at my door, a little while ago, I supposed you were sworn confederates."

"What's the good of masked balls, if you can't talk to people you've never met ? I've never met him, but I'm one of his admirers. I like his little poems. And I'm the happy possessor of a portrait of him. It's a print after a photograph. I cut it from an illustrated paper."

"I really almost wish I *was* Victor Field. I should feel such a glow of gratified vanity."

"And the Countess Wohenhoffen has at least twenty portraits of the Invisible Prince—photographs, miniatures, life-size paintings, taken from the time he was born, almost, to the time of his disappearance. Victor Field and Louis Leczinski have countenances as like each other as two halfpence."

"An accidental resemblance, doubtless."

"No, it isn't an accidental resemblance."

"Oh, then you think it's intentional ? "

"Don't be absurd. I might have thought it accidental, except for one or two odd little circumstances. *Primo*, Victor Field is a guest at the Wohenhoffens' ball."

"Oh, he *is* a guest here ? "

"Yes, he is. You are wondering how I know. Nothing simpler. The same costumier who made my domino, supplied his Chinese dress. I noticed it at his shop. It struck me as rather nice, and I asked whom it was for. The costumier said, for an Englishman at the Hôtel de Bade. Then he looked in his book, and told me the Englishman's name. It was Victor Field. So, when I saw the same Chinese dress here to-night, I knew it covered the person of one of my favourite authors. But I own, like you, I was a good deal surprised. What on earth should a little London literary man be doing at the Countess Wohenhoffen's ?

hoffen's ? And then I remembered the astonishing resemblance
between Victor Field and Louis Leczinski ; and I remembered
that to Louis Leczinski the Countess Wohenhoffen had been a
second mother ; and I reflected that though he chose to be as one
dead and buried for the rest of the world, Louis Leczinski might very
probably keep up private relations with the Countess. He might
very probably come to her ball, incognito, and safely masked. I
observed also that the Countess's rooms were decorated throughout with *white lilac*. But the white lilac is the emblematic flower
of the Leczinskis ; green and white are their family colours.
Wasn't the choice of white lilac on this occasion perhaps designed
as a secret compliment to the Prince ? I was taught in the
schoolroom that two and two make four."

   " Oh, one can see that you've enjoyed a liberal education. But
where were you taught to jump to conclusions ? You do it with a
grace, an assurance. I too have heard that two and two make
four ; but first you must catch your two and two. Really, as if
there couldn't be more than one Chinese costume knocking
about Vienna, during carnival week ! Dear, good, sweet lady,
it's of all disguises the disguise they're driving hardest, this
particular season. And then to build up an elaborate theory of
identities upon the mere chance resemblance of a pair of photographs ! Photographs indeed ! Photographs don't give the com-
plexion. Say that your Invisible Prince is dark, what's to prevent
your literary man from being fair or sandy ? Or *vice versâ ?*
And then, how is a little German Polish princeling to write poems
and things in English ? No, no, no ; your reasoning hasn't a leg
to stand on."

   " Oh, I don't mind its not having legs, so long as it convinces
me. As for writing poems and things in English, you yourself
said that everybody is more or less English, in these days.
                                                      German

German princes are especially so. They all learn English, as a
second mother-tongue. You see, like Circassian beauties, they
are mostly bred up for the marriage market ; and nothing is a
greater help towards a good sound remunerative English marriage,
than a knowledge of the language. However, don't be frightened.
I must take it for granted that Victor Field would prefer not to
let the world know who he is. I happen to have discovered his
secret. He may trust to my discretion."

" You still persist in imagining that I'm Victor Field ? "

" I should have to be extremely simple-minded to imagine
anything else. You wouldn't be a male human being if you had
sat here for half an hour patiently talking about another man."

" Your argument, with a meretricious air of subtlety, is facile
and superficial. I thank you for teaching me that word. I'd sit
here till doomsday talking about my worst enemy, for the pleasure
of talking with you."

"Perhaps we have been talking of your worst enemy. Whom
do the moralists pretend a man's worst enemy is wont to be ? "

" I wish you would tell me the name of the person the moralists
would consider *your* worst enemy."

" I'll tell you directly, as I said before, if you'll own up."

" Your price is prohibitive. I've nothing to own up to."

" Well then—good-night."

Lightly, swiftly, she fled from the conservatory, and was soon
irrecoverable in the crowd.

.

The next morning Victor Field left Vienna for London ; but
before he left he wrote a letter to Peter Wohenhoffen. In the
course of it he said : " There was an Englishwoman at your ball
last night with the reasoning powers of a detective in a novel.

By

By divers processes of elimination and induction, she had formed all sorts of theories about no end of things. Among others, for instance, she was willing to bet her halidom that a certain Prince Louis Leczinski, who seems to have gone on the spree some years ago, and never to have come home again—she was willing to bet anything you like that Leczinski and I—*moi qui vous parle* —were to all intents and purposes the same. Who was she, please ? Rather a tall woman, in a black domino, with grey eyes, or greyish blue, and a nice voice."

In the answer which he received from Peter Wohenhoffen towards the end of the week, Peter said : "There were nineteen Englishwomen at my mother's party, all of them rather tall, with nice voices, and grey or blue-grey eyes. I don't know what colours their dominoes were. Here is a list of them."

The names that followed were names of people whom Victor Field almost certainly would never meet. The people Victor knew in London were the sort of people a little literary man might be expected to know. Most of them were respectable ; some of them even deemed themselves rather smart—and patronised him right Britishly. But the nineteen names in Peter Wohenhoffen's list ("Oh, me ! Oh, my !" cried Victor) were names to make you gasp.

All the same, he went a good deal to Hyde Park during the season, and watched the driving.

"Which of all those haughty high-born beauties is she ?" he wondered futilely.

And then the season passed, and then the year ; and little by little, of course, he ceased to think about her.

* * *

One afternoon last May, a man habited in accordance with the

the fashion of the period, stopped before a hairdresser's shop in Knightsbridge somewhere, and, raising his hat, bowed to the three waxen ladies who simpered from the window.

"Oh! It's Mr. Field!" a voice behind him cried. "What are these cryptic rites that you're performing? What on earth are you bowing into a hairdresser's window for?"—a smooth, melodious voice, tinged by an inflection that was half ironical, half bewildered.

"I was saluting the type of English beauty," he answered, turning. "Fortunately, there are divergencies from it," he added, as he met the puzzled smile of his interlocutrice; a puzzled smile indeed, but, like the voice, by no means without its touch of irony.

She gave a little laugh; and then, examining the models critically, "Oh?" she questioned. "Would you call that the type? You place the type high. Their features are quite fault-less, and who ever saw such complexions?"

"It's the type, all the same," said he. "Just as the imitation marionette is the type of English breeding."

"The imitation marionette? I'm afraid I don't follow," she confessed.

"The imitation marionettes. You've seen them at little theatres in Italy. They're actors who imitate puppets. Men and women who try to behave as if they weren't human, as if they were made of starch and whalebone instead of flesh and blood."

"Ah, yes," she assented, with another little laugh. "That *would* be rather typical of our insular methods. But do you know what an engaging, what a reviving spectacle you presented, as you stood there flourishing your hat? What do you imagine people thought? And what would have happened to you if I had just chanced to be a policeman, instead of a friend?"

"Would

"Would you have clapped your handcuffs on me ? I suppose my conduct did seem rather suspicious. I was in the deepest depths of dejection. One must give some expression to one's sorrow."

"Are you going towards Kensington ? " she asked, preparing to move on.

"Before I commit myself, I should like to be sure whether you are," he replied.

"You can easily discover with a little perseverance."

He placed himself beside her, and together they walked towards Kensington.

She was rather taller than the usual woman, and slender. She was exceedingly well-dressed ; smartly, becomingly : a jaunty little hat of strangely twisted straw, with an aigrette springing defiantly from it ; a jacket covered with mazes and labyrinths of embroidery ; at her throat a big knot of white lace, the ends of which fell winding in a creamy cascade to her waist (do they call the thing a *jabot ?*) ; and then. . . . . But what can a man trust himself to write of these esoteric matters ? She carried herself extremely well, too : with grace, with distinction, her head held high, even thrown back a little, superciliously. She had an immense quantity of very lovely hair. Red hair ? Yellow hair ? Red hair with yellow lights burning in it ? Yellow hair with red fires shimmering through it ? In a single loose, full billow it swept away from her forehead, and then flowed into half-a-thousand rippling, crinkling, capricious undulations. And her skin had the sensitive colouring the fineness of texture, that are apt to accompany red hair when it's yellow, yellow hair when it's red. Her face, with its pensive, quizzical eyes, its tip-tilted nose, its rather large mouth, and the little mocking quirks and curves the lips took, was an alert, arch, witty face, a delicate
high-bred

high-bred face, and withal a somewhat sensuous, emotional face ;
the face of a woman with a vast deal of humour in her soul, a vast
deal of mischief, of a woman who would love to tease you and
mystify you, and lead you on, and put you off, and yet who, in
her own way, at her own time, would know supremely well how
to be kind.

But it was mischief rather than kindness that glimmered in her
eyes at present, as she asked, " You were in the deepest depths of
dejection ? Poor man ! Why ? "

" I can't precisely determine," said he, " whether the sympathy that seems to vibrate in your voice is genuine or counterfeit."

" Perhaps it's half and half. But my curiosity is unmixed.
Tell me your troubles."

" The catalogue is long. I've sixteen hundred million. The
weather, for example. The shameless beauty of this radiant
spring day. It's enough to stir all manner of wild pangs and
longings in the heart of an octogenarian. But, anyhow, when
one's life is passed in a dungeon, one can't perpetually be singing
and dancing from mere exuberance of joy, can one ? "

" Is your life passed in a dungeon ? "

" Indeed, indeed, it is. Isn't yours ? "

" It had never occurred to me that it was."

" You're lucky. Mine is passed in the dungeons of Castle
Ennui."

" Oh, Castle Ennui. Ah, yes. You mean you're bored ? "

" At this particular moment I'm savouring the most exquisite
excitement. But in general, when I am not working or sleeping,
I'm bored to extermination—incomparably bored. If only one
could work and sleep alternately, twenty-four hours a day, the
year round ! There's no use trying to play in London. It's so

hard

hard to find a playmate. The English people take their pleasures without salt."

"The dungeons of Castle Ennui," she repeated meditatively. "Yes, we are fellow-prisoners. I'm bored to extermination too. Still," she added, "one is allowed out on parole, now and again. And sometimes one has really quite delightful little experiences."

"It would ill become me, in the present circumstances, to dispute that."

"But the Castle waits to reclaim us afterwards, doesn't it ? That's rather a happy image, Castle Ennui."

"I'm extremely glad you approve of it ; Castle Ennui is the Bastille of modern life. It is built of prunes and prisms ; it has its outer court of Convention, and its inner court of Propriety ; it is moated round by Respectability ; and the shackles its inmates wear are forged of dull little duties and arbitrary little rules. You can only escape from it at the risk of breaking your social neck, or remaining a fugitive from social justice to the end of your days. Yes, it *is* a fairly decent little image."

"A bit out of something you're preparing for the press ? " she suggested.

"Oh, how unkind of you ! " he cried. "It was absolutely extemporaneous."

"One can never tell, with *vous autres gens-de-lettres.*"

"It would be friendlier to say *nous autres gens d'esprit.*"

"Aren't we proving to what degree *nous autres gens d'esprit sont bêtes,*" she remarked, "by continuing to walk along this narrow pavement, when we can get into Kensington Gardens by merely crossing the street ? Would it take you out of your way ? "

"I have no way. I was sauntering for pleasure, if you can believe me. I wish I could hope that you have no way either. Then

Then we could stop here, and crack little jokes together the livelong afternoon," he said, as they entered the Gardens.

"Alas, my way leads straight back to the Castle. I've promised to call on an old woman in Campden Hill."

"Disappoint her. It's good for old women to be disappointed. It whips up their circulation."

"I shouldn't much regret disappointing the old woman, and I should rather like an hour or two of stolen freedom. I don't mind owning that I've generally found you, as men go, a moderately interesting man to talk with. But the deuce of it is. . . . . You permit the expression?"

"I'm devoted to the expression."

"The deuce of it is, I'm supposed to be driving."

"Oh, that doesn't matter. So many suppositions in this world are baseless."

"But there's the prison-van. It's one of the tiresome rules in the female wing of Castle Ennui that you're always supposed, more or less, to be driving. And though you may cheat the authorities by slipping out of the prison-van directly it's turned the corner, and sending it on ahead, there it remains, a factor that can't be eliminated. The prison-van will relentlessly await my arrival in the old woman's street."

"That only adds to the sport. Let it wait. When a factor can't be eliminated, it should be haughtily ignored. Besides, there are higher considerations. If you leave me, what shall I do with the rest of this weary day?"

"You can go to your club."

"Merciful lady! What sin have I committed? I never go to my club, except when I've been wicked, as a penance. If you will permit me to employ a metaphor—oh, but a tried and trusty metaphor—when one ship on the sea meets another in distress, it

stops

stops and comforts it, and forgets all about its previous engagements and the prison-van and everything. Shall we cross to the north, and see whether the Serpentine is in its place ? Or would you prefer to inspect the eastern front of the Palace ? Or may I offer you a penny chair ? "

" I think a penny chair would be the maddest of the three dissipations."

And they sat down in penny chairs.

" It's rather jolly here, isn't it ? " said he. " The trees, with their black trunks, and their leaves, and things. Have you ever seen such sumptuous foliage ? And the greensward, and the shadows, and the sunlight, and the atmosphere, and the mistiness—isn't it like pearl-dust and gold-dust floating in the air ? It's all got up to imitate the background of a Watteau. We must do our best to be frivolous and ribald, and supply a proper foreground. How big and fleecy and white the clouds are. Do you think they're made of cotton-wool ? And what do you suppose they paint the sky with ? There never was such a brilliant, breath-taking blue. It's much too nice to be natural. And they've sprinkled the whole place with scent, haven't they ? You notice how fresh and sweet it smells. If only one could get rid of the sparrows—the cynical little beasts ! hear how they're chortling—and the people, and the nursemaids and children. I have never been able to understand why they admit the public to the parks."

" Go on," she encouraged him. " You're succeeding admirably in your effort to be ribald."

" But that last remark wasn't ribald in the least—it was desperately sincere. I do think it's inconsiderate of them to admit the public to the parks. They ought to exclude all the lower classes, the People, at one fell swoop, and then to discriminate tremendously amongst the others."

" Mercy,

"Mercy, what undemocratic sentiments! The People, the poor dear People—what have they done?"

"Everything. What haven't they done? One could forgive their being dirty and stupid and noisy and rude; one could forgive their ugliness, the ineffable banality of their faces, their goggle-eyes, their protruding teeth, their ungainly motions; but the trait one can't forgive is their venality. They're so mercenary. They're always thinking how much they can get out of you—everlastingly touching their hats and expecting you to put your hand in your pocket. Oh, no, believe me, there's no health in the People. Ground down under the iron heel of despotism, reduced to a condition of hopeless serfdom, I don't say that they might not develop redeeming virtues. But free, but sovereign, as they are in these days, they're everything that is squalid and sordid and offensive. Besides, they read such abominably bad literature."

"In that particular they're curiously like the aristocracy, aren't they?" said she. "By-the-bye, when are you going to publish another book of poems?"

"Apropos of bad literature?"

"Not altogether bad. I rather like your poems."

"So do I," said he. "It's useless to pretend that we haven't tastes in common."

They were both silent for a bit. She looked at him oddly, an inscrutable little light flickering in her eyes. All at once she broke out with a merry trill of laughter.

"What are you laughing at?" he demanded.

"I'm hugely amused," she answered.

"I wasn't aware that I'd said anything especially good."

"You're building better than you know. But if I am amused, *you* look ripe for tears. What is the matter?"

"Every heart knows its own bitterness. Don't pay the least
attention

attention to me.   You mustn't let moodiness of mine cast a blight upon your high spirits."

" No fear.   There are pleasures that nothing can rob of their sweetness.   Life is not all dust and ashes.   There are bright spots."

" Yes, I've no doubt there are."

" And thrilling little adventures—no ? "

" For the bold, I dare say."

" None but the bold deserve them.   Sometimes it's one thing, and sometimes it's another."

" That's very certain."

" Sometimes, for instance, one meets a man one knows, and speaks to him.   And he answers with a glibness !   And then, almost directly, what do you suppose one discovers ? "

" What ? "

" One discovers that the wretch hasn't the ghost of a notion who one is—that he's totally and absolutely forgotten one ! "

" Oh, I say !   Really ? "

" Yes, really.   You can't deny that *that's* an exhilarating little adventure."

" I should think it might be.   One could enjoy the man's embarrassment."

" Or his lack of embarrassment.   Some men are of an assurance, of a *sang froid !*   They'll place themselves beside you, and walk with you, and talk with you, and even propose that you should pass the livelong afternoon cracking jokes with them in a garden, and never breathe a hint of their perplexity.   They'll brazen it out."

" That's distinctly heroic, Spartan, of them, don't you think ? Internally, poor dears, they're very likely suffering agonies of discomfiture."

" We'll

" We'll hope they are. Could they decently do less ? "

" And fancy the mental struggles that must be going on in
their brains. If I were a man in such a situation I'd throw
myself upon the woman's mercy. I'd say, ' Beautiful, sweet lady,
I know I know you. Your name, your entirely charming and
appropriate name, is trembling on the tip of my tongue. But, for
some unaccountable reason, my brute of a memory chooses to play
the fool. If you've a spark of Christian kindness in your soul,
you'll come to my rescue with a little clue.' "

" If the woman had a Christian sense of the ridiculous in her
soul, I fear you'd throw yourself on her mercy in vain."

" What *is* the good of tantalising people ? "

" Besides, the woman might reasonably feel slightly humiliated
to find herself forgotten in that bare-faced manner."

" The humiliation surely would be all the man's. Have you
heard from the Wohenhoffens lately ? "

" The—what ? The—who ? "

" The Wohenhoffens."

" What are the Wohenhoffens ? Are they persons ? Are they
things ? "

" Oh, nothing. My enquiry was merely dictated by a thirst
for knowledge. It occurred to me vaguely that you might have
worn a black domino at a masked ball they gave, the Wohenhoffens. Are you sure you didn't."

" I've a great mind to punish your forgetfulness by pretending
that I did."

" She was rather tall, like you, and she had grey eyes, and a
nice voice, and a laugh that was sweeter than the singing of
nightingales. She was monstrously clever, too, with a flow of
language that would have made her a leader in any sphere. She
was also a perfect fiend. I have always been anxious to meet her
again,

again, in order that I might ask her to marry me. I'm strongly disposed to believe that she was you. Was she ? "

" If I say yes, will you at once proceed to ask me to marry you ? "

" Try it and see."

" *Ce n'est pas la peine.* It occasionally happens that a woman's already got a husband."

" She said she was an old maid."

" Do you dare to insinuate that I look like an old maid ? "

" Yes."

" Upon my word ! "

" Would you wish me to insinuate that you look like anything so insipid as a young girl ? *Were* you the woman of the black domino ? "

" I should need further information, before being able to make up my mind. Are the—what's their name ?—Wohenheimer ?— are the Wohenheimers people one can safely confess to knowing ? Oh, you're a man, and don't count. But a woman ? It sounds a trifle Jewish, Wohenheimer. But of course there are Jews and Jews."

" You're playing with me like the cat in the adage. It's too cruel. No one is responsible for his memory."

" And to think that this man took me down to dinner not two months ago ! " she murmured in her veil.

" You're as hard as nails. In whose house ? Or—stay. Prompt me a little. Tell me the first syllable of your name. Then the rest will come with a rush."

" My name is Matilda Muggins."

" I've a great mind to punish your untruthfulness by pretending to believe you," said he. " Have you really got a husband ? "

" Why do you doubt it ? "

" I don't

" I don't doubt it.   Have you ? "

" I don't know what to answer."

" Don't you know whether you've got a husband ? "

" I don't know what I'd better let you believe.   Yes, on the whole, I think you may as well assume that I've got a husband."

" And a lover, too ? "

" Really !   I like your impertinence ! "

" I only asked to show a polite interest.   I knew the answer would be an indignant negative.   You're an Englishwoman, and you're *nice*.   Oh, one can see with half an eye that you're *nice*. But that a nice Englishwoman should have a lover is as inconceivable as that she should smoke a pipe.   It's only the reg'lar bad-uns in England who have lovers.   There's nothing between the family pew and the divorce court.   One nice Englishwoman is a match for the whole Eleven Thousand Virgins of Cologne."

" To hear you talk, one might fancy you were not English yourself.   For a man of the name of Field, you're uncommonly foreign.   You *look* rather foreign too, you know, by-the-bye. You haven't at all an English cast of countenance."

" I've enjoyed the advantages of a foreign education.   I was brought up abroad."

" Where your features unconsciously assimilated themselves to a foreign type ?   Where you learned a hundred thousand strange little foreign things, no doubt ?   And imbibed a hundred thousand unprincipled little foreign notions ?   And all the ingenuous little foreign prejudices and misconceptions concerning England ? "

" Most of them."

" *Perfide Albion ?*   English hypocrisy ? "

" Oh, yes, the English are consummate hypocrites.   But there's
only

only one objection to their hypocrisy—it so rarely covers any wickedness. It's such a disappointment to see a creature stalking towards you, laboriously draped in sheep's clothing, and then to discover that it's only a sheep. You, for instance, as I took the liberty of intimating a moment ago, in spite of your perfectly respectable appearance, are a perfectly respectable woman. If you weren't, wouldn't I be making furious love to you, though ! "

" As I am, I can see no reason why you shouldn't make furious love to me, if it would amuse you. There's no harm in firing your pistol at a person who's bullet-proof."

" No ; it's merely a wanton waste of powder and shot. However, I shouldn't stick at that. The deuce of it is. . . . You permit the expression ? "

" I'm devoted to the expression."

" The deuce of it is, you profess to be married."

" Do you mean to say that you, with your unprincipled foreign notions, would be restrained by any such consideration as that ? "

" I shouldn't be for an instant—if I weren't in love with you."

" *Comment donc ? Déjà ?* " she cried with a laugh.

" Oh, *déjà !* Why not ? Consider the weather—consider the scene. Is the air soft, is it fragrant ? Look at the sky—good heavens !—and the clouds, and the shadows on the grass, and the sunshine between the trees. The world is made of light to-day, of light and colour, and perfume and music. *Tutt' intorno canta amor, amor, amore !* What would you have ? One recognises one's affinity. One doesn't need a lifetime. You began the business at the Wohenhoffens' ball. To-day you've merely put on the finishing touches."

" Oh, then I *am* the woman you met at the masked ball ? "

" Look me in the eye, and tell me you're not."

                                               " I haven't

"I haven't the faintest interest in telling you I'm not. On the contrary, it rather pleases me to let you imagine that I am."

"She owed me a grudge, you know. I hoodwinked her like everything."

"Oh, did you ? Then, as a sister woman, I should be glad to serve as her instrument of vengeance Do you happen to have such a thing as a watch about you ? "

"Yes."

"Will you be good enough to tell me what o'clock it is ? "

"What are your motives for asking ? "

"I'm expected at home at five."

"Where do you live ? "

"What are your motives for asking ? "

"I want to call upon you."

"You might wait till you're invited."

"Well, invite me—quick ! "

"Never."

"Never ? "

"Never, never, never. A man who's forgotten me as you have ! "

"But if I've only met you once at a masked ball. . . . ."

"Can't you be brought to realise that every time you mistake me for that woman of the masked ball you turn the dagger in the wound ? "

"But if you won't invite me to call upon you, how and when am I to see you again ? "

"I haven't an idea," she answered, cheerfully. "I must go now. Good bye." She rose.

"One moment. Before you go will you allow me to look at the palm of your left hand ? "

"What for ? "

"I can

" I can tell fortunes. I'm extremely good at it. I'll tell you yours."

" Oh, very well," she assented, sitting down again : and guile-lessly she pulled off her glove.

He took her hand, a beautifully slender, nervous hand, warm and soft, with rosy, tapering fingers.

" Oho ! you *are* an old maid after all," he cried. " There's no wedding ring."

" You villain ! " she gasped, snatching the hand away.

" I promised to tell your fortune. Haven't I told it correctly ? "

" You needn't rub it in, though. Eccentric old maids don't like to be reminded of their condition."

" Will you marry *me* ? "

" Why do you ask ? "

" Partly from curiosity. Partly because it's the only way I can think of, to make sure of seeing you again. And then, I like your hair. Will you ? "

" I can't."

" Why not ? "

" The stars forbid. And I'm ambitious. In my horoscope it is written that I shall either never marry at all, or—marry royalty."

" Oh, bother ambition ! Cheat your horoscope. Marry me. Will you ? "

" If you care to follow me," she said, rising again, " you can come and help me to commit a little theft."

He followed her to an obscure and sheltered corner of a flowery path, where she stopped before a bush of white lilac.

" There are no keepers in sight, are there ? " she questioned.

" I don't see any," said he.

" Then allow me to make you a receiver of stolen goods," said she, breaking off a spray, and handing it to him.

" Thank

"Thank you.   But I'd rather have an answer to my question."

"Isn't that an answer ? "

"Is it ? "

"White lilac—to the Invisible Prince ? "

"The Invisible Prince . . . .   Then you *are* the black domino ! "

"Oh, I suppose so."

"And you *will* marry me ? "

"I'll tell the aunt I live with to ask you to dinner."

"But will you marry me ? "

"I thought you wished me to cheat my horoscope ? "

"How could you find a better means of doing so ? "

"What ! if I should marry Louis Leczinski . . . . ? "

"Oh, to be sure.   You would have it that I was Louis Leczinski.   But, on that subject, I must warn you seriously——"

"One instant," she interrupted.   "People must look other people straight in the face when they're giving serious warnings. Look straight into my eyes, and continue your serious warning."

"I must really warn you seriously," said he, biting his lip, "that if you persist in that preposterous delusion about my being Louis Leczinski, you'll be most awfully sold.   I have nothing on earth to do with Louis Leczinski.   Your ingenious little theories, as I tried to convince you at the time, were absolute romance."

Her eyebrows raised a little, she kept her eyes fixed steadily on his—oh, in the drollest fashion, with a gaze that seemed to say "How admirably you do it !   I wonder whether you imagine I believe you.   Oh, you fibber !   Aren't you ashamed to tell me such abominable fibs ? " . . . .

They stood still, eyeing each other thus, for something like twenty seconds, and then they both laughed and walked on.

Reticence in Literature
Some Roundabout Remarks

By Hubert Crackanthorpe

URING the past fifty years, as every one knows, the art of
fiction has been expanding in a manner exceedingly
remarkable, till it has grown to be the predominant branch of
imaginative literature. But the other day we were assured that
poetry only thrives in limited and exquisite editions; that the
drama, here in England at least, has practically ceased to be literature at all. Each epoch instinctively chooses that literary vehicle
which is best adapted for the expression of its particular temper :
just as the drama flourished in the robust age of Shakespeare and
Ben Jonson ; just as that outburst of lyrical poetry, at the beginning of the century in France, coincided with a period of extreme
emotional exaltation ; so the novel, facile and flexible in its conventions, with its endless opportunities for accurate delineation of
reality, becomes supreme in a time of democracy and of science—
to note but these two salient characteristics.

And, if we pursue this light of thought, we find that, on all
sides, the novel is being approached in one especial spirit, that it
would seem to be striving, for the moment at any rate, to perfect
itself within certain definite limitations. To employ a hackneyed,

and

and often quite unintelligent, catchword—the novel is becoming realistic.

Throughout the history of literature, the jealous worship of beauty—which we term idealism—and the jealous worship of truth —which we term realism—have alternately prevailed. Indeed, it is within the compass of these alternations that lies the whole fundamental diversity of literary temper.

Still, the classification is a clumsy one, for no hard and fast line can be drawn between the one spirit and the other. The so-called idealist must take as his point of departure the facts of Nature ; the so-called realist must be sensitive to some one or other of the forms of beauty, if each would achieve the fineness of great art. And the pendulum of production is continually swinging, from degenerate idealism to degenerate realism, from effete vapidity to slavish sordidity.

Either term, then, can only be employed in a purely limited and relative sense. Completely idealistic art—art that has no point of contact with the facts of the universe, as we know them—is, of course, an impossible absurdity ; similarly, a complete reproduction of Nature by means of words is an absurd impossibility. Neither emphasization nor abstraction can be dispensed with : the one, eliminating the details of no import ; the other, exaggerating those which the artist has selected. And, even were such a thing possible, it would not be Art. The invention of a highly perfected system of coloured photography, for instance, or a skilful recording by means of the phonograph of scenes in real life, would not subtract one whit from the value of the painter's or the playwright's interpretation. Art is not invested with the futile function of perpetually striving after imitation or reproduction of Nature ; she endeavours to produce, through the adaptation of a restricted number of natural facts, an harmonious and satisfactory whole. Indeed, in

this

this very process of adaptation and blending together, lies the main
and greater task of the artist. And the novel, the short story,
even the impression of a mere incident, convey each of them, the
imprint of the temper in which their creator has achieved this
process of adaptation and blending together of his material. They
are inevitably stamped with the hall-mark of his personality. A
work of art can never be more than a corner of Nature, seen
through the temperament of a single man. Thus, all literature is,
must be, essentially subjective ; for style is but the power of
individual expression. The disparity which separates literature
from the reporter's transcript is ineradicable. There is a quality
of ultimate suggestiveness to be achieved ; for the business of art
is, not to explain or to describe, but to suggest. That attitude of
objectivity, or of impersonality towards his subject, consciously or
unconsciously, assumed by the artist, and which nowadays provokes
so considerable an admiration, can be attained only in a limited
degree. Every piece of imaginative work must be a kind of
autobiography of its creator—significant, if not of the actual facts
of his existence, at least of the inner working of his soul. We are
each of us conscious, not of the whole world, but of our own
world ; not of naked reality, but of that aspect of reality which
our peculiar temperament enables us to appropriate. Thus, every
narrative of an external circumstance is never anything else than
the transcript of the impression produced upon ourselves by that
circumstance, and, invariably, a degree of individual interpretation
is insinuated into every picture, real or imaginary, however
objective it may be. So then, the disparity between the so-called
idealist and the so-called realist is a matter, not of æsthetic philosophy, but of individual temperament. Each is at work, according
to the especial bent of his genius, within precisely the same limits.
Realism, as a creed, is as ridiculous as any other literary creed.

Now,

Now, it would have been exceedingly curious if this recent specialisation of the art of fiction, this passion for draining from the life, as it were, born, in due season, of the general spirit of the latter half of the nineteenth century, had not provoked a considerable amount of opposition—opposition of just that kind which every new evolution in art inevitably encounters. Between the vanguard and the main body there is perpetual friction.

But time flits quickly in this hurried age of ours, and the opposition to the renascence of fiction as a conscientious interpretation of life is not what it was; its opponents are not the men they were. It is not so long since a publisher was sent to prison for issuing English translations of celebrated specimens of French realism; yet, only the other day, we vied with each other in doing honour to the chief figure-head of that tendency across the Channel, and there was heard but the belated protest of a few worthy individuals, inadequately equipped with the jaunty courage of ignorance, or the insufferable confidence of second-hand knowledge.

And during the past year things have been moving very rapidly. The position of the literary artist towards Nature, his great inspirer, has become more definite, more secure. A sound, organised opinion of men of letters is being acquired; and in the little bouts with the *bourgeois*—if I may be pardoned the use of that wearisome word—no one has to fight single-handed. Heroism is at a discount; Mrs. Grundy is becoming mythological; a crowd of unsuspected supporters collect from all sides, and the deadly conflict of which we had been warned becomes but an interesting skirmish. Books are published, stories are printed, in old-established reviews, which would never have been tolerated a few years ago. On all sides, deference to the tendency of the time is spreading. The truth must be admitted: the roar of unthinking prejudice is dying away.

All

All this is exceedingly comforting : and yet, perhaps, it is not a matter for absolute congratulation. For, if the enemy are not dying as gamely as we had expected, if they are, as I am afraid, losing heart, and in danger of sinking into a condition of passive indifference, it should be to us a matter of not inconsiderable apprehension. If this new evolution in the art of fiction—this general return of the literary artist towards Nature, on the brink of which we are to-day hesitating—is to achieve any definite, ultimate fineness of expression, it will benefit enormously by the continued presence of a healthy, vigorous, if not wholly intelligent, body of opponents. Directly or indirectly, they will knock a lot of nonsense out of us, will these opponents ;—why should we be ashamed to admit it ? They will enable us to find our level, they will spur us on to bring out the best—and only the best—that is within us.

Take, for instance, the gentleman who objects to realistic fiction on moral grounds. If he does not stand the most conspicuous to-day, at least he was pre-eminent the day before yesterday. He is a hard case, and it is on his especial behalf that I would appeal. For he has been dislodged from the hill top, he has become a target for all manner of unkind chaff, from the ribald youth of Fleet Street and Chelsea. He has been labelled a Philistine : he has been twitted with his middle-age ; he has been reported to have compromised himself with that indecent old person, Mrs. Grundy. It is confidently asserted that he comes from Putney, or from Sheffield, and that, when he is not busy abolishing the art of English literature, he is employed in safeguarding the interests of the grocery or tallow-chandler's trade. Strange and cruel tales of him have been printed in the monthly reviews ; how, but for him, certain well-known popular writers would have written masterpieces ; how, like the ogre in the fairy tale, he consumes every morning at break-

fast

fast a hundred pot-boiled young geniuses. For the most part they have been excellently well told, these tales of this moral ogre of ours ; but why start to shatter brutally their dainty charm by a soulless process of investigation ? No, let us be shamed rather into a more charitable spirit, into making generous amends, into rehabilitating the greatness of our moral ogre.

He is the backbone of our nation ; the guardian of our mediocrity ; the very foil of our intelligence. Once, you fancied that you could argue with him, that you could dispute his dictum. Ah! how we cherished that day-dream of our extreme youth. But it was not to be. He is still immense ; for he is unassailable ; he is flawless, for he is complete within himself ; his lucidity is yet unimpaired ; his impartiality is yet supreme. Who amongst us could judge with a like impartiality the productions of Scandinavia and Charpentier, Walt Whitman, and the Independent Theatre ? Let us remember that he has never professed to understand Art, and the deep debt of gratitude that every artist in the land should consequently owe to him ; let us remember that he is above us, for he belongs to the great middle classes ; let us remember that he commands votes, that he is candidate for the County Council ; let us remember that he is delightful, because he is intelligible.

Yes, he is intelligible ; and of how many of us can that be said ? His is no complex programme, no subtly exacting demand. A plain moral lesson is all that he asks, and his voice is as of one crying in the ever fertile wilderness of Smith and of Mudie.

And he is right, after all—if he only knew it. The business of art is to create for us fine interests, to make of our human nature a more complete thing : and thus, all great art is moral in the wider and the truer sense of the word. It is precisely on this point of the meaning of the word "moral" that we and our ogre

part

part company. To him, morality is concerned only with the
established relations between the sexes and with fair dealing between
man and man : to him the subtle, indirect morality of Art is
incomprehensible.

Theoretically, Art is non-moral. She is not interested in any
ethical code of any age or any nation, except in so far as the
breach or observance of that code may furnish her with material
on which to work. But, unfortunately, in this complex world of
ours, we cannot satisfactorily pursue one interest—no, not even the
interest of Art, at the expense of all others—let us look that fact in
the face, doggedly, whatever pangs it may cost us—pleading mag-
nanimously for the survival of our moral ogre, for there will be
danger to our cause when his voice is no more heard.

If imitation be the sincerest form of flattery, then our moral
ogre must indeed have experienced a proud moment, when a
follower came to him from the camp of the lovers of Art, and the
artistic objector to realistic fiction started on his timid career. I
use the word timid in no disparaging sense, but because our
artistic objector, had he ventured a little farther from the vicinity
of the coat-tails of his powerful protector, might have secured a
more adequate recognition of his performances. For he is by no
means devoid of adroitness. He can patter to us glibly of the
" gospel of ugliness " ; of the " cheerlessness of modern literature " ;
he can even juggle with that honourable property-piece, the maxim
of Art for Art's sake. But there have been moments when even
this feat has proved ineffective, and some one has started scoffing
at his pretended " delight in pure rhythm or music of the phrase,"
and flippantly assured him that he is talking nonsense, and that
style is a mere matter of psychological suggestion. You fancy
our performer nonplussed, or at least boldly bracing himself to
brazen the matter out. No, he passes dexterously to his curtain
                                                          effect

effect—a fervid denunciation of express trains, evening newspapers, Parisian novels, or the first number of THE YELLOW
BOOK. Verily, he is a versatile person.

Sometimes, to listen to him you would imagine that pessimism
and regular meals were incompatible ; that the world is only
ameliorated by those whom it completely satisfies, that good pre-
dominates over evil, that the problem of our destiny had been
solved long ago. You begin to doubt whether any good thing
can come out of this miserable, inadequate age of ours, unless it
be a doctored survival of the vocabulary of a past century. The
language of the coster and cadger resound in our midst, and,
though Velasquez tried to paint like Whistler, Rudyard Kipling
cannot write like Pope. And a weird word has been invented to
explain the whole business. Decadence, decadence : you are all
decadent nowadays. Ibsen, Degas, and the New English Art
Club ; Zola, Oscar Wilde, and the Second Mrs. Tanqueray.
Mr. Richard Le Gallienne is hoist with his own petard ; even the
British playwright has not escaped the taint. Ah, what a hideous
spectacle. All whirling along towards one common end. And
the elegant voice of the artistic objector floating behind : " *Après
vous le déluge.*" A wholesale abusing of the tendencies of the age
has ever proved, for the superior mind, an inexhaustible source
of relief. Few things breed such inward comfort as the contemplation of one's own pessimism—few things produce such
discomfort as the remembrance of our neighbour's optimism.

And yet, pessimists though we may be dubbed, some of us, on
this point at least, how can we compete with the hopelessness
enjoyed by our artistic objector, when the spectacle of his despond-
ency makes us insufferably replete with hope and confidence, so
that while he is loftily bewailing or prettily denouncing the com-
pleteness of our degradation, we continue to delight in the evil of

                                                              our

our ways? Oh, if we could only be sure that he would persevere in reprimanding this persistent study of the pitiable aspects of life, how our hearts would go out towards him? For the man who said that joy is essentially, regrettably inartistic, admitted in the same breath that misery lends itself to artistic treatment twice as easily as joy, and resumed the whole question in a single phrase. Let our artistic objector but weary the world sufficiently with his despair concerning the permanence of the cheerlessness of modern realism, and some day a man will arise who will give us a study of human happiness, as fine, as vital as anything we owe to Guy de Maupassant or to Ibsen. That man will have accomplished the infinitely difficult, and in admiration and in awe shall we bow down our heads before him.

In one radical respect the art of fiction is not in the same position as the other arts. They—music, poetry, painting, sculpture, and the drama—possess a magnificent fabric of accumulated tradition. The great traditions of the art of fiction have yet to be made. Ours is a young art, struggling desperately to reach expression, with no great past to guide it. Thus, it should be a matter for wonder, not that we stumble into certain pitfalls, but that we do not fall headlong into a hundred more.

But, if we have no great past, we have the present and the future—the one abundant in facilities, the other abundant in possibilities. Young men of to-day have enormous chances : we are working under exceedingly favourable conditions. Possibly we stand on the threshold of a very great period. I know, of course, that the literary artist is shamefully ill-paid, and that the man who merely caters for the public taste, amasses a rapid and respectable fortune. But how is it that such an arrangement seems other than entirely equitable? The essential conditions of the two cases are entirely distinct. The one man is free to give untrammelled
expression

expression to his own soul, free to fan to the full the flame that burns in his heart : the other is a seller of wares, a unit in national commerce. To the one is allotted liberty and a living wage ; to the other, captivity and a consolation in Consols. Let us whine, then, no more concerning the prejudice and the persecution of the Philistine, when even that misanthrope, Mr. Robert Buchanan, admits that there is no power in England to prevent a man writing exactly as he pleases. Before long the battle for literary freedom will be won. A new public has been created—appreciative, eager and determined ; a public which, as Mr. Gosse puts it, in one of those admirable essays of his, " has eaten of the apple of know-ledge, and will not be satisfied with mere marionnettes. Whatever comes next," Mr. Gosse continues, " we cannot return, in serious novels, to the inanities and impossibilites of the old well-made plot, to the children changed at nurse, to the madonna-heroine and the god-like hero, to the impossible virtues and melodramatic vices. In future, even those who sneer at realism and misrepre-sent it most wilfully, will be obliged to put their productions more in accordance with veritable experience. There will still be novel-writers who address the gallery, and who will keep up the gaudy old convention, and the clumsy *Family Herald* evolution, but they will no longer be distinguished men of genius. They will no longer sign themselves George Sand or Charles Dickens."

Fiction has taken her place amongst the arts. The theory that writing resembles the blacking of boots, the more boots you black, the better you do it, is busy evaporating. The excessive admira-tion for the mere idea of a book or a story is dwindling ; so is the comparative indifference to slovenly treatment. True is it that the society lady, dazzled by the brilliancy of her own conversation, and the serious-minded spinster, bitten by some sociological theory, still decide in the old jaunty spirit, that fiction is the obvious

                                                    medium

medium through which to astonish or improve the world. Let us beware of the despotism of the intelligent amateur, and cease our toying with that quaint and winsome bogey of ours, the British Philistine, whilst the intelligent amateur, the deadliest of Art's enemies, is creeping up in our midst.

For the familiarity of the man in the street with the material employed by the artist in fiction, will ever militate against the acquisition of a sound, fine, and genuine standard of workmanship. Unlike the musician, the painter, the sculptor, the architect, the artist in fiction enjoys no monopoly in his medium. The word and the phrase are, of necessity, the common property of everybody ; the ordinary use of them demands no special training. Hence the popular mind, while willingly acknowledging that there are technical difficulties to be surmounted in the creation of the sonata, the landscape, the statue, the building, in the case of the short story, or of the longer novel, declines to believe even in their existence, persuaded that in order to produce good fiction, an ingenious idea, or "plot," as it is termed, is the one thing needed. The rest is a mere matter of handwriting.

The truth is, and, despite Mr. Waugh, we are near recognition of it, that nowadays there is but scanty merit in the mere selection of any particular subject, however ingenious or daring it may appear at first sight ; that a man is not an artist, simply because he writes about heredity or the *demi-monde*, that to call a spade a spade requires no extraordinary literary gift, and that the essential is contained in the frank, fearless acceptance by every man of his entire artistic temperament, with its qualities and its flaws.

Credo

By Arthur Symons

EACH, in himself, his hour to be and cease
Endures alone, yet few there be who dare
  Sole with himself his single burden bear,
All the long day until the night's release.

Yet, ere the night fall, and the shadows close,
  This labour of himself is each man's lot;
  All a man hath, yet living, is forgot,
Himself he leaves behind him when he goes.

If he have any valiancy within,
  If he have made his life his very own,
  If he have loved and laboured, and ha.e known
A strenuous virtue, and the joy of sin;

Then, being dead, he has not lived in vain,
  For he has saved what most desire to lose,
  And he has chosen what the few must choose,
Since life, once lived, returns no more again.

For

For of our time we lose so large a part
    In serious trifles, and so oft let slip
    The wine of every moment at the lip
Its moment, and the moment of the heart.

We are awake so little on the earth,
    And we shall sleep so long, and rise so late,
    If there is any knocking at that gate
Which is the gate of death, the gate of birth.

The Foolish Virgin

By George Gissing

COMING down to breakfast, as usual, rather late, Miss Jewell was surprised to find several persons still at table. Their conversation ceased as she entered, and all eyes were directed to her with a look in which she discerned some special meaning. For several reasons she was in an irritable humour ; the significant smiles, the subdued " Good mornings," and the silence that followed, so jarred upon her nerves that, save for curiosity, she would have turned and left the room.

Mrs. Banting (generally at this hour busy in other parts of the house) inquired with a sympathetic air whether she would take porridge ; the others awaited her reply as if it were a matter of general interest. Miss Jewell abruptly demanded an egg. The awkward pause was broken by a high falsetto.

" I believe you know who it is all the time, Mr. Drake," said Miss Ayres, addressing the one man present.

" I assure you I don't. Upon my word, I don't. The whole thing astonishes me."

Resolutely silent, Miss Jewell listened to a conversation the drift of which remained dark to her, until some one spoke the name " Mr. Cheeseman ; " then it was with difficulty that she controlled her face and her tongue. The servant brought her an egg. She

struck

struck it clumsily with the edge of the spoon, and asked in an
affected drawl :

" What are you people talking about ? "

Mrs. Sleath, smiling maliciously, took it upon herself to
reply.

" Mr. Drake has had a letter from Mr. Cheeseman. He writes
that he's engaged, but doesn't say who to. Delicious mystery,
isn't it ? "

The listener tried to swallow a piece of bread-and-butter, and
seemed to struggle with a constriction of the throat. Then, looking round the table, she said with contemptuous pleasantry :

" Some lodging-house servant, I shouldn't wonder."

Every one laughed. Then Mr. Drake declared he must be off
and rose from the table. The ladies also moved, and in a minute
or two Miss Jewell sat at her breakfast alone.

She was a tall, slim person, with unremarkable, not ill-moulded
features. Nature meant her to be graceful in form and pleasantly
feminine of countenance ; unwholesome habit of mind and body
was responsible for the defects that now appeared in her. She had
no colour, no flesh ; but an agreeable smile would well have
become her lips, and her eyes needed only the illumination of
healthy thought to be more than commonly attractive. A few
months would see the close of her twenty-ninth year ; but Mrs.
Banting's boarders, with some excuse, judged her on the wrong
side of thirty.

Her meal, a sad pretence, was soon finished. She went to the
window and stood there for five minutes looking at the cabs and
pedestrians in the sunny street. Then, with the languid step
which had become natural to her, she ascended the stairs and
turned into the drawing-room. Here, as she had expected, two
ladies sat in close conversation. Without heeding them, she
walked

walked to the piano, selected a sheet of music, and sat down to play.

Presently, whilst she drummed with vigour on the keys, some one approached; she looked up and saw Mrs. Banting; the other persons had left the room.

"If it's true," murmured Mrs. Banting, with genuine kindliness on her flabby lips, "all I can say is that it's shameful—shameful!"

Miss Jewell stared at her.

"What do you mean?"

"Mr. Cheeseman—to go and——"

"I don't understand you. What is it to me?"

The words were thrown out almost fiercely, and a crash on the piano drowned whatever Mrs. Banting meant to utter in reply. Miss Jewell now had the drawing-room to herself.

She "practised" for half an hour, careering through many familiar pieces with frequent mechanical correction of time-honoured blunders. When at length she was going up to her room, a grinning servant handed her a letter which had just arrived. A glance at the envelope told her from whom it came, and in privacy she at once opened it. The writer's address was Glasgow.

"My dear Rosamund," began the letter, "I can't understand why you write in such a nasty way. For some time now your letters have been horrid. I don't show them to William because if I did he would get into a tantrum. What I have to say to you now is this, that we simply can't go on sending you the money. We haven't it to spare, and that's the plain truth. You think we're rolling in money, and it's no use telling you we are not. William said last night that you *must* find some way of supporting yourself, and I can only say the same. You are a lady and had a

                                                      thorough

thorough good education, and I am sure you have only to exert yourself. William says I may promise you a five-pound note twice a year, but more than that you must not expect. Now do just think over your position——"

She threw the sheet of paper aside, and sat down to brood miserably. This little back bedroom, at no time conducive to good spirits, had seen Rosamund in many a dreary or exasperated mood; to-day it beheld her on the very verge of despair. Illuminated texts of Scripture spoke to her from the walls in vain; portraits of admired clergymen smiled vainly from the mantelpiece. She was conscious only of a dirty carpet, an ill-made bed, faded curtains, and a window that looked out on nothing. One cannot expect much for a guinea a week, when it includes board and lodging; the bedroom was at least a refuge, but even that, it seemed, would henceforth be denied her. Oh, the selfishness of people! And oh, the perfidy of man!

For eight years, since the breaking up of her home, Rosamund had lived in London boarding-houses. To begin with, she could count on a sufficient income, resulting from property in which she had a legitimate share. Owing to various causes, the value of this property had steadily diminished, until at length she became dependent upon the subsidies of kinsfolk; for more than a twelve-month now, the only person able and willing to continue such remittances had been her married sister, and Rosamund had hardly known what it was to have a shilling of pocket-money. From time to time she thought feebly and confusedly of " doing something," but her aims were so vague, her capabilities so inadequate, that she always threw aside the intention in sheer hopelessness. Whatever will she might once have possessed had evaporated in the boarding-house atmosphere. It was hard to believe that her brother-in-law would ever withhold the poor five pounds a month

And

And—what is the use of boarding-houses if not to renew indefi-nitely the hope of marriage?

She was not of the base order of women. Conscience yet lived in her, and drew support from religion; something of modesty, of self-respect, still clad her starving soul. Ignorance and ill-luck had once or twice thrown her into such society as may be found in establishments outwardly respectable; she trembled and fled. Even in such a house as this of Mrs. Banting's, she had known sickness of disgust. Herself included, four single women abode here at the present time; and the scarcely disguised purpose of every one of them was to entrap a marriageable man. In the others, it seemed to her detestable, and she hated all three, even as they in their turn detested her. Rosamund flattered herself with the persuasion that she did not aim merely at marriage and a sub-sistence; she would not marry *any* one; her desire was for sym-pathy, true companionship. In years gone by she had used to herself a more sacred word; nowadays the homely solace seemed enough. And of late a ray of hope had glimmered upon her dusty path. Mr. Cheeseman, with his plausible airs, his engaging smile, had won something more than her confidence; an acquaintance of six months, ripening at length to intimacy, justified her in regarding him with sanguine emotion. They had walked toge-ther in Kensington Gardens; they had exchanged furtive and significant glances at table and elsewhere; every one grew aware of the mutual preference. It shook her with a painful misgiving when Mr. Cheeseman went away for his holiday and spoke no word; but probably he would write. He had written—to his friend Drake; and all was over.

Her affections suffered, but that was not the worst. Her pride had never received so cruel a blow.

After a life of degradation which might well have unsexed her,
Rosamund

Rosamund remained a woman. The practice of affections numberless had taught her one truth, that she could never hope to charm save by reliance upon her feminine qualities. Boarding-house girls, such numbers of whom she had observed, seemed all intent upon disowning their womanhood; they cultivated masculine habits, wore as far as possible male attire, talked loud slang, threw scorn (among themselves at all events) upon domestic virtues; and not a few of them seemed to profit by the prevailing fashion. Rosamund had tried these tactics, always with conscious failure. At other times, and vastly to her relief, she aimed in precisely the opposite direction, encouraging herself in feminine extremes. She would talk with babbling *naïveté*, exaggerate the languor induced by idleness, lack of exercise, and consequent ill-health; betray timidities and pruderies, let fall a pious phrase, rise of a morning for "early celebration" and let the fact be known. These and the like extravagances had appeared to fascinate Mr. Cheeseman, who openly professed his dislike for androgynous persons. And Rosamund enjoyed the satisfaction of moderate sincerity. Thus, or very much in this way, would she be content to live. Romantic passion she felt to be beyond her scope. Long ago—ah! perhaps long ago, when she first knew Geoffrey Hunt——

The name, as it crossed her mind, suggested an escape from the insufferable *ennui* and humiliation of hours till evening. It must be half a year since she called upon the Hunts, her only estimable acquaintances in or near London. They lived at Teddington, and the railway fare was always a deterrent; nor did she care much for Mrs. Hunt and her daughters, who of late years had grown reserved with her, as if uneasy about her mode of life. True, they were not at all snobbish; homely, though well-to-do people; but they had such strict views, and could not understand
the

the existence of a woman less energetic than themselves. In her
present straits, which could hardly be worse, their counsel might
prove of value; though she doubted her courage when it came to
making confessions.

She would do without luncheon (impossible to sit at table with
those "creatures") and hope to make up for it at tea; in truth
appetite was not likely to trouble her. Then for dress. Wearily
she compared this garment with that, knowing beforehand that
all were out of fashion and more or less shabby. Oh, what did
it matter! She had come to beggary, the result that might have
been foreseen long ago. Her faded costume suited fitly enough
with her fortunes—nay, with her face. For just then she caught
a sight of herself in the glass, and shrank. A lump choked her:
looking desperately, as if for help, for pity, through gathering
tears, she saw the Bible verse on the nearest wall: "Come unto
me——" Her heart became that of a woful child; she put her
hands before her face, and prayed in the old, simple words of
childhood.

As her call must not be made before half-past three, she could
not set out upon the journey forthwith; but it was a relief to get
away from the house. In this bright weather, Kensington
Gardens, not far away, seemed a natural place for loitering, but
the alleys would remind her too vividly of late companionship;
she walked in another direction, sauntered for an hour by the
shop windows of Westbourne Grove, and, when she felt tired, sat
at the railway station until it was time to start. At Teddington,
half a mile's walk lay before her; though she felt no hunger, long
abstinence and the sun's heat taxed her strength to the point of
exhaustion; on reaching her friend's door, she stood trembling
with nervousness and fatigue. The door opened, and to her
dismay she learnt that Mrs. Hunt was away from home.

Happily,

Happily, the servant added that Miss Caroline was in the garden.

"I'll go round," said Rosamund at once. "Don't trouble——"

The pathway round the pleasant little house soon brought her within view of a young lady who sat in a garden-chair, sewing. But Miss Caroline was not alone ; near to her stood a man in shirt-sleeves and bare-headed, vigorously sawing a plank ; he seemed to be engaged in the construction of a summer-house, and Rosamund took him at first sight for a mechanic, but when he turned round, exhibiting a ruddy face all agleam with health and good humour, she recognised the young lady's brother, Geoffrey Hunt. He, as though for the moment puzzled, looked fixedly at her.

"Oh, Miss Jewell, how glad I am to see you ! "

Enlightened by his sister's words, Geoffrey dropped the saw, and stepped forward with still heartier greeting. Had civility permitted, he might easily have explained his doubts. It was some six years since his last meeting with Rosamund, and she had changed not a little ; he remembered her as a graceful and rather pretty girl, with life in her, even if it ran for the most part to silliness, gaily dressed, sprightly of manner ; notwithstanding the account he had received of her from his relatives, it astonished him to look upon this limp, faded woman. In Rosamund's eyes, Geoffrey was his old self ; perhaps a trifle more stalwart, and if anything handsomer, but with just the same light in his eyes, the same smile on his bearded face, the same cordiality of utterance. For an instant, she compared him with Mr. Cheeseman, and flushed for very shame. Unable to command her voice, she stammered incoherent nothings ; only when a seat supported her weary body did she lose the dizziness which had threatened downright collapse ; then she closed her eyes, and forgot everything but the sense of rest.

Geoffrey

Geoffrey drew on his coat, and spoke jestingly of his amateur
workmanship. Such employment, however, seemed not inappro-
priate to him, for his business was that of a timber-merchant.
Of late years he had lived abroad, for the most part in Canada.
Rosamund learnt that at present he was having a longish holiday.

"And you go back to Canada ?"

This she asked when Miss Hunt had stepped into the house to
call for tea. Geoffrey answered that it was doubtful ; for various
reasons he rather hoped to remain in England, but the choice
did not altogether rest with him.

"At all events "—she gave a poor little laugh—" you haven't
pined in exile."

"Not a bit of it. I have always had plenty of hard work—
the one thing needful."

"Yes—I remember—you always used to say that. And I
used to protest. You granted, I think, that it might be different
with women."

"Did I ?"

He wished to add something to the point, but refrained out of
compassion. It was clear to him that Miss Jewell, at all events,
would have been none the worse for exacting employment.
Mrs. Hunt had spoken of her with the disapprobation natural in
a healthy, active woman of the old school, and Geoffrey himself
could not avoid a contemptuous judgment.

"You have lived in London all this time ?" he asked, before
she could speak.

"Yes. Where else should I live ? My sister at Glasgow
doesn't want me there, and—and there's nobody else, you know."
She tried to laugh. "I have friends in London—well, that is to
say—at all events I'm not *quite* solitary."

The man smiled, and could not allow her to suspect how pro-
foundly

foundly he pitied such a condition. Caroline Hunt had reappeared ; she began to talk of her mother and sister, who were enjoying themselves in Wales. Her own holiday would come upon their return ; Geoffrey was going to take her to Switzerland.

Tea arrived just as Rosamund was again sinking into bodily faintness and desolation of spirit. It presently restored her, but she could hardly converse. She kept hoping that Caroline would offer her some invitation—to lunch, to dine, anything ; but as yet no such thought seemed to occur to the young hostess. Suddenly the aspect of things was altered by the arrival of new callers, a whole family, man, wife and three children, strangers to Rosamund. For a time it seemed as if she must go away without any kind of solace ; for Geoffrey had quitted her, and she sat alone. On the spur of irrational resentment, she rose and advanced to Miss Hunt.

"Oh, but you are not going ! I want you to stay and have dinner with us, if you can. Would it make you too late ? "

Rosamund flushed and could scarce contain her delight. In a moment she was playing with the youngest of the children, and even laughing aloud, so that Geoffrey glanced curiously towards her. Even the opportunity of private conversation which she had not dared to count upon was granted before long; when the callers had departed Caroline excused herself, and left her brother alone with the guest for half an hour. There was no time to be lost ; Rosamund broached almost immediately the subject uppermost in her mind.

"Mr. Hunt, I know how dreadful it is to have people asking for advice, but if I *might*—if you could have patience with me——"

"I haven't much wisdom to spare," he answered, with easy good-nature.

"Oh,

"Oh, you are very rich in it, compared with poor me.—And my position is *so* difficult. I want—I am trying to find some way of being useful in the world. I am tired of living for myself. I seem to be such a useless creature. Surely even *I* must have *some* talent, which it's my duty to put to use! Where should I turn ? Could you help me with a suggestion ? "

Her words, now that she had overcome the difficulty of beginning, chased each other with breathless speed, and Geoffrey was all but constrained to seriousness ; he took it for granted, however, that Miss Jewell frequently used this language ; doubtless it was part of her foolish, futile existence to talk of her soul's welfare, especially in *tête-à-tête* with unmarried men. The truth he did not suspect, and Rosamund could not bring herself to convey it in plain words.

"I do so envy the people who have something to live for ! " Thus she panted. "I fear I have *never* had a purpose in life— I'm sure I don't know why. Of course I'm only a woman, but even women nowadays are doing so much. You don't despise their efforts, do you ? "

"Not indiscriminately."

"If I could feel myself a profitable member of society !—I want to be lifted above my wretched self. Is there no great end to which I could devote myself ? "

Her phrases grew only more magniloquent, and all the time she was longing for courage to say : "How can I earn money ? " Geoffrey, confirmed in the suspicion that she talked only for effect, indulged his natural humour.

"I'm such a groveller, Miss Jewell. I never knew these aspirations. I see the world mainly as cubic feet of timber."

"No, no, you won't make me believe that. I *know* you have ideals ! "

"That

"That word reminds me of poor old Halliday. You remember Halliday, don't you?"

In vexed silence, Rosamund shook her head.

"But I think you must have met him, in the old days. A tall, fair man—no? He talked a great deal about ideals, and meant to move the world. We lost sight of each other when I first left England, and only met again a day or two ago. He is married, and has three children, and looks fifty years old, though he can't be much more than thirty. He took me to see his wife —they live at Forest Hill."

Rosamund was not listening, and the speaker became aware of it. Having a purpose in what he was about to say, he gently claimed her attention.

"I think Mrs. Halliday is the kind of woman who would interest you. If ever any one had a purpose in life, *she* has."

"Indeed? And what?"

"To keep house admirably, and bring up her children as well as possible, on an income which would hardly supply some women with shoe-leather."

"Oh, that's very dreadful!"

"Very fine, it seems to me. I never saw a woman for whom I could feel more respect. Halliday and she suit each other perfectly; they would be the happiest people in England if they had any money. As he walked back with me to the station he talked about their difficulties. They can't afford to engage a good servant (if one exists nowadays), and cheap sluts have driven them frantic, so that Mrs. Halliday does everything with her own hands."

"It must be awful."

"Pretty hard, no doubt. She is an educated woman—otherwise, of course, she couldn't, and wouldn't, manage it. And, by-the-
bye

bye "—he paused for quiet emphasis—" she has a sister, unmarried, who lives in the country and does nothing at all. It occurs to one—doesn't it ?—that the idle sister might pretty easily find scope for *her* energies."

Rosamund stared at the ground. She was not so dull as to lose the significance of this story, and she imagined that Geoffrey reflected upon herself in relation to her own sister. She broke the long silence by saying awkwardly :

" I'm sure *I* would never allow a sister of mine to lead such a life."

" I don't think you would," replied the other. And, though he spoke genially, Rosamund felt it a very moderate declaration of his belief in her. Overcome by strong feeling, she exclaimed :

" I would do *anything* to be of use in the world. You don't think I mean it, but I do, Mr. Hunt. I——"

Her voice faltered ; the all-important word stuck in her throat. And at that moment Geoffrey rose.

" Shall we walk about ? Let me show you my mother's fernery she is very proud of it."

That was the end of intimate dialogue. Rosamund felt aggrieved, and tried to shape sarcasms, but the man's imperturbable good-humour soon made her forget everything save the pleasure of being in his company. It was a bitter-sweet evening, yet perhaps enjoyment predominated. Of course, Geoffrey would conduct her to the station ; she never lost sight of this hope. There would be another opportunity for plain speech. But her desire was frustrated ; at the time of departure, Caroline said that they might as well all go together. Rosamund could have wept for chagrin.

She returned to the detested house, the hateful little bedroom, and there let her tears have way. In dread lest the hysterical sobs should be overheard, she all but stifled herself.

                     Then,

Then, as if by blessed inspiration, a great thought took shape in her despairing mind. At the still hour of night she suddenly sat up in the darkness, which seemed illumined by a wondrous hope. A few minutes motionless; the mental light grew dazzling; she sprang out of bed, partly dressed herself, and by the rays of a candle sat down to write a letter:

" DEAR MR. HUNT,

"Yesterday I did not tell you the whole truth. I have nothing to live upon, and I *must* find employment or starve. My brother-in-law has been supporting me for a long time—I am ashamed to tell you, but I *will*, and he can do so no longer. I wanted to ask you for practical advice, but I did not make my meaning clear. For all that, you *did* advise me, and very well indeed. I wish to offer myself as domestic help to poor Mrs. Halliday. Do you think she would have me? I ask no wages—only food and lodging. I will work harder and better than any general servants—I *will indeed*. My health is not bad, and I am fairly strong. Don't—don't throw scorn on this! Will you recommend me to Mrs. Halliday—or ask Mrs. Hunt to do so? I beg that you will. Please write to me at once, and say yes. I shall be ever grateful to you.

"Very sincerely yours,

"ROSAMUND JEWELL."

This she posted as early as possible. The agonies she endured in waiting for a reply served to make her heedless of boarding-house spite, and by the last post that same evening came Geoffrey's letter. He wrote that her suggestion was startling. "Your motive seems to me very praiseworthy, but whether the thing would be possible is another question. I dare not take upon myself the responsibility of counselling you to such a step. Pray, take time, and think. I am most grieved to hear of your difficulties, but is there not some better way out of them?"

Yes,

Yes, there it was! Geoffrey Hunt could not believe in her power to *do* anything praiseworthy. So had it been six years ago, when she would have gone through flood and flame to win his admiration. But in those days she was a girlish simpleton; she had behaved idiotically. It should be different now; were it at the end of her life, she would prove to him that he had slighted her unjustly!

Brave words, but Rosamund attached some meaning to them. The woman in her—the ever-prevailing woman—was wrought by fears and vanities, urgencies and desires, to a strange point of exaltation. Forthwith, she wrote again: "Send me, I entreat you, Mrs. Halliday's address. I will go and see her. No, I can't do anything but work with my hands. I am no good for anything else. If Mrs. Halliday refuses me, I shall go as a servant into some other house. Don't mock at me; I don't deserve it. Write at once."

Till midnight she wept and prayed.

Geoffrey sent her the address, adding a few dry words: "If you are willing and able to carry out this project, your ambition ought to be satisfied. You will have done your part towards solving one of the gravest problems of the time." Rosamund did not at once understand; when the writer's meaning grew clear, she kept repeating the words, as though they were a new gospel. Yes! she would be working nobly, helping to show a way out of the great servant difficulty. It would be an example to poor ladies, like herself, who were ashamed of honest work. And Geoffrey Hunt was looking on. He must needs marvel; perhaps he would admire greatly; perhaps—oh, oh!

Of course, she found a difficulty in wording her letter to the lady who had never heard of her, and of whom she knew practically nothing. But zeal surmounted obstacles. She began by saying
that

that she was in search of domestic employment, and that, through her friends at Teddington, she had heard of Mrs. Halliday as a lady who might perhaps consider her application. Then followed an account of herself, tolerably ingenuous, and an amplification of the phrases she had addressed to Geoffrey Hunt. On an after-thought, she enclosed a stamped envelope.

Whilst the outcome remained dubious, Rosamund's behaviour to her fellow-boarders was a pattern of offensiveness. She no longer shunned them—seemed, indeed, to challenge their observation for the sake of meeting it with arrogant defiance. She rudely interrupted conversations, met sneers with virulent retorts, made herself the common enemy. Mrs. Banting was appealed to; ladies declared that they could not live in a house where they were exposed to vulgar insult. When nearly a week had passed Mrs. Banting found it necessary to speak in private with Miss Jewell, and to make a plaintive remonstrance. Rosamund's flashing eye and contemptuous smile foretold the upshot.

"Spare yourself the trouble, Mrs. Banting. I leave the house to-morrow."

"Oh, but——"

"There is no need for another word. Of course, I shall pay the week in lieu of notice. I am busy, and have no time to waste."

The day before, she had been to Forest Hill, had seen Mrs. Halliday, and entered into an engagement. At midday on the morrow she arrived at the house which was henceforth to be her home, the scene of her labours.

Sheer stress of circumstance accounted for Mrs. Halliday's decision. Geoffrey Hunt, a dispassionate observer, was not misled in forming so high an opinion of his friend's wife. Only a year or two older than Rosamund, Mrs. Halliday had the mind and the

temper

temper which enable woman to front life as a rational combatant, instead of vegetating as a more or less destructive parasite. Her voice declared her ; it fell easily upon a soft, clear note ; the kind of voice that expresses good-humour and reasonableness, and many other admirable qualities ; womanly, but with no suggestion of the feminine gamut ; a voice that was never likely to test its compass in extremes. She had enjoyed a country breeding ; something of liberal education assisted her natural intelligence ; thanks to a good mother, she discharged with ability and content the prime domestic duties. But physically she was not inexhaustible, and the laborious, anxious years had taxed her health. A woman of the ignorant class may keep house, and bring up a family, with her own hands ; she has to deal only with the simplest demands of life ; her home is a shelter, her food is primitive, her children live or die according to the law of natural selection. Infinitely more complex, more trying, is the task of the educated wife and mother ; if to conscientiousness be added enduring poverty, it means not seldom an early death. Fatigue and self-denial had set upon Mrs. Halliday's features a stamp which could never be obliterated. Her husband, her children, suffered illnesses ; she, the indispensable, durst not confess even to a headache. Such servants as from time to time she had engaged merely increased her toil and anxieties ; she demanded, to be sure, the diligence and efficiency which in this new day can scarce be found among the menial ranks ; what she obtained was sluttish stupidity, grotesque presumption, and every form of female viciousness. Rosamund Jewell, honest in her extravagant fervour, seemed at first a mocking apparition ; only after a long talk, when Rosamund's ingenuousness had forcibly impressed her, would Mrs. Halliday agree to an experiment. Miss Jewell was to live as one of the family ; she did not ask this, but consented to it. She was to

receive

receive ten pounds a year, for Mrs. Halliday insisted that payment there must be.

"I can't cook," Rosamund had avowed. "I never boiled a potato in my life. If you teach me, I shall be grateful to you."

"The cooking I can do myself, and you can learn if you like."

"I should think I might wash and scrub by the light of nature?"

"Perhaps. Good will and ordinary muscles will go a long way."

"I can't sew, but I will learn."

Mrs. Halliday reflected.

"You know that you are exchanging freedom for a hard and a very dull life?"

"My life has been hard and dull enough, if you only knew. The work will seem hard at first, no doubt. But I don't think I shall be dull with you."

Mrs. Halliday held out her work-worn hand, and received a clasp of the fingers attenuated by idleness.

It was a poor little house; built—of course—with sham display of spaciousness in front, and huddling discomfort at the rear. Mrs. Halliday's servants never failed to urge the smallness of the rooms as an excuse for leaving them dirty; they had invariably been accustomed to lordly abodes, where their virtues could expand. The furniture was homely and no more than sufficient, but here and there on the walls shone a glimpse of summer landscape, done in better days by the master of the house, who knew something of various arts, but could not succeed in that of money-making. Rosamund bestowed her worldly goods in a tiny chamber which Mrs. Halliday did her best to make inviting and comfortable; she had less room here than at Mrs. Banting's, but the cleanliness of surroundings would depend upon herself, and she was not likely

to

to spend much time by the bedside in weary discontent. Halliday, who came home each evening at half-past six, behaved to her on their first meeting with grave, even respectful, courtesy; his tone flattered Rosamund's ear, and nothing could have been more seemly than the modest gentleness of her replies.

At the close of the first day, she wrote to Geoffrey Hunt : " I do believe I have made a good beginning. Mrs. Halliday is perfect and I quite love her. Please do not answer this; I only write because I feel that I owe it to your kindness. I shall never be able to thank you enough."

When Geoffrey obeyed her and kept silence, she felt that he acted prudently; perhaps Mrs. Halliday might see the letter, and know his hand. But none the less she was disappointed.

Rosamund soon learnt the measure of her ignorance in domestic affairs. Thoroughly practical and systematic, her friend (this was to be their relation) set down a scheme of the day's and the week's work; it made a clear apportionment between them, with no preponderance of unpleasant drudgery for the new-comer's share. With astonishment, which she did not try to conceal, Rosamund awoke to the complexity and endlessness of home duties even in so small a house as this.

" Then you have *no* leisure ? " she exclaimed, in sympathy, not remonstrance.

" I feel at leisure when I'm sewing—and when I take the children out. And there's Sunday."

The eldest child was about five years old, the others three and a twelvemonth, respectively. Their ailments gave a good deal of trouble, and it often happened that Mrs. Halliday was awake with one of them the greater part of the night. For children Rosamund had no natural tenderness ; to endure the constant sound of their voices proved, in the beginning, her hardest trial ; but

the

the resolve to school herself in every particular soon enabled her to tend the little ones with much patience, and insensibly she grew fond of them. Until she had overcome her awkwardness in every task, it cost her no little effort to get through the day ; at bedtime she ached in every joint, and morning oppressed her with a sick lassitude. Conscious however, of Mrs. Halliday's forbearance, she would not spare herself, and it soon surprised her to discover that the rigid performance of what seemed an ignoble task brought its reward. Her first success in polishing a grate gave her more delight than she had known since childhood. She summoned her friend to look, to admire, to praise.

"Haven't I done it well ? Could you do it better yourself ? "
"Admirable ! "

Rosamund waved her black-lead brush and tasted victory.

The process of acclimatisation naturally affected her health. In a month's time she began to fear that she must break down ; she suffered painful disorders, crept out of sight to moan and shed a tear. Always faint, she had no appetite for wholesome food. Tossing on her bed at night she said to herself a thousand times : "I must go on even if I die ! " Her religion took the form of asceticism and bade her rejoice in her miseries ; she prayed constantly and at times knew the solace of an infinite self-glorification. In such a mood she once said to Mrs. Halliday :

"Don't you think I deserve some praise for the step I took ? "
"You certainly deserve both praise and thanks from me."
"But I mean—it isn't every one who could have done it ? I've a right to feel myself superior to the ordinary run of girls ? "

The other gave her an embarrassed look, and murmured a few satisfying words. Later in the same day she talked to Rosamund about her health and insisted on making certain changes which allowed her to take more open-air exercise. The result of this

was

was a marked improvement; at the end of the second month
Rosamund began to feel and look better than she had done for
several years. Work no longer exhausted her. And the labour
in itself seemed to diminish, a natural consequence of perfect
co-operation between the two women. Mrs. Halliday declared
that life had never been so easy for her as now; she knew the
delight of rest in which there was no self-reproach. But for
sufficient reasons she did not venture to express to Rosamund all
the gratitude that was due.

About Christmas a letter from Forest Hill arrived at Teddington; this time it did not forbid a reply. It spoke of struggles
sufferings, achievements. "Do I not deserve a word of praise?
Have I not done something, as you said, towards solving the
great question? Don't you believe in me a little?" Four
more weeks went by, and brought no answer. Then, one
evening, in a mood of bitterness, Rosamund took a singular step;
she wrote to Mr. Cheeseman. She had heard nothing of him, had
utterly lost sight of the world in which they met; but his place
of business was known to her, and thither she addressed the note.
A few lines only: "You are a very strange person, and I really
take no interest whatever in you. But I have sometimes thought
you would like to ask my forgiveness. If so, write to the above
address—my sister's. I am living in London, and enjoying
myself, but I don't choose to let you know where." Having an
opportunity on the morrow, Sunday, she posted this in a remote
district.

The next day, a letter arrived for her from Canada. Here
was the explanation of Geoffrey's silence. His words could
hardly have been more cordial, but there were so few of them.
On nourishment such as this no illusion could support itself; for
the moment Rosamund renounced every hope. Well, she was no

worse

worse off than before the renewal of their friendship. But could it be called friendship? Geoffrey's mother and sisters paid no heed to her; they doubtless considered that she had finally sunk below their horizon; and Geoffrey himself, for all his fine words, most likely thought the same at heart. Of course they would never meet again. And for the rest of her life she would be nothing more than a domestic servant in genteel disguise—happy were the disguise preserved.

However, she had provided a distraction for her gloomy thoughts. With no more delay than was due to its transmission by way of Glasgow, there came a reply from Mr. Cheeseman: two sheets of notepaper. The writer prostrated himself; he had been guilty of shameful behaviour; even Miss Jewell, with all her sweet womanliness, must find it hard to think of him with charity. But let her remember what " the poets " had written about Remorse, and apply to *him* the most harrowing of their descriptions. He would be frank with her; he would " a plain, unvarnished tale unfold." Whilst away for his holiday he by chance encountered *one* with whom, in days gone by, he had held tender relations. She was a young widow; his foolish heart was touched; he sacrificed honour to the passing emotion. Their marriage would be delayed, for his affairs were just now anything but flourishing. " Dear Miss Jewell, will you not be my friend, my sister? Alas, I am not a happy man; but it is too late to lament." And so on to the squeezed signature at the bottom of the last page.

Rosamund allowed a fortnight to pass—not before writing, but before her letter was posted. She used a tone of condescension, mingled with airy banter. " From my heart I feel for you, but, as you say, there is no help. I am afraid you are very impulsive —yet I thought that was a fault of youth. Do not give way to despair.

despair. I really don't know whether I shall feel it right to let you hear again, but if it soothes you I don't think there would be any harm in your letting me know the cause of your troubles."

This odd correspondence, sometimes with intervals of three weeks, went on until late summer. Rosamund would soon have been a year with Mrs. Halliday. Her enthusiasm had long since burnt itself out; she was often a prey to vapours, to cheerless lassitude, even to the spirit of revolt against things in general, but on the whole she remained a thoroughly useful member of the household; the great experiment might fairly be called successful. At the end of August it was decided that the children must have sea air; their parents would take them away for a fortnight. When the project began to be talked of, Rosamund, perceiving a domestic difficulty, removed it by asking whether she would be at liberty to visit her sister in Scotland. Thus were things arranged.

Some days before that appointed for the general departure. Halliday received a letter which supplied him with a subject of conversation at breakfast.

"Hunt is going to be married," he remarked to his wife, just as Rosamund was bringing in the children's porridge.

Mrs. Halliday looked at her helper—for no more special reason than the fact of Rosamund's acquaintance with the Hunt family; she perceived a change of expression, an emotional play of feature, and at once averted her eyes.

"Where? In Canada?" she asked, off-hand.

"No, he's in England. But the lady is a Canadian.—I wonder he troubles to tell me. Hunt's a queer fellow. When we meet, once in two years, he treats me like a long-lost brother; but I don't think he'd care a bit if he never saw me or heard of me again."

"It's

" It's a family characteristic," interposed Rosamund with a dry laugh.

That day she moved about with the gait and the eyes of a somnambulist. She broke a piece of crockery, and became hysterical over it. Her afternoon leisure she spent in the bedroom, and at night she professed a headache which obliged her to retire early.

A passion of wrath inflamed her; as vehement—though so utterly unreasonable—as in the moment when she learnt the perfidy of Mr. Cheeseman. She raged at her folly in having submitted to social degradation on the mere hint of a man who uttered it in a spirit purely contemptuous. The whole hateful world had conspired against her. She banned her kinsfolk and all her acquaintances, especially the Hunts; she felt bitter even against the Hallidays—unsympathetic, selfish people, utterly indifferent to her private griefs, regarding her as a mere domestic machine. She would write to Geoffrey Hunt, and let him know very plainly what she thought of his behaviour in *urging* her to become a servant. Would such a thought have ever occurred to a *gentleman!* And her poor life was wasted, oh! oh! She would soon be thirty—thirty! The glass mocked her with savage truth. And she had not even a decent dress to put on. Self-neglect had made her appearance vulgar; her manners, her speech, doubtless, had lost their note of social superiority. Oh, it was hard! She wished for death, cried for divine justice in a better world.

On the morning of release, she travelled to London Bridge, ostensibly *en route* for the north. But, on alighting, she had her luggage taken to the cloak-room, and herself went by omnibus to the West-end. By noon she had engaged a lodging, one room in a street where she had never yet lived. And hither before night was transferred her property.

The

The next day she spent about half of her ready-money in the purchase of clothing—cheap, but such as the self-respect of a "lady" imperatively demands. She bought cosmetics; she set to work at removing from her hands the traces of ignoble occupation. On the day that followed—Sunday—early in the afternoon, she repaired to a certain corner of Kensington Gardens, where she came face to face with Mr. Cheeseman.

"I have come," said Rosamund, in a voice of nervous exhilaration which tried to subdue itself. "Please to consider that it is more than you could expect."

"It is! A thousand times more! You are goodness itself."

In Rosamund's eyes the man had not improved since a year ago. The growth of a beard made him look older, and he seemed in indifferent health; but his tremulous delight, his excessive homage, atoned for the defect. She, on the other hand, was so greatly changed for the better that Cheeseman beheld her with no less wonder than admiration. Her brisk step, her upright bearing, her clear eye, and pure-toned skin contrasted remarkably with the lassitude and sallowness he remembered; at this moment, too, she had a pleasant rosiness of cheek which made her girlish, virginal. All was set off by the new drapery and millinery, which threw a shade upon Cheeseman's very respectable but somewhat time-honoured, Sunday costume.

They spent several hours together, Cheeseman talking of his faults, his virtues, his calamities, and his hopes, like the impulsive, well-meaning, but nerveless fellow that he was. Rosamund gathered from it all, as she had vaguely learnt from his recent correspondence, that the alluring widow no longer claimed him; but he did not enter into details on this delicate subject. They had tea at a restaurant by Notting Hill Gate; then, Miss Jewell appearing indefatigable, they again strolled in unfrequented ways.

At

At length was uttered the question for which Rosamund had long ago prepared her reply.

" You cannot expect me," she said sweetly, " to answer at once."

" Of course not ! I shouldn't have dared to hope——"

He choked and swallowed ; a few beads of perspiration shining on his troubled face.

" You have my address ; most likely I shall spend a week or two there. Of course you may write. I shall probably go to my sister's in Scotland, for the autumn——"

" Oh ! don't say that—don't. To lose you again—so soon——"

" I only said, ' probably '——"

" Oh, thank you !—To go so far away—And the autumn ; just when I have a little freedom ; the very best time—if I dared to hope such a thing——"

Rosamund graciously allowed him to bear her company as far as to the street in which she lived.

A few days later she wrote to Mrs. Halliday, heading her letter with the Glasgow address. She lamented the sudden impossibility of returning to her domestic duties. Something had happened. "In short, dear Mrs. Halliday, I am going to be married. I could not give you warning of this, it has come so unexpectedly. Do forgive me ! I so earnestly hope that you will find some one to take my place, some one better and more of a help to you. I know I haven't been much use. Do write home at Glasgow and say I may still regard you as a dear friend."

This having been dispatched, she sat musing over her prospects. Mr. Cheeseman had honestly confessed the smallness of his income ; he could barely count upon a hundred and fifty a year ; but things *might* improve. She did not dislike him—no, she did not dislike him. He would be a very tractable husband. Compared, of course, with——

A letter

A letter was brought up to her room. She knew the flowing commercial hand, and broke the envelope without emotion. Two sheets—three sheets—and a half. But what was all this? "Despair . . . thoughts of self-destruction . . . ignoble publicity . . . practical   ruin . . . impossible . . . despise   and forget . . . Dante's   hell . . . deeper   than   ever   plummet sounded . . . forever ! . . . ." So again he had deceived her ! He must have known that the widow was dangerous ; his reticence was mere shuffling. His behaviour to that other woman had perhaps exceeded in baseness his treatment of herself; else, how could he be so sure that a jury would give her " ruinous damages " ? Or was it all a mere illustration of a man's villainy ? Why should not *she* also sue for damages ? Why not ? Why not ?

The three months that followed were a time of graver peril, of darker crisis, than Rosamund, with all her slip-slop experiences, had ever known. An observer adequately supplied with facts, psychological and material, would more than once have felt that it depended on the mere toss of a coin whether she kept or lost her social respectability. She sounded all the depths possible to such a mind and heart—save only that from which there could have been no redemption. A saving memory lived within her, and at length, in the yellow gloom of a November morning—her tarnished, draggle-tailed finery thrown aside for the garb she had worn in lowliness—Rosamund betook herself to Forest Hill. The house of the Hallidays looked just as usual. She slunk up to the door, rang the bell, and waited in fear of a strange face. There appeared Mrs. Halliday herself. The surprised but friendly smile at once proved her forgiveness of Rosamund's desertion. She had written, indeed, with calm good sense, hoping only that all would be well.

"Let me see you alone, Mrs. Halliday.—How glad I am to sit in this room again ! Who is helping you now ? "

"No

"No one. Help such as I want is not easy to find."

"Oh, let me come back!—I am *not* married.—No, no, there is nothing to be ashamed of. I am no worse than I ever was. I'll tell you everything—the whole silly, wretched story."

She told it, blurring only her existence of the past three months.

"I would have come before, but I was so bitterly ashamed. I ran away so disgracefully. Now I'm penniless—all but suffering hunger. Will you have me again, Mrs. Halliday ? I've been a horrid fool, but—I do believe—for the last time in my life. Try me again, dear Mrs. Halliday ! "

There was no need of the miserable tears, the impassioned pleading. Her home received her as though she had been absent but for an hour. That night she knelt again by her bedside in the little room, and at seven o'clock next morning she was lighting fires, sweeping floors, mute in thankfulness.

Halliday heard the story from his wife, and shook a dreamy, compassionate head.

"For goodness' sake," urged the practical woman, "don't let her think she's a martyr."

"No, no ; but the poor girl should have her taste of happiness."

"Of course I'm sorry for her, but there are plenty of people more to be pitied. Work she must, and there's only one kind of work she's fit for. It's no small thing to find your vocation—is it ? Thousands of such women—all meant by nature to scrub and cook—live and die miserably because they think themselves too good for it."

"The whole social structure is rotten ! "

"It'll last our time," rejoined Mrs. Halliday, as she gave a little laugh and stretched her weary arms.

Two Songs

By Rosamund Marriott-Watson

I—Requiescat

Bury me deep when I am dead,
   Far from the woods where sweet birds sing;
Lap me in sullen stone and lead,
   Lest my poor dust should feel the spring.

Never a flower be near me set,
   Nor starry cup nor slender stem,
Anemone nor violet,
   Lest my poor dust remember them.

And you—wherever you may fare—
   Dearer than birds, or flowers, or dew—
Never, ah me, pass never there,
   Lest my poor dust should dream of you.

FAIR

II—The Isle of Voices

F<small>AIR</small> blows the wind to-day, fresh along the valleys,
    Strange with the sounds and the scents of long ago;
Sinks in the willow-grove; shifts, and sighs, and rallies—
Whence, Wind? and why, Wind? and whither do you go?

Why, Wind, and whence, Wind?—yet well and well I know it—
Word from a lost world, a world across the sea;
No compass guides there, never chart will show it,
Green grows the grave there that holds the heart of me.

Sunk lies my ship, and the cruel sea rejoices,
Sharp are the reefs where the hungry breakers fret—
Land so long lost to me—Youth, the Isle of Voices—
Call never more to me—I who must forget.

A Defence of Cosmetics

NAY, but it is useless to protest. Artifice must queen it once
more in the town, and so, if there be any whose hearts chafe
at her return, let them not say, "We have come into evil times,"
and be all for resistance, reformation or angry cavilling. For did
the king's sceptre send the sea retrograde, or the wand of the
sorcerer avail to turn the sun from its old course? And what
man or what number of men ever stayed that reiterated process by
which the cities of this world grow, are very strong, fail and grow
again? Indeed, indeed, there is charm in every period, and only
fools and flutterpates do not seek reverently for what is charming
in their own day. No martyrdom, however fine, nor satire, however splendidly bitter, has changed by a little tittle the known
tendency of things. It is the times that can perfect us, not we
the times, and so let all of us wisely acquiesce. Like the little
wired marionettes, let us acquiesce in the dance.

For behold! The Victorian era comes to its end and the day
of sancta simplicitas is quite ended. The old signs are here and
the portents to warn the seer of life that we are ripe for a new
epoch of artifice. Are not men rattling the dice-box and ladies
dipping their fingers in the rouge-pots? At Rome, in the keenest
time of her degringolade, when there was gambling even in the holy
temples,

temples, great ladies (does not Lucian tell us?) did not scruple to squander all they had upon unguents from Arabia. Nero's mistress and unhappy wife, Poppæa, of shameful memory, had in her travelling retinue fifteen—or, as some say, fifty—she-asses, for the sake of their milk, that was thought an incomparable guard against cosmetics with poison in them. Last century, too, when life was lived by candle-light, and ethics was but etiquette, and even art a question of punctilio, women, we know, gave the best hours of the day to the crafty farding of their faces and the towering of their coiffures. And men, throwing passion into the wine-bowl to sink or swim, turned out thought to browse upon the green cloth. Cannot we even now in our fancy see them, those silent exquisites round the long table at Brooks', masked, all of them, "lest the countenance should betray feeling," in quinze masks, through whose eyelets they sat peeping, peeping, while macao brought them riches or ruin? We can see them, those silent rascals, sitting there with their cards and their rouleaux and their wooden money-bowls, long after the dawn had crept up St. James' and pressed its haggard face against the window of the little club. Yes, we can raise their ghosts—and, more, we can see manywhere a devotion to hazard fully as meek as theirs. In England there has been a wonderful revival of cards. Roulette may rival dead faro in the tale of her devotees. Her wheel is spinning busily in every house and ere long it may be that tender parents will be waiting to complain of the compulsory baccarat in our public schools.

In fact, we are all gamblers once more, but our gambling is on a finer scale than ever it was. We fly from the card-room to the heath, and from the heath to the City, and from the City to the coast of the Mediterranean. And just as no one seriously encourages the clergy in its frantic efforts to lay the spirit of chance, that has thus resurged among us, so no longer are many faces set
against

against that other great sign of a more complicated life, the love for cosmetics. No longer is a lady of fashion blamed if, to escape the outrageous persecution of time, she fly for sanctuary to the toilet-table; and if a damosel, prying in her mirror, be sure that with brush and pigment she can trick herself into more charm, we are not angry. Indeed, why should we ever have been? Surely it is laudable, this wish to make fair the ugly and overtop fairness, and no wonder that within the last five years the trade of the makers of cosmetics has increased immoderately—twenty-fold, so one of these makers has said to me. We need but walk down any modish street and peer into the little broughams that flit past, or (in Thackeray's phrase) under the bonnet of any woman we meet, to see over how wide a kingdom rouge reigns. We men, who, from Juvenal down to that discourteous painter of whom Lord Chesterfield tells us, have especially shown a dislike of cosmetics, are quite yielding; and there are, I fancy, many such husbands as he who, suddenly realising that his wife was painted, bad her sternly, " Go up and take it all off," and, on her reappearance, bad her with increasing sternness, " Go up and put it all on again."

But now that the use of pigments is becoming general, and most women are not so young as they are painted, it may be asked curiously how the prejudice ever came into being. Indeed, it is hard to trace folly, for that it is inconsequent, to its start; and perhaps it savours too much of reason to suggest that the prejudice was due to the tristful confusion man has made of soul and surface. Through trusting so keenly to the detection of the one by keeping watch upon the other, and by force of the thousand errors following, he has come to think of surface even as the reverse of soul. He supposes that every clown beneath his paint and lip-salve is moribund and knows it, (though in verity, I am told, clowns are as cheerful

a

a class of men as any other), that the fairer the fruit's rind and the more delectable its bloom, the closer are packed the ashes within it. The very jargon of the hunting-field connects cunning with a mask. And so perhaps came man's anger at the embellishment of women—that lovely mask of enamel with its shadows of pink and tiny pencilled veins, what must lurk behind it? Of what treacherous mysteries may it not be the screen? Does not the heathen lacquer her dark face, and the harlot paint her cheeks, because sorrow has made them pale?

After all, the old prejudice is a-dying. We need not pry into the secret of its birth. Rather is this a time of jolliness and glad indulgence. For the era of rouge is upon us, and as only in an elaborate era can man by the tangled accrescency of his own pleasures and emotions reach that refinement which is his highest excellence, and by making himself, so to say, independent of Nature, come nearest to God, so only in an elaborate era is woman perfect. Artifice is the strength of the world, and in that same mask of paint and powder, shadowed with vermeil tint and most trimly pencilled, is woman's strength.

For see! We need not look so far back to see woman under the direct influence of Nature. Early in this century, our grand-mothers, sickening of the odour of faded exotics and spilt wine, came out into the daylight once more and let the breezes blow around their faces and enter, sharp and welcome, into their lungs. Artifice they drove forth, and they set Martin Tupper upon a throne of mahogany to rule over them. A very reign of terror set in. All things were sacrificed to the fetish Nature. Old ladies may still be heard to tell how, when they were girls, affectation was not; and, if we verify their assertion in the light of such literary authorities as Dickens, we find that it is absolutely true. Women appear to have been in those days utterly natural in their
conduct

conduct—flighty, gushing, blushing, fainting, giggling and shaking
their curls. They knew no reserve in the first days of the
Victorian era. No thought was held too trivial, no emotion too
silly, to express. To Nature everything was sacrificed. Great
heavens! And in those barren days what influence was exerted
by women? By men they seem not to have been feared nor loved,
but regarded rather as " dear little creatures " or " wonderful little
beings," and in their relation to life as foolish and ineffectual as the
landscapes they did in water-colour. Yet, if the women of those
years were of no great account, they had a certain charm and they
at least had not begun to trespass upon men's ground; if they
touched not thought, which is theirs by right, at any rate they
refrained from action, which is ours. Far more serious was it
when, in the natural trend of time, they became enamoured of
rinking and archery and galloping along the Brighton Parade.
Swiftly they have sped on since then from horror to horror. The
invasion of the tennis-courts and of the golf-links, the seizure of
the tricycle and of the type-writer, were but steps preliminary in
that campaign which is to end with the final victorious occupation
of St. Stephen's. But stay! The horrific pioneers of womanhood
who gad hither and thither and, confounding wisdom with the
device on her shield, shriek for the unbecoming, are doomed.
Though they spin their tricycle-treadles so amazingly fast, they
are too late. Though they scream victory, none follow them.
Artifice, that fair exile, has returned.

Yes, though the pioneers know it not, they are doomed already.
For of the curiosities of history not the least strange is the manner
in which two social movements may be seen to overlap, long after
the second has, in truth, given its deathblow to the first. And,
in like manner as one has seen the limbs of a murdered thing in
lively movement, so we need not doubt that, though the voices of
those

those who cry out for reform be very terribly shrill, they will soon be hushed. Dear Artifice is with us. It needed but that we should wait.

Surely, without any of my pleading, women will welcome their great and amiable protectrix, as by instinct. For (have I not said?) it is upon her that all their strength, their life almost, depends. Artifice's first command to them is that they should repose. With bodily activity their powder will fly, their enamel crack. They are butterflies who must not flit, if they love their bloom. Now, setting aside the point of view of passion, from which very many obvious things might be said, (and probably have been by the minor poets), it is, from the intellectual point of view, quite necessary that a woman should repose. Hers is the resupinate sex. On her couch she is a goddess, but so soon as ever she put her foot to the ground—lo, she is the veriest little sillypop and quite done for. She cannot rival us in action, but she is our mistress in the things of the mind. Let her not by second-rate athletics, nor indeed by any exercise soever of the limbs, spoil the pretty procedure of her reason. Let her be content to remain the guide, the subtle suggester of what *we* must do, the strategist whose soldiers we are, the little architect whose workmen.

"After all," as a pretty girl once said to me, "women are a sex by themselves, so to speak," and the sharper the line between their worldly functions and ours, the better. This greater swiftness and less erring subtlety of mind, their forte and privilege, justifies the painted mask that Artifice bids them wear. Behind it their minds can play without let. They gain the strength of reserve. They become important, as in the days of the Roman Empire were the Emperor's mistresses, as was the Pompadour at Versailles, as was our Elizabeth. Yet do not their faces become
lined

lined with thought; beautiful and without meaning are their faces.

And, truly, of all the good things that will happen with the full renascence of cosmetics, one of the best is that surface will finally be severed from soul. That damnable confusion will be solved by the extinguishing of a prejudice which, as I suggest, itself created. Too long has the face been degraded from its rank as a thing of beauty to a mere vulgar index of character or emotion. We had come to troubling ourselves, not with its charm of colour and line, but with such questions as whether the lips were sensuous, the eyes full of sadness, the nose indicative of determination. I have no quarrel with physiognomy. For my own part, I believe in it. But it has tended to degrade the face æsthetically, in such wise as the study of cheirosophy has tended to degrade the hand. And the use of cosmetics, the masking of the face, will change this. We shall gaze at a woman merely because she is beautiful, not stare into her face anxiously, as into the face of a barometer.

How fatal it has been, in how many ways, this confusion of soul and surface! Wise were the Greeks in making plain masks for their mummers to play in, and dunces we not to have done the same! Only the other day, an actress was saying that what she was most proud of in her art—next, of course, to having appeared in some provincial pantomime at the age of three—was the deftness with which she contrived, in parts demanding a rapid succession of emotions, to dab her cheeks quite quickly with rouge from the palm of her right hand, or powder from the palm of her left. Gracious goodness! why do not we have masks upon the stage? Drama is the presentment of the soul in action. The mirror of the soul is the voice. Let the young critics, who seek a cheap reputation for austerity, by cavilling at "incidental music," set

their

their faces rather against the attempt to justify inferior dramatic
art by the subvention of a quite alien art like painting, of any art,
indeed, whose sphere is only surface.   Let those, again, who sneer,
so rightly, at the "painted anecdotes of the Academy," censure
equally the writers who trespass on painter's ground.   It is a
proclaimed sin that a painter should concern himself with a good
little girl's affection for a Scotch greyhound, or the keen enjoyment
of their port by elderly gentlemen of the early 'forties.   Yet, for a
painter to prod the soul with his paint-brush is no worse than for
a novelist to refuse to dip under the surface, and the fashion of
avoiding a psychological study of grief by stating that the owner's
hair turned white in a single night, or of shame by mentioning a
sudden rush of scarlet to the cheeks, is as lamentable as may
be.   But!   But with the universal use of cosmetics and the
consequent secernment of soul and surface, which, at the risk of
irritating a reader, I must again insist upon, all those old properties
that went to bolster up the ordinary novel—the trembling lips, the
flashing eyes, the determined curve of the chin, the nervous trick of
biting the moustache—aye and the hectic spot of red on either
cheek—will be made spiflicate, as the puppets were spiflicated by
Don Quixote.   Yes, even now Demos begins to discern.   The same
spirit that has revived rouge, smote his mouth as it grinned at
the wondrous painter of mist and river, and now sends him
sprawling for the pearls that Meredith dived for in the deep
waters of romance.

Indeed the revival of cosmetics must needs be so splendid an
influence, conjuring boons innumerable, that one inclines almost
to mutter against the inexorable law by which Artifice must
perish from time to time.   That such branches of painting as the
staining of glass or the illuminating of manuscripts should fall into
disuse seems, in comparison, so likely; these were esoteric arts;
they

they died with the monastic spirit. But personal appearance is art's very basis. The painting of the face is the first kind of painting man can have known. To make beautiful things— is it not an impulse laid upon few? But to make oneself beautiful is an universal instinct. Strange that the resultant art could never perish! So fascinating an art too! So various in its materials from stimmis, psimythium and fuligo to bismuth and arsenic, so simple in that its ground and its subject-matter are one, so marvellous in that its very subject-matter becomes lovely when an artist has selected it! For surely this is no idle nor fantastic saying. To deny that "make-up" is an art, on the pretext that the finished work of its exponents depends for beauty and excellence upon the ground chosen for the work, is absurd. At the touch of a true artist, the plainest face turns comely. As subject-matter the face is no more than suggestive, as ground, merely a loom round which the beatus artifex may spin the threads of any gold fabric:

> "Quae nunc nomen habent operosi signa Maronis
>   Pondus iners quondam duraque massa fuit.
> Multa viros nescire decet; pars maxima rerum
>   Offendat, si non interiora tegas,"

and, as Ovid would seem to suggest, by pigments any tone may be set aglow on a woman's cheek, from enamel the features take any form. Insomuch that surely the advocates of soup-kitchens and free-libraries and other devices for giving people what providence did not mean them to receive, should send out pamphlets in the praise of self-embellishment. For it will place Beauty within easy reach of many who could not otherwise hope to attain it.

But of course Artifice is rather exacting. In return for the repose she forces—so wisely!—upon her followers when the sun is

high

high or the moon is blown across heaven, she demands that
they should pay her long homage at the sun's rising. The initiate
may not enter lightly upon her mysteries. For, if a bad com-
plexion be inexcusable, to be ill-painted is unforgiveable; and when
the toilet is laden once more with the fulness of its elaboration, we
shall hear no more of the proper occupation for women. And
think, how sweet an energy, to sit at the mirror of coquetry!
See the dear merits of the toilet as shown upon old vases, or upon
the walls of Roman dwellings, or, rather still, read Böttiger's
alluring, scholarly description of " Morgenscenen im Puttzimmer
Einer Reichen Römerin." Read of Sabina's face as she comes
through the curtain of her bed-chamber to the chamber of her
toilet. The slave-girls have long been chafing their white feet
upon the marble floor. They stand, those timid Greek girls,
marshalled in little battalions. Each has her appointed task, and
all kneel in welcome as Sabina stalks, ugly and frowning, to the
toilet chair. Scaphion steps forth from among them, and, dipping a
tiny sponge in a bowl of hot milk, passes it lightly, ever so lightly,
over her mistress' face. The Poppæan pastes melt beneath it like
snow. A cooling lotion is poured over her brow and is fanned
with feathers. Phiale comes after, a clever girl, captured in some
sea-skirmish in the Aegean. In her left hand she holds the ivory
box wherein are the phucus and that white powder, psimythium;
in her right a sheaf of slim brushes. With how sure a touch does
she mingle the colours, and in what sweet proportion blushes
and blanches her lady's upturned face. Phiale is the cleverest of all
the slaves. Now Calamis dips her quill in a certain powder that
floats, liquid and sable, in the hollow of her palm. Standing upon
tip-toe and with lips parted, she traces the arch of the eyebrows.
The slaves whisper loudly of their lady's beauty, and two of them
hold up a mirror to her. Yes, the eyebrows are rightly arched.

But

But why does Psecas abase herself? She is craving leave to powder Sabina's hair with a fine new powder. It is made of the grated rind of the cedar-tree, and a Gallic perfumer, whose stall is near the Circus, gave it to her for a kiss. No lady in Rome knows of it. And so, when four special slaves have piled up the head-dress, out of a perforated box this glistening powder is showered. Into every little brown ringlet it enters, till Sabina's hair seems like a pile of gold coins. Lest the breezes send it flying, the girls lay the powder with sprinkled attar. Soon Sabina will start for the Temple of Cybele.

Ah! Such are the lures of the toilet that none will for long hold aloof from them. Cosmetics are not going to be a mere prosaic remedy for age or plainness, but all ladies and all young girls will come to love them. Does not a certain blithe Marquise, whose *lettres intimes* from the Court of Louis Seize are less read than their wit would merit, tell us how she was scandalised to see "*même les toutes jeunes demoiselles émaillées comme ma tabatière?*" So it shall be with us. Surely the common prejudice against painting the lily can but be based on mere ground of economy. That which is already fair is complete, it may be urged—urged implausibly, for there are not so many lovely things in this world that we can afford not to know each one of them by heart. There is only one white lily, and who that has ever seen—as I have —a lily really well painted could grudge the artist so fair a ground for his skill? Scarcely do you believe through how many nice metamorphoses a lily may be passed by him. In like manner, we all know the young girl, with her simpleness, her goodness, her wayward ignorance. And a very charming ideal for England must she have been, and a very natural one, when a young girl sat even on the throne. But no nation can keep its ideal for ever and it needed none of Mr. Gilbert's delicate satire in " Utopia " to
remind

remind us that she had passed out of our ken with the rest of the early Victorian era. What writer of plays, as lately asked some pressman, who had been told off to attend many first nights and knew what he was talking about, ever dreams of making the young girl the centre of his theme ? Rather he seeks inspiration from the tried and tired woman of the world, in all her intricate maturity, whilst, by way of comic relief, he sends the young girl flitting in and out with a tennis-racket, the poor εἴδωλον ἀμαυρόν of her former self. The season of the unsophisticated is gone by, and the young girl's final extinction beneath the rising tides of cosmetics will leave no gap in life and will rob art of nothing.

" Tush," I can hear some damned flutterpate exclaim, " girlishness and innocence are as strong and as permanent as womanhood itself! Why, a few months past, the whole town went mad over Miss Cissie Loftus! Was not hers a success of girlish innocence and the absence of rouge ? If such things as these be outmoded, why was she so wildly popular ? " Indeed, the triumph of that clever girl, whose début made London nice even in August, is but another witness to the truth of my contention. In a very sophisticated time, simplicity has a new dulcedo. Hers was a success of contrast. Accustomed to clever malaperts like Miss Lloyd or Miss Reeve, whose experienced pouts and smiles under the sun-bonnet are a standing burlesque of innocence and girlishness, Demos was really delighted, for once and away, to see the real presentment of these things upon his stage. Coming after all those sly serios, coming so young and mere with her pink frock and straightly combed hair, Miss Cissie Loftus had the charm which things of another period often do possess. Besides, just as we adored her for the abrupt nod with which she was wont at first to acknowledge the applause, so we were glad for her to come

upon

upon the stage with nothing to tinge the ivory of her cheeks. It seemed so strange, that neglect of convention. To be behind footlights and not rouged! Yes, hers was a success of contrast. She was like a daisy in the window at Solomons'. She was delightful. And yet, such is the force of convention, that when last I saw her, playing in some burlesque at the Gaiety, her fringe was curled and her pretty face rouged with the best of them. And, if further need be to show the absurdity of having called her performance " a triumph of naturalness over the jaded spirit of modernity," let us reflect that the little mimic was not a real old-fashioned girl after all. She had none of that restless naturalness that would seem to have characterised the girl of the early Victorian days. She had no pretty ways—no smiles nor blushes nor tremors. Possibly Demos could not have stood a presentment of girlishness unrestrained.

But with her grave insouciance, Miss Cissie Loftus had much of the reserve that is one of the factors of feminine perfection, and to most comes only, as I have said, with artifice. Her features played very, very slightly. And in truth, this may have been one of the reasons of her great success. For expression is but too often the ruin of a face; and, since we cannot as yet so order the circumstances of life that women shall never be betrayed into " an unbecoming emotion," when the brunette shall never have cause to blush, and the lady who looks well with parted lips be kept in a permanent state of surprise, the safest way by far is to create, by brush and pigments, artificial expressions for every face.

And this—say you?—will make monotony? You are mistaken, *toto cœlo* mistaken. When your mistress has wearied you with one expression, then it will need but a few touches of that pencil, a backward sweep of that brush, and lo, you will be revelling in another. For though, of course, the painting of the

face

face is, in manner, most like the painting of canvas, in outcome it is rather akin to the art of music—lasting, like music's echo, not for very long. So that, no doubt, of the many little appurtenances of the Reformed Toilet Table, not the least vital will be a list of the emotions that become its owner, with recipes for simulating them. According to the colour she wills her hair to be for the time—black or yellow or, peradventure, burnished red —she will blush for you, sneer for you, laugh or languish for you. The good combinations of line and colour are nearly numberless, and by their means poor restless woman will be able to realise her moods in all their shades and lights and dappledoms, to live many lives and masquerade through many moments of joy. No monotony will be. And for us men matrimony will have lost its sting.

But be it remembered! Though we men will garner these oblique boons, it is into the hands of women that Artifice gives her pigments. I know, I know that many men in a certain sect of society have shown a marked tendency to the use of cosmetics. I speak not of the countless gentlemen who walk about town in the time of its desertion from August to October, artificially bronzed, as though they were fresh from the moors or from the Solent. This, I conceive, is done for purely social reasons and need not concern me here. Rather do I speak of those who make themselves up, seemingly with an æsthetic purpose. Doubtless—I wish to be quite just—there are many who look the better for such embellishment; but, at the hazard of being thought old-fashioned and prejudiced, I cannot speak of the custom with anything but strong disapproval. If men are to lie among the rouge-pots, inevitably it will tend to promote that amalgamation of the sexes which is one of the chief planks in the decadent platform and to obtund that piquant contrast between him and her, which

is

is one of the redeeming features of creation.   Besides, really, men
have not the excuse of facial monotony, that holds in the case of
women.   Have we not hair upon our chins and upper lips ?   And
can we not, by diverting the trend of our moustache or by growing
our beard in this way or that, avoid the boredom of looking the same
for long ?   Let us beware.   For if, in violation of unwritten
sexual law, men take to trifling with the paints and brushes that
are feminine heritage, it may be that our great ladies will don false
imperials, and the little doner deck her pretty chin with a Newgate
fringe !   After all, I think we need not fear that many men will
thus trespass.   Most of them are in the City nowadays, and the
great wear and tear of that place would put their use of rouge—
that demands bodily repose from its dependents—quite outside the
range of practical æsthetics.

   But that in the world of women they will not neglect this art,
so ripping in itself, in its result so wonderfully beneficent, I am
sure indeed.   Much, I have said, is already done for its full
renascence.   The spirit of the age has made straight the path of
its professors.   Fashion has made Jezebel surrender her monopoly
of the rouge-pot.   As yet, the great art of self-embellishment is
for us but in its infancy.   But if Englishwomen can bring it to
the flower of an excellence so supreme as never yet has it known,
then, though Old England may lose her martial and commercial
supremacy, we patriots will have the satisfaction of knowing that
she has been advanced at one bound to a place in the councils of
æsthetic Europe.   And, in sooth, is this hoping too high of my
countrywomen ?   True that, as the art seems always to have
appealed to the ladies of Athens, and it was not until the waning
time of the Republic that Roman ladies learned to love the practice
of it, so Paris, Athenian in this as in all other things, has been noted
hitherto as a far more vivid centre of the art than London. But it was
in

in Rome, under the Emperors, that unguentaria reached its zenith, and shall it not be in London, soon, that unguentaria shall outstrip its Roman perfection? Surely there must be among us artists as cunning in the use of brush and puff as any who lived at Versailles. Surely the splendid, impalpable advance of good taste, as shown in dress and in the decoration of houses, may justify my hope of the preëminence of Englishwomen in the cosmetic art. By their innate delicacy of touch they will accomplish much, and much, of course, by their swift feminine perception. Yet it were well that they should know something also of the theoretical side of the craft. Modern authorities upon the mysteries of the toilet are, it is true, rather few; but among the ancients many a writer would seem to have been fascinated by them. Archigenes, a man of science at the Court of Cleopatra, and Criton at the Court of the Emperor Trajan, both wrote treatises upon cosmetics—doubtless most scholarly treatises that would have given many a precious hint. It is a pity they are not extant. From Lucian or from Juvenal, with his bitter picture of a Roman *levée*, much may be learnt; from the staid pages of Xenophon and Aristophanes' dear farces. But best of all is that fine book of the Ars Amatoria that Ovid has set aside for the consideration of dyes, perfumes and pomades. Written by an artist who knew the allurements of the toilet and understood its philosophy, it remains without rival as a treatise upon Artifice. It is more than a poem, it is a manual; and if there be left in England any lady who cannot read Latin in the original, she will do well to procure a discreet translation. In the Bodleian Library there is treasured the only known copy of a very poignant and delightful rendering of this one book of Ovid's masterpiece. It was made by a certain Wye Waltonstall, who lived in the days of Elizabeth, and, seeing that he dedicated it to " the Vertuous Ladyes and Gentlewomen of Great Britain," I am

sure

sure that the gallant writer, could he know of our great renascence of cosmetics, would wish his little work to be placed once more within their reach. " Inasmuch as to you, ladyes and gentle-women," so he writes in his queer little dedication, " my booke of pigments doth first addresse itself, that it may kisse your hands and afterward have the lines thereof in reading sweetened by the odour of your breath, while the dead letters formed into words by your divided lips may receive new life by your passionate expression, and the words marryed in that Ruby coloured temple may thus happily united, multiply your contentment." It is rather sad to think that, at this crisis in the history of pigments, the Vertuous Ladyes and Gentlewomen cannot read the libellus of Wye Walton-stall, who did so dearly love pigments.

But since the days when these great critics wrote their treatises, with what gifts innumerable has Artifice been loaded by Science! Many little partitions must be added to the narthecium before it can comprehend all the new cosmetics that have been quietly devised since classical days, and will make the modern toilet chalks away more splendid in its possibilities. A pity that no one has devoted himself to the compiling of a new list; but doubtless all the newest devices are known to the admirable unguentarians of Bond Street, who will impart them to their clients. Our thanks, too, should be given to Science for ridding us of the old danger that was latent in the use of cosmetics. Nowadays they cannot, being purged of any poisonous element, do harm to the skin that they make beautiful. There need be no more sowing the seeds of destruction in the furrows of time, no martyrs to the cause like Georgina Gunning, that fair dame but infelix, who died, so they relate, from the effect of a poisonous rouge upon her lips. No, we need have no fears now. Artifice will claim not another victim from among her worshippers.

Loveliness

Loveliness shall sit at the toilet, watching her oval face in the oval mirror.   Her smooth fingers shall flit among the paints and powder, to tip and mingle them, catch up a pencil, clasp a phial, and what not and what *not*, until the mask of vermeil tinct has been laid aptly, the enamel quite hardened.   And, heavens, how she will charm us and ensorcel our eyes !   Positively rouge will rob us for a time of all our reason; we shall go mad over masks.   Was it not at Capua that they had a whole street where nothing was sold but dyes and unguents ?   We must have such a street, and, to fill our new Seplasia, our Arcade of the Unguents, all herbs and minerals and live creatures shall give of their substance.   The white cliffs of Albion shall be ground to powder for loveliness, and perfumed by the ghost of many a little violet.   The fluffy eider-ducks, that are swimming round the pond, shall lose their feathers, that the powder-puff may be moonlike as it passes over loveliness's lovely face.   Even the camels shall become ministers of delight, giving their hair in many tufts to be stained by the paints in her colour-box, and across her cheek the swift hare's foot shall fly as of old.   The sea shall offer her the phucus, its scarlet weed.   We shall spill the blood of mulberries at her bidding.   And, as in another period of great ecstasy, a dancing wanton, la belle Aubrey, was crowned upon a church's lighted altar, to Arsenic, that " green-tress'd goddess," ashamed at length of skulking between the soup of the unpopular and the test-tubes of the Queen's analyst, shall be exalted to a place of highest honour upon loveliness's toilet-table.

All these things shall come to pass.   Times of jolliness and glad indulgence !   For Artifice, whom we drove forth, has returned among us, and, though her eyes are red with crying, she is smiling forgiveness.   She is kind.   Let us dance and be glad, and trip the cockawhoop !   Artifice, sweetest exile, is come into her kingdom.   Let us dance her a welcome !

The Death Mask

By Ella D'Arcy

THE Master was dead; and Peschi, who had come round to
the studio to see about some repairs—part of the ceiling had
fallen owing to the too lively proceedings of Dubourg and his
eternal visitors overhead—Peschi displayed a natural pride that it
was he who had been selected from among the many *mouleurs* of
the Quarter, to take a mask of the dead man.

All Paris was talking of the Master, although not, assuredly,
under that title. All Paris was talking of his life, of his genius,
of his misery, and of his death. Peschi, for the moment, was sole
possessor of valuable unedited details, to the narration of which
Hiram P. Corner, who had dropped in to pass the evening with
me, listened with keenly attentive ears.

Corner was a recent addition to the American Art Colony;
ingenuous as befitted his eighteen years, and of a more than
improbable innocence. Paris, to him, represented the Holiest of
Holies; the dead Master, by the adorable impeccability of his
writings, figuring therein as one of the High Priests. Needless
to say, he had never come in contact with that High Priest, had
never even seen him; while the Simian caricatures which so
frequently

155

frequently embellished the newspapers, made as little impression on the lad's mind as did the unequivocal allusions, jests, and epigrams, for ever flung up like sea-spray against the rock of his unrevered name.

The absorbing interest Corner felt glowed visibly on his fresh young western face, and it was this, I imagine, which led Peschi to propose that we should go back with him to his *atelier* and see the mask for ourselves.

Peschi is a Genoese; small, lithe, very handsome; a skilled workman, a little demon of industry; full of enthusiasms, with the real artist-soul. He works for Felon the sculptor, and it was Felon who had been commissioned to do the bust for which the death mask would serve as model.

It is always pleasant to hear Peschi talk; and to-night, as we walked from the Rue Fleurus to the Rue Notre-Dame-des-Champs he told us something of mask-taking in general, with illustrations from this particular case.

On the preceding day, barely two hours after death had taken place, Rivereau, one of the dead man's intimates, had rushed into Peschi's workroom, and carried him off, with the necessary materials, to the Rue Monsieur, in a cab. Rivereau, though barely twenty, is perhaps the most notorious of the *bande*. Peschi described him to Corner as having dark, evil, narrow eyes set too close together in a perfectly white face, framed by falling, lustre-less black hair; and with the stooping shoulders, the troubled walk, the attenuated hands common to his class.

Arrived at the house, Rivereau led the way up the dark and dirty staircase to the topmost landing, and as they paused there an instant, Peschi could hear the long-drawn, hopeless sobs of a woman within the door.

On being admitted he found himself in an apartment
consisting

consisting of two small, inconceivably squalid rooms, opening one
from the other.

In the outer room, five or six figures, the disciples, friends, and
lovers of the dead poet, conversed together ; a curious group in a
medley of costumes. One in an opera-hat, shirt-sleeves, and
soiled grey trousers tied up with a bit of stout string ; another in
a black coat buttoned high to conceal the fact that he wore no shirt
at all ; a third in clothes crisp from the tailor, with an immense
bunch of Parma violets in his buttonhole. But all were alike in
the strangeness of their eyes, their voices, their gestures.

Seen through the open door of the further room, lay the corpse
under a sheet, and by the bedside knelt the stout, middle-aged
mistress, whose sobs had reached the stairs.

Madame Germaine, as she was called in the Quarter, had
loved the Master with that complete, self-abnegating, sublime
love of which certain women are capable—a love uniting that of
the mother, the wife, and the nurse all in one. For years she
had cooked for him, washed for him, mended for him ; had
watched through whole nights by his bedside when he was ill ;
had suffered passively his blows, his reproaches, and his neglect,
when, thanks to her care, he was well again. She adored him
dumbly, closed her eyes to his vices, and magnified his gifts,
without in the least comprehending them. She belonged to the
ouvrière class, could not read, could not write her own name ; but
with a characteristic which is as French as it is un-British, she
paid her homage to intellect, where an Englishwoman only
gives it to inches and muscle. Madame Germaine was prouder
perhaps of the Master's greatness, worshipped him more devoutly,
than any one of the super-cultivated, ultra-corrupt group, who
by their flatteries and complaisances had assisted him to his ruin.

It was with the utmost difficulty, Peschi said, that Rivereau
and

and the rest had succeeded in persuading the poor creature to leave the bedside and go into the other room while the mask was being taken.

The operation, it seems, is a sufficiently horrible one, and no relative is permitted to be present. As you cover the dead face over with the plaster, a little air is necessarily forced back again into the lungs, and this air as it passes along the windpipe causes strange rattlings, sinister noises, so that you might swear that the corpse was returned to life. Then, as the mould is removed, the muscles of the face drag and twitch, the mouth opens, the tongue lolls out; and Peschi declared that this always remains for him a gruesome moment. He has never accustomed himself to it; on every recurring occasion it fills him with the same repugnance; and this, although he has taken so many masks, is so deservedly celebrated for them, that *la bande* had instantly selected him to perpetuate the Master's lineaments.

"But it's an excellent likeness," said Peschi; "you see they sent for me so promptly that he had not changed at all. He does not look as though he were dead, but just asleep."

Meanwhile we had reached the unshuttered shop-front, where Peschi displays, on Sundays and week-days alike, his finished works of plastic art to the *gamins* and *filles* of the Quarter.

Looking past the statuary, we could see into the living-room beyond, it being separated from the shop only by a glass partition. It was lighted by a lamp set in the centre of the table, and in the circle of light thrown from beneath its green shade, we saw a charming picture: the young head of Madame Peschi bent over her baby, whom she was feeding at the breast. She is eighteen, pretty as a rose, and her story and Peschi's is an idyllic one; to be told, perhaps, another time. She greeted us with the smiling, cordial, unaffected kindliness which in France warms your blood
with

with the constant sense of brotherhood ; and, giving the boy to his
father—a delicious opalescent trace of milk hanging about the little
mouth—she got up to see about another lamp which Peschi had
asked for.

Holding this lamp to guide our steps, he preceded us now across
a dark yard to his workshop at the further end, and while we
went we heard the young mother's exquisite nonsense-talk
addressed to the child, as she settled back in her place again to her
nursing.

Peschi, unlocking a door, flashed the light down a long room,
the walls of which, the trestle-tables, the very floor, were hung,
laden, and encumbered with a thousand heterogeneous objects.
Casts of every description and dimension, finished, unfinished,
broken ; scrolls for ceilings ; caryatides for chimney-pieces ;
cornucopias for the entablatures of buildings ; chubby Cupids
jostling emaciated Christs ; broken columns for Père Lachaise, or
consolatory upward-pointing angels ; hands, feet, and noses for the
Schools of Art ; a pensively posed *échorché* contemplating a Venus
of Milo fallen upon her back ; these, and a crowd of nameless,
formless things, seemed to spring at our eyes, as Peschi raised or
lowered the lamp, moved it this way or the other.

"There it is," said he, pointing forwards ; and I saw lying flat
upon a modelling-board, with upturned features, a grey, immobile
simulacrum of the curiously mobile face I remembered so well.

"Of course you must understand," said Peschi, "it's only in
the rough, just exactly as it came from the *creux*. Fifty copies
are to be cast altogether, and this is the first one. But I must
prop it up for you. You can't judge of it as it is."

He looked about him for a free place on which to set the lamp.
Not finding any, he put it down on the floor. For a few moments
he stood busied over the mask with his back to us.

"Now

" Now you can see it properly," said he, and stepped aside.

The lamp threw its rays upwards, illuminating strongly the lower portion of the cast, throwing the upper portion into deepest shadow, with the effect that the inanimate mask was become suddenly a living face, but a face so unutterably repulsive, so hideously bestial, that I grew cold to the roots of my hair. . . . . A fat, loose throat, a retreating chinless chin, smeared and bleared with the impressions of the meagre beard ; a vile mouth, lustful, flaccid, the lower lip disproportionately great ; ignoble lines ; hateful puffiness ; something inhuman and yet worse than inhuman in its travesty of humanity ; something that made you hate the world and your fellows, that made you hate yourself for being ever so little in *this* image. A more abhorrent spectacle I have never seen. . . . .

So soon as I could turn my eyes from the ghastly thing, I looked at Corner. He was white as the plaster faces about him. His immensely opened eyes showed his astonishment and his terror. For what I experienced was intensified in his case by the unexpected and complete disillusionment. He had opened the door of the tabernacle, and out had crawled a noisome spider ; he had lifted to his lips the communion cup, and therein squatted a toad. A sort of murmur of frantic protestation began to rise in his throat ; but Peschi, unconscious of our agitation, now lifted the lamp, passed round with it behind the mask, held it high, and let the rays stream downwards from above.

The astounding way the face changed must have been seen to be believed in. It was exactly as though, by some cunning sleight of hand, the mask of a god had been substituted for that of a satyr. . . . . You saw a splendid dome-like head, Shakespearean in contour ; a broad, smooth, finely-modelled brow ; thick, regular horizontal eyebrows, casting a shadow which diminished the too

great

great distance separating them from the eyes ; while the deeper
shadow thrown below the nose altered its character entirely. Its
snout-like appearance was gone, its deep, wide-open, upturned
nostrils were hidden, but you noticed the well-marked transition
from forehead to nose-base, the broad ridge denoting extraordinary
mental power. Over the eyeballs the lids had slidden down
smooth and creaseless ; the little tell-tale palpebral wrinkles
which had given such libidinous lassitude to the eye had vanished
away. The lips no longer looked gross, and they closed together
in a beautiful, sinuous line, now first revealed by the shadow on
the upper one. The prominence of the jaws, the muscularity of
the lower part of the face, which gave it so painfully microcephalous
an appearance, were now unnoticeable ; on the contrary, the whole
face looked small beneath the noble head and brow. You
remarked the medium-sized and well-formed ears, with the
" swan " distinct in each, the gently-swelling breadth of head
above them, the full development of the forehead over the orbits of
the eyes. You discerned the presence of those higher qualities
which might have rendered him an ascetic or a saint ; which
led him to understand the beauty of self-denial, to appreciate
the wisdom of self-restraint : and you did not see how these
qualities remained inoperative in him, being completely over-
balanced by the size of the lower brain, the thick, bull throat,
and the immense length from the ear to the base of the skull at
the back.

I had often seen the Master in life : I had seen him sipping
absinthe at the d'Harcourt ; reeling, a Silemus-like figure, among
the nocturnal Bacchantes of the Boul' Miche ; lying in the gutter
outside his house, until his mistress should come to pick him up
and take him in. I had seen in the living man more traces than
a few of the bestiality which the death-mask had completely
verified ;

verified ; but never in the living man had I suspected anything of the beauty, of the splendour, that I now saw.

For that the Master had somewhere a beautiful soul you divined from his works ; from the exquisite melody of all of them, from the pure, the ecstatic, the religious altitude of some few. But in actual daily life, his loose and violent will-power, his insane passions, held that soul bound down so close a captive, that those who knew him best were the last to admit its existence.

And here, a mere accident of lighting displayed not only that existence, but its visible, outward expression as well. In these magnificent lines and arches of head and brow, you saw what the man might have been, what God had intended him to be ; what his mother had foreseen in him, when, a tiny infant like Peschi's yonder, she had cradled the warm, downy, sweet-smelling little head upon her bosom, and dreamed day-dreams of all the high, the great, the wonderful things her boy later on was to do. You saw what the poor, purblind, middle-aged mistress was the only one to see in the seamed and ravaged face she kissed so tenderly for the last time before the coffin-lid was closed.

You saw the head of gold ; you could forget the feet of clay, or, remembering them, you found for the first time some explanation of the anomalies of his career.

You understood how he who could pour out passionate protestations of love and devotion to God in the morning, offering up body and soul, flesh and blood in his service ; dedicating his brow as a footstool for the Sacred Feet ; his hands as censers for the glowing coals, the precious incense ; condemning his eyes, misleading lights, to be extinguished by the tears of prayer ; you understood how, nevertheless, before evening was come, he would set every law of God and decency at defiance, use every member, every faculty, in the service of sin.

It

It was given to him, as it is given to few, to see the Best, to reverence it, to love it; and the blind, groping hesitatingly forward in the darkness, do not stray as far as he strayed.

He knew the value of work, its imperative necessity; that in the sweat of his brow the artist, like the day-labourer, must produce, must produce: and he spent his slothful days shambling from café to café.

He never denied his vices; he recognised them and found excuses for them, high moral reasons even, as the intellectual man can always do. To indulge them was but to follow out the dictates of Nature, who in herself is holy; cynically to expose them to the world was but to be absolutely sincere.

And his disciples, going further, taught with a vague poetic mysticism that he was a fresh Incarnation of the Godhead; that what was called his immorality was merely his scorn of truckling to the base conventions of the world. But in his saner moments he described himself more accurately as a man blown hither and thither by the winds of evil chance, just as a withered leaf is blown in autumn; and having received great and exceptional gifts, with Shakespeare's length of years in which to turn them to account, he had chosen instead to wallow in such vileness that his very name was anathema among honourable men.

Chosen? Did he choose? Can one say after all that he chose to resemble the leaf rather than the tree? The gates of gifts close on the child with the womb, and all we possess comes to us from afar, and is collected from a thousand diverging sources.

If that splendid head and brow were contained in the seed, so also were the retreating chin, the debased jaw, the animal mouth. One as much as the other was the direct inheritance of former generations. Considered in a certain aspect, it seems that a man

by

by taking thought, may as little hope to thwart the implanted propensities of his character, as to alter the shape of his skull or the size of his jawbone.

I lost myself in mazes of predestination and free-will. Life appeared to me as a huge kaleidoscope turned by the hand of Fate. The atoms of glass coalesce into patterns, fall apart, unite together again, are always the same, but always different, and, shake the glass never so slightly, the precise combination you have just been looking at is broken up for ever. It can never be repeated. This particular man, with his faults and his virtues, his unconscious brutalities, his unexpected gentlenesses, his furies of remorse ; this man with the lofty brain, the perverted tastes, the weak, irresolute, indulgent heart, will never again be met with to the end of time ; in all the endless combinations to come, this precise combination will never be found. Just as of all the faces the world will see, a face like the mask there will never again exchange glances with it. . . . .

I looked at Corner, and saw his countenance once more aglow with the joy of a recovered ideal ; while Peschi's voice broke in on my reverie, speaking with the happy pride of the artist in a good and conscientious piece of work.

"Eh bien, how do you find it ? " said he ; " it is beautiful, is it not ? "

Fleet Street Eclogue

St. George's Day

By John Davidson

BASIL. MENZIES. PERCY. BRIAN. HERBERT. SANDY.

MENZIES.

WHAT thought may burst the bond
          Of rasping spleen?
What hope its victim soothe?
What dream assuage his pains?

HERBERT.

An old stile stands between
Two beeches silvery smooth,
All carved and kissed by lovers fond.

MENZIES.

The foolish country swains!

HERBERT.

165

HERBERT.

Oh ! but the old stile stands,
For ever dear to me—
Foot-worn, its bars by many hands
Polished like ebony !

MENZIES.

But me my city spleen
Holds in a fretting bond.

HERBERT.

And the quickset hedges mantle green,
And the fields roll green beyond ;
While the antique footpath winds about
By farms and little towns,
By waterways, and in and out,
And up and over the downs.

MENZIES.

I hear the idle workmen's sighs ;
I hear their children's hungry cries ;
I hear the burden of the years ;
I hear the drip of women's tears ;
I hear despair, whose tongue is dumb,
Speak thunder in the ruthless bomb.

SANDY.

But why keep brooding over ill ?
Why hearken such discordant tones ?

HERBERT.

HERBERT.

We dream, we sing; we drive the quill
To keep the flesh upon our bones :
Therefore what trade have we with wrongs,
With ways and woes that spoil our songs ?

MENZIES.

None, none !   Alas, there lies the sting !
We see, we feel, but cannot aid ;
We hide our foolish heads and sing ;
We live, we die ; and all is said.

HERBERT.

To wonder-worlds of old romance
Our aching thoughts for solace run.

BRIAN.

And some have stolen fire from France.

SANDY.

And some adore the Midnight Sun.

MENZIES.

I, too, for light the world explore,
And, trembling, tread where angels trod ;
Devout at every shrine adore,
And follow after each new god.

But

But by the altar everywhere
I find the money-changer's stall;
And littering every temple-stair
The sick and sore like maggots crawl.

BRIAN.

Hush, hush!

MENZIES.

          I cannot hush! The poor,
The maimed, the halt, the starving come,
Crying for help at every door;
But loud the ecclesiastic drum
Outbids them; and behind it wait
The bones and cleavers of the State.

SANDY.

This smacks of Disestablishment!

BRIAN.

We'll find him next attacking Rent!

BASIL.

Your talk is vain; your voice is hoarse.

MENZIES.

I would they were as hoarse and vain
As their wide-weltering spring and source
Of helpless woe, of wrath insane.

HERBERT.

By John Davidson

HERBERT.

Why will you hug the coast of Hell?

BRIAN.

Why antedate the Judgment Day?

MENZIES.

Nay, flout me not; you know me well.

BASIL.

Right, comrade! Give your fancy way.

MENZIES.

I cannot see the stars and flowers,
Nor hear the lark's soprano ring,
Because a ruddy darkness lowers
For ever, and the tempests sing.
I see the strong coerce the weak,
And labour overwrought rebel;
I hear the useless treadmill creak,
The prisoner, cursing in his cell;
I see the loafer-burnished wall;
I hear the rotting match-girl whine;
I see the unslept switchman fall;
I hear the explosion in the mine;
I see along the heedless street
The sandwichmen trudge through the mire;
I hear the tired quick-tripping feet

Of

Of sad, gay girls who ply for hire;
I hear the gibbering of the mad;
Sinister workhouse folk I note;
I mark the sable ironclad
In every sound and channel float,
The growl of armies, bound in chains
Of parchment peace that chafes and frets
Their seven-leagued limbs and bristled manes
Of glittering bayonets,
The glowing blast, the fire-shot smoke,
Where guns are forged and armour-plate,
The mammoth hammer's pounding stroke—
The din of our dread iron date;
And always divers undertones
Within the roaring tempest throb—
The chink of gold, the labourer's groans,
The infant's wail, the woman's sob:
Hoarsely they beg of Fate to give
A little lightening of their woe,
A little time to love, to live,
A little time to think and know.
I see where in the East may rise
Some unexpected dreadful dawn—
The gleam of steeled and scowling eyes,
A flash of women's faces wan!

BASIL.

This is St. George's Day.

MENZIES.

St. George? A wretched thief, I vow.

HERBERT.

HERBERT.

Nay, Menzies, you should rather say,
St. George for Merry England, now!

SANDY.

That surely is a phantom cry,
Hollow and vain for many years.

MENZIES.

I hear the idle workmen sigh;
I hear the drip of women's tears.

BASIL.

I hear the laughing, singing voice
Of Shakespeare warming England through;
His birthday, this.

HERBERT.

      Again rejoice,
For this is Wordsworth's birthday, too.

MENZIES.

I hear the agitator shout;
I hear the broker cheapen love;
I hear poor ladies crying out
For license men are weary of.

                           HERBERT.

HERBERT.

I hear the lofty lark,
The lowly nightingale.

BASIL.

The Present is a dungeon dark
Of social problems.   Break the gaol!
Get out into the splendid Past,
Or bid the splendid Future hail.

MENZIES.

Nor then, nor now, nor first, nor last,
I know.   The slave of ruthless Law,
To me Time seems a dungeon vast
Where Life lies rotting in the straw.

BASIL.

I care not for your images
Of Life and Law.   I want to sing
Of England and of Englishmen
Who made our country what it is.

HERBERT.

And I to praise the English Spring.

PERCY.

St. George for Merry England, then !

MENZIES.

MENZIES.

There is no England now, I fear.

BASIL.

No England, say you; and since when?

MENZIES.

Cockney and Celt and Scot are here,
And Democrats and " ans " and " ists "
In clubs and cliques and divers lists;
But now we have no Englishmen.

BASIL.

You utter what you never felt,
I know.   By bog and mount and fen,
No Saxon, Norman, Scot, or Celt
I find, but only Englishmen.

HERBERT.

In all our hedges roses bud.

BASIL.

And thought and speech are more than blood.

HERBERT.

Away with spleen, and let us sing
The English Spring, the English Spring!

BASIL.

BASIL.

In weeds of gold and purple hues
Glad April bursts with piping news
Of swifts and swallows come again,
And of the tender pensive strain
The bullfinch sings from bush to bush.

PERCY.

And oh ! the blackbird and the thrush
Interpret as no maestro may
The meaning of the night and day.

SANDY.

They catch the whispers of the breeze
And weave them into melodies.

BRIAN.

They utter for the hours that pass
The purpose of their moments bright.

BASIL.

They speak the passion of the grass,
That grows so stoutly day and night.

HERBERT.

St. George for Merry England then !
For we are all good Englishmen !

                                        PERCY.

PERCY.

We stand as our forefathers stood
For Liberty's and Conscience' sake.

HERBERT.

We are the sons of Robin Hood,
The sons of Hereward the Wake.

PERCY.

The sons of yeomen, English-fed,
Ready to feast or drink or fight.

HERBERT.

The sons of kings—of Hal and Ned,
Who kept their island right and tight.

PERCY.

The sons of Cromwell's Ironsides,
Who knew no king but God above.

BASIL.

We are the sons of English brides,
Who married Englishmen for love.

SANDY.

Oh, now I see Fate's means and ends!
The Bruce and Wallace wight I ken,

Who

Who saved old Scotland from its friends,
Were mighty northern Englishmen.

BRIAN.

And Parnell, who so greatly fought
To make a mob people, then
With Fate inevitably wrought
That Irish should be Englishmen.

BASIL.

By bogland, highland, down, and fen,
All Englishmen, all Englishmen!

MENZIES.

There is no England now, I say—

BRIAN.

No England now? My grief, my grief!

MENZIES.

We lie widespread, the dragon-prey
Of any Cappadocian thief.
In Arctic and Pacific seas
We lounge and loaf; and either pole
We reach with sprawling colonies—
Unwieldy limbs that lack a soul.

       BASIL.

BASIL.

St. George for Greater England, then!
The Boreal and the Austral men!
They reverence the heroic roll
Of Englishmen who sang and fought:
They have a soul, a mighty soul,
The soul of English speech and thought.

SANDY.

And when the soul of England slept—

BASIL.

St. George for foolish England, then!—

SANDY.

Lo! Washington and Lincoln kept
America for Englishmen!

BASIL.

Hurrah! The English people reigns
Across the wide Atlantic flood!
It could not bind itself in chains,
For Yankee blood is English blood!

HERBERT.

And here the spring is queen
In robes of white and green.

                              PERCY.

PERCY.

In chestnut sconces opening wide
Tapers shall burn some fresh May morn.

BRIAN.

And the elder brightens the highway side,
And the bryony binds the thorn.

SANDY.

White is the snow of the leafless sloe,
The saxifrage by the sedge,
And white the lady-smocks a-row
And sauce-alone in the hedge.

BASIL.

England is in her Spring;
She only begins to be.
Oh! for an organ voice to sing
The summer I can see!
But the Past is there; and a mole may know,
And a bat may understand,
That we are the people wherever we go—
Kings by sea and land!

HERBERT.

And the spring is crowned and stoled
In purple and in gold.

PERCY.

PERCY.

Wherever light, wherever shade is,
Gold and purple may be seen.

BRIAN.

Gold and purple lords-and-ladies
Tread a measure on the green.

SANDY.

Among the long brown furrow lines
The charlock's mustard flowers come up.

HERBERT.

On happy banks the primrose shines;
In lustrous meads, the buttercup.

HERBERT.

In deserts where the wild wind blows
Blossoms the magic hæmony.

PERCY.

Deep in the Chiltern woodland glows
The purple pasque anemone.

BASIL.

And England still grows great,
And never shall grow old;

                                        Within

Within our hands we hold
The world's fate.

MENZIES.

We hold the world's fate?
The cry seems out of date.

BASIL.

Not while a single Englishman
Can work with English brains and bones!
Awaiting us since time began,
The swamps of ice, the wastes of flame
In Boreal and Austral zones
Took life and meaning when we came.
The Sphinx that watches by the Nile
Has seen great empires pass away :
The mightiest lasted but a while ;
Yet ours shall not decay.
Because, although red blood may flow,
And ocean shake with shot,
Not England's sword but England's Word
Undoes the Gordian Knot.
Bold tongue, stout heart, strong hand, brave brow
The world's four quarters win ;
And patiently with axe and plough
We bring the deserts in.

MENZIES.

Whence comes this patriotic craze?
Spare us at least the hackneyed brag
About the famous English flag.

BASIL.

By John Davidson 181

BASIL.

I'll spare no flourish of its praise.
Where'er our flag floats in the wind
Order and justice dawn and shine.
The dusky myriads of Ind,
The swarthy tribes far south the line,
And all who fight with lawless law.
And all with lawless men who cope,
Look hitherward across the brine,
For we are the world's forlorn hope.

MENZIES.

That makes my heart leap up! Hurrah!
We are the world's forlorn hope!

HERBERT.

And with the merry birds we sing
The English Spring, the English Spring.

PERCY.

Iris and orchis now unfold.

BRIAN.

The drooping-leaved laburnums ope
In thunder-showers of greenish gold.

MENZIES.

And we are the world's forlorn hope!

SANDY

SANDY.

The lilacs shake their dancing plumes
Of lavender, mauve, and heliotrope.

HERBERT.

The speedwell on the highway blooms.

MENZIES.

And we are the world's forlorn hope !

SANDY.

Skeletons lurk in every street.

HERBERT.

We push and strike for air and scope.

BRIAN.

The pulses of rebellion beat
Where want and hunger sulk and mope.

MENZIES.

But though we wander far astray,
And oft in utter darkness grope,
Fearless we face the roughest day,
For we are the world's forlorn hope.

SANDY.

By John Davidson

SANDY.

St. George for Merry England then !
For we are all good Englishmen !

BASIL.

St. George for Greater England then !
The Boreal and the Austral men !

ALL.

By bogland, highland, down, and fen,
All Englishmen, all Englishmen !
Who with their latest breath shall sing
Of England and the English Spring !

Long Odds

By Kenneth Grahame

For every honest reader there exist some half-dozen honest books, which he re-reads at regular intervals of six months or thereabouts. Whatever the demands on him, however alarming the arrears that gibber and grin in menacing row, for these he somehow generally manages to find time. Nay, as the years flit by, the day is only too apt to arrive when he reads no others at all; the hour will even come, in certain instances, when the number falls to five, to four—perhaps to three. With this same stride of time comes another practice too—that of formulating general principles to account for or excuse one's own line of action; and yet it ought not to be necessary to put forward preface or apology for finding oneself immersed in *Treasure Island* for about the twentieth time. The captain's capacities for the consumption of rum must always be a new delight and surprise; the approaching tap of the blind man's stick, the moment of breathless waiting in the dark and silent inn, are ever sure of their thrill; hence it came about that the other night I laid down the familiar book at the end of Part the Second—where vice and virtue spar a moment ere the close grip—with the natural if common-place reflection that nineteen to six was good healthy odds.

But somehow I was in no hurry to take the book up again. The

The mental comment with which I had laid it down had set up a yeasty ferment and a bubble in my brain ; till at last, with a start, I asked myself how long was it since I had been satisfied with such a pitiful majority on the side of evil ? Why, a certain number of years ago it would have been no majority at all—none, at least, worth speaking of. What a change must have been taking place in me unsuspected all this time, that I could tamely accept, as I had just done, this pitiful compromise (I can call it nothing else) with the base law of probabilities ! What a totally different person I must have now become, from the hero who sallied out to deal with a horde of painted Indians, armed only with his virtue and his unerring smoothbore ! Well, there was some little comfort in the fact that the fault was not entirely my own, nor even that of the irresistible years.

Frankly, in the days I look back to, this same *Treasure Island* would not have gone down at all. It was not that we were in the least exacting. We did not ask for style ; the evolution of character possessed no interest whatever for us ; and all scenery and description we sternly skipped. One thing we *did* insist on having, and that was good long odds against the hero ; and in those fortunate days we generally got them. Just at present, however, a sort of moral cowardice seems to have set in among writers of this noblest class of fiction ; a truckling to likelihood, and a dirty regard for statistics. Needless to say, this state of things is bringing about its inevitable consequence. Already one hears rumours that the boy of the period, instead of cutting down impalpable bandits or blowing up imaginary mines and magazines, is moodily devoting himself to golf. The picture is a pitiful one. Heaven hath blessed him, this urchin, with a healthy appetite for pirates, a neat hand at the tomahawk, and a simple passion for being marooned ; instead of which, he now plods about the country playing

playing golf. The fault is not his, of course ; the honest heart of
him beats sound as ever. The real culprits are these defaulting
writers, who, tainted by realism, basely shirk their duty, fall away
from the high standard of former days, and endeavour to represent
things as they possibly might have happened. Nineteen to six,
indeed ! No lad of spirit will put up with this sort of thing. He
will even rather play golf ; and play golf he consequently does.

The magnificent demand of youth for odds—long odds, whatever the cost !—has a pathetic side to it, once one is in a position
to look back, thereon squinting gloomily through the wrong end of
the telescope. At the age of six or seven, the boy (in the person
of his hero of the hour) can take on a Genie, an Afreet or two, a
few Sultans and a couple of hostile armies, with a calmness re-
sembling indifference. At twelve he is already less exacting.
Three hundred naked Redskins, mounted on mustangs and yelling
like devils, pursue him across the prairie and completely satisfy his
more modest wants. At fifteen, 'tis enough if he may only lay his
frigate alongside of two French ships of the line ; and among the
swords he shall subsequently receive on his quarter-deck he will
not look for more than one Admiral's ; while a year or two later
it suffices if he can but win fame and fortune at twenty-five, and
marry the Earl's daughter in the face of a whole competitive
House of Lords. Henceforward all is declension. One really has
not the heart to follow him, step by dreary step, to the time when
he realises that a hero may think himself lucky if he can only hold
his own, and so on to the point when it dawns on him at last that
the gods have a nasty habit of turning the trump, and have even
been accused of playing with loaded dice—an aphorism any honest
boy would laugh to scorn.

Indeed, the boy may well be excused for rejecting with indignation these unworthy sneers at the *bona fides* of the autocrats who,
from

from afar, shift the pieces on this little board, and chuck them aside when done with, one by one. For he but sees the world without through the chequered lattice of the printed page, and there invariably the hero, buffeted though he may be of men, kicked by parents and guardians, reviled by colonels and first lieutenants, always has the trump card up his sleeve, ready for production in the penultimate chapter. What wonder, then, that the gods appear to him as his cheerful backers, ready to put their money on him whatever the starting price? Nay, even willing to wink and look the other way when he, their darling, gets a quiet lift from one of themselves, who (perhaps) may " have a bit on ? " Meanwhile, to the wistful gazer through the lattice, his cloistral life begins to irk terribly. 'Tis full time he was up and doing. Through the garden gate, beyond the parish common, somewhere over the encircling horizon, lie fame and fortune, and the title and the bride. Pacific seas are calling, the thunder of their rollers seems to thrill to him through the solid globe that interposes between. Savages are growing to dusky manhood solely that he may flesh his sword on them ; maidens are already entangling themselves in perilous situations that he, and he alone, may burst the bonds, eliminate the dragon, and swing them forth to freedom and his side. The scarlet sunsets scorn him, a laggard and a recreant ; behind them lie arrogant cities, plains of peril, and all the tingling adventure of the sea. The very nights are big with reproach, in their tame freedom from the watch-fire, the war-whoop, the stealthy ambuscade ; and every hedgerow is a boundary, every fence another bond. From this point his decadence dates. At first the dice spring merrily out on the board. The gods throw, and he ; and they again, and then he, and still with no misgivings ; those blacklegs know enough to permit an occasional win. All the same, early or late, comes that period in the game when

when suspicion grows a sickening certainty. He asked for long odds against him, and he has got them with a vengeance; the odds of the loaded dice. While as for that curled darling he dreamed of, who was to sweep the board and declare himself the chosen, where is he? He has dropped by the roadside, many a mile behind. From henceforth on they must not look to join hands again.

Some there are who have the rare courage, at the realising point, to kick the board over and declare against further play. Stout-hearted ones they, worthy of marble and brass; but you meet them not at every turn of the way. Such a man I forgathered with by accident, one late autumn, on the almost deserted Lido. The bathing-ladders were drawn up, the tramway was under repair; but the slant sun was still hot on the crinkled sand, and it was not so much a case of paddling suggesting itself as of finding oneself barefoot and paddling without any conscious process of thought. So I paddled along dreamily, and thought of Ulysses, and how he might have run the prow of his galley up on these very sands, and sprung ashore and paddled; and then it was that I met him—not Ulysses, but the instance in point.

He was barelegged also, this elderly man of sixty or thereabouts; and he had just found a *cavallo del mare*, and exhibited it with all the delight of a boy; and as we wandered together, cool-footed, eastwards, I learnt by degrees how such a man as this, with the mark of Cheapside still evident on him, came to be pacing the sands of the Lido that evening with me. He had been Secretary, it transpired, to some venerable Company or Corporation that dated from Henry the Seventh; and among his duties, which were various and engrossing, was in especial that of ticking off, with a blue pencil, the members of his governing body, as they made their appearance at their weekly meeting; in accordance with the practice
dating

dating from Henry the Seventh. His week, as I have said, was a busy one, and hinged on a Board day ; and as time went on these Board days raced up and disappeared with an ever-increasing rapidity, till at last his life seemed to consist of but fifty-two days in the year—all Board days. And eternally he seemed to be ticking off names with a feverish blue pencil. These names, too, that he ticked—they flashed into sight and vanished with the same nightmare gallop ; the whole business was a great humming Zoetrope. Anon the Board would consist of Smith, Brown, Jackson, &c., Life Members all ; in the briefest of spaces Smith would drop out, and on would come Price, a neophyte—a mere youngling, this Price. A few more Board days flash by, and out would go Brown and maybe Jackson—on would come Cattermole, Fraser, Davidson—beardless juniors every one. Round spun the unceasing wheel ; in a twinkling Davidson, the fledgling, sat reverend in the chair, while as for those others——! And all the time his blue pencil, with him, its slave, fastened to one end of it, ticked steadily on. To me, the hearer, it was evident that he must have been gradually getting into the same state of mind as Rudyard Kipling's delightful lighthouse keeper, whom solitude and the ceaseless tides caused to see streaks and lines in all things, till at last he barred a waterway of the world against the ships that persisted in making the water streaky. And this may account for an experience of his in the Underground Railway one evening, when he was travelling home after a painful Board day on which he had ticked up three new boys into vacant places which seemed to have been hardly filled an hour. He was alone, he said, and rather sleepy, and he hardly looked at the stranger who got in at one of the stations, until he saw him deposit in the hat-rack—where ordinary people put their umbrellas —what might have been an umbrella, but looked, in the dim light of the Underground, far more like a scythe. Then he sat up and

begpan

began to take notice. The elderly stranger—for he was both
gaunt and elderly—nay, as he looked at him longer he saw he was
old—oh so very old ! And one long white tuft of hair hung down
on his wrinkled forehead from under his top hat,—the stranger
squatted on the seat opposite him, produced a note-book and a pencil—a *blue* pencil too !—and leaning forward, with a fiendish grin,
said, " *Now* I'm going to tick off all you fellows—all you Secre-
taries—right back from the days of Henry the Seventh ! "

The Secretary fell back helplessly in his seat. Terror-stricken,
he strove to close his ears against the raucous voice that was already
rattling off those quaint old Tudor names he remembered having
read on yellowing parchment; but all was of no avail. The
stranger went steadily on, and each name as read was ruthlessly
scored out by the unerring blue pencil. The pace was tremendous.
Already they were in the Commonwealth ; past flew the Restora-
tion like a racehorse—the blue pencil wagged steadily like a nightmare—Queen Anne and her coffee-houses,—in a second they were
left far behind ; and as they turned the corner and sped down the
straight of the Georgian era, the Secretary sweated, a doomed man.
The gracious reign of Victoria was full in sight—nay, on the
stranger's lips was hovering the very name of Fladgate—Fladgate
whom the Secretary could himself just remember, a doddering old
pensioner—when the train shivered and squealed into St. James's
Park Station. The Secretary flung the door open and fled like a
hare, though it was not his right station. He ran as far as the
Park itself, and there on the bridge over the water he halted,
mopped his brow, and gradually recovered his peace of mind. The
evening was pleasant, full of light and laughter and the sound of
distant barrel-organs. Before him, calm and cool, rose the walls
of the India Office, which in his simple way he had always considered a dream in stone. Beneath his feet a whole family of ducks
circled

circled aimlessly, with content written on every feature ; or else, reversing themselves in a position denoting supreme contempt for all humanity above the surface, explored a new cool underworld a few inches below. It was then (he said) that a true sense of his situation began to steal over him ; and it was then that he awoke to the fact of another life open to him should he choose to grasp it. Neither the ducks nor the India Office (so he affirmed) carried blue pencils, and why should he ? The very next Board day he sent in his resignation, and, with a comfortable pension and some reminiscence (perhaps) of that frontage of the India Office, crossed the Channel and worked South till he came to Venice, where the last trace of blue-pencil nightmare finally faded away.

"And are you never bored ? " I tenderly inquired of him, as we rocked homewards in a gondola between an apricot sky and an apricot sea.

"During the first six months I was," he answered, frankly ; " then it passed away altogether, even as influenza does in time, or the memory of a *gaucherie*. And now every day lasts as long as a year of those Board days of old, and is fifty-two times as interesting. Why, only take this afternoon, for example. I didn't get over here till two, but first I met some newly-arrived Americans, and talked for a cycle with them ; and you never know what an American will be surprised at, or, better still, what he will not be surprised at ; and if you only think what that means—— Well, presently they left (they had to get on to Rome), so I went up to the platform over the sea and had oysters and a bottle of that delightful yellow wine I always forget the name of ; and æons passed away in the consumption. Each oyster lasted a whole Board day, and each glass of yellow wine three. Then I strolled along the sands for a century or so, thinking of nothing in particular. Lastly, I met you, and for some twelve months I've been boring

you

you with my uninteresting story. And even yet there's the whole evening to come ! Oh, I had lots of leeway to make up when I came over here ; but I think I shall manage it yet—in Venice ! "

I could not help thinking, as I parted from him at the Piazzetta steps, that (despite a certain incident in the Underground Railway) here was one of the sanest creatures I had ever yet happened upon.

But examples such as this (as I said) are rare ; the happy-starred ones who know when to cut their losses. The most of us prefer to fight on—mainly, perhaps, from cowardice, and the dread of a plunge into a new element, new conditions, new surroundings—a fiery trial for any humble, mistrustful creature of use-and-wont. And yet it is not all merely a matter of funk. For a grim love grows up for the sword-play itself, for the push and the hurtle of battle, for the grips and the give-and-take—in fine, for the fight itself, whatever the cause. In this exaltation, far from ignoble, we push and worry along until a certain day of a mist and a choke, and we are ticked off and done with.

This is the better way ; and the history of our race is ready to justify us. With the tooth-and-claw business we began, and we mastered it thoroughly ere we learnt any other trade. Since that time we may have achieved a thing or two besides—evolved an art, even, here and there, though the most of us bungled it. But from first to last fighting was the art we were always handiest at ; and we are generally safe if we stick to it, whatever the foe, whatever the weapons—most of all, whatever the cause.

Two Prose Fancies

By Richard Le Gallienne

I—Variations upon Whitebait

A VERY Pre-Raphaelite friend of mine came to me one day
and said apropos of his having designed a very Early English
chair: "After all, if one has anything to say one might as well
put it into a chair!"

I thought the remark rather delicious, as also his other remark
when one day in a curiosity-shop we were looking at another
chair, which the dealer declared to be Norman. My friend
seated himself in it very gravely, and after softly moving about
from side to side, testing it, it would appear, by the sensation it
imparted to the sitting portion of his limbs, he solemnly decided
" I don't think the *flavour* of this chair is Norman!"

I thought of this Pre-Raphaelite brother as the Sphinx and I
were seated a few evenings ago at our usual little dinner, in our
usual little sheltered corner, on the Lover's Gallery of one of the
great London restaurants. The Sphinx says that there is only
one place in Europe where one can really dine, but as it is
impossible to be always within reasonable train service of that
Montsalvat of cookery, she consents to eat with me—she cannot
call it dine—at the restaurant of which I speak. I being very

simple-minded,

simple-minded, untravelled, and unlanguaged, think it, in my
Cockney heart, a very fine place indeed, with its white marble
pillars surrounding the spacious peristyle, and flashing with a
thousand brilliant lights and colours; with its stately cooks, clothed
in white samite, mystic, wonderful, ranged behind a great altar
loaded with big silver dishes, and the sacred musicians of the
temple ranged behind them—while in and out go the waiters
clothed in white and black, waiters so good and kind that I am
compelled to think of Elijah being waited on by angels.

They have such an eye for a romance, too, and really take it personally to heart if it should befall that our little table is usurped by others
that know not love.   I like them, too, because they really seem to
have an eye for the strange beauty and charm of the Sphinx, quite
an unexpected taste for Botticelli.   They ill conceal their envy of
my lot, and sometimes in the meditative pauses between the
courses I see them romantically reckoning how it might be possible
by desperately saving up, by prodigious windfalls of tips, from
unexampled despatch and sweetness in their ministrations, how it
might be possible in ten years' time, perhaps even in five—the
lady would wait five years! and her present lover could be artisti-
cally poisoned meanwhile!—how it might be possible to come and
sue for her beautiful hand.   Then a harsh British cry for " waiter "
comes like a rattle and scares away that beautiful dream-bird,
though, as the poor dreamer speeds on the quest of roast beef for
four, you can see it still circling with its wonderful blue feathers
around his pomatumed head.

Ah, yes, the waiters know that the Sphinx is no ordinary woman.
She cannot conceal even from them the mystical star of her face;
they too catch far echoes of the strange music of her brain; they
too grow dreamy with dropped hints of fragrance from the rose of
her wonderful heart.

How

By Richard Le Gallienne   195

How reverently do they help her doff her little cloak of silk and
lace; with what a worshipful inclination of the head, as in the
presence of a deity, do they await her verdict of choice between
rival soups—shall it be " clear or thick ? "   And when she decides
on " thick " how relieved they seem to be, as if—well, some few
matters remain undecided in the universe, but never mind, this
is settled for ever, no more doubts possible on one portentous
issue, at any rate—Madame will take her soup " thick."

" On such a night " our talk fell upon whitebait.

As the Sphinx's silver fork rustled among the withered silver
upon her plate, she turned to me and said:

" Have you ever thought what beautiful little things these
whitebait are ? "

" Oh, yes," I replied, " they are the daisies of the deep sea, the
threepenny-pieces of the ocean."

" You dear ! " said the Sphinx, who is alone in the world in
thinking me awfully clever.   " Go on, say something else, something pretty about whitebait—there's a subject for you ! "

Then it was that, fortunately, I remembered my Pre-Raphaelite
friend, and I sententiously remarked: " Of course, if one has anything to say one cannot do better than say it about whitebait. . . .
Well, whitebait. . . ."

But here, providentially, the band of the beef—that is, the band
behind the beef; that is, the band that nightly hymns the beef
(the phrase is to be had in three qualities)—struck up the overture
from " Tannhäuser," which is not the only music that makes
the Sphinx forget my existence; and thus, forgetting me, she
momentarily forgot the whitebait.   But I remembered, remembered hard—worked at pretty things, as metal-workers punch out
their flowers of brass and copper.   The music swirled about us
like golden waves, in which swam myriad whitebait, like showers
of

of tiny stars, like falling snow. To me it was one grand processional of whitebait, silver ripples upon streams of gold.

The music stopped. The Sphinx turned to me with the soul of Wagner in her eyes, and then she turned to the waiter: " Would it be possible," she said, " to persuade the bandmaster to play that wonderful thing over again ? "

The waiter seemed a little doubtful, even for the Sphinx, but he went off to the bandmaster with the air of a man who has at last an opportunity to show that he can dare all for love. Personally, I have a suspicion that he poured his month's savings at the bandmaster's feet, and begged him to do this thing for the most wonderful lady in the world; or perhaps the bandmaster was really a musician, and his musician's heart was touched—lonely there amid the beef—to think that there was really some one, invisible though she were to him, some shrouded silver presence, up there among the beefeaters, who really loved to hear great music. Perhaps it was thus made a night he has never forgotten; perhaps it changed the whole course of his life—who knows ? The sweet reassuring request may have come to him at a moment when, sick of heart, he was deciding to abandon real music for ever, and settle down amid the beef and the beef-music of Old England.

Well, however it was, the waiter came back radiant with a " Yes " on every shining part of him, and if the " Tannhäuser " had been played well at first, certainly the orchestra surpassed themselves this second time.

When the great jinnee of music had once more passed out of the hall, the Sphinx turned with shining eyes to the waiter:

" Take," she said, " take these tears to the bandmaster. He has indeed earned them."

" Tears, little one," I said. " See how they swim like whitebait in the fishpools of your eyes ! "

" Oh,

" Oh, yes, the whitebait," rejoined the Sphinx, glad of a subject to hide her emotion.   " Now tell me something nice about them, though the poor little things have long since disappeared.   Tell me, for instance, how they get their beautiful little silver water-proofs ? "

" Electric Light of the World," I said, " it is like this.   While they are still quite young and full of dreams, their mother takes them out in picnic parties of a billion or so at a time to where the spring moon is shining, scattering silver from its purse of pearl far over the wide waters, silver, silver, for every little whitebait that cares to swim and pick it up.   The mother, who has a contract with some such big restaurateur as ours here, chooses a convenient area of moonlight, and then at a given sign they all turn over on their sides, and bask and bask in the rays, little fin pressed lovingly against little fin—for this is the happiest time in the young white-bait's life: it is at these silvering parties that matches are made and future consignments of whitebait arranged for.   Well, night after night, they thus lie in the moonlight, first on one side then on the other, till by degrees, tiny scale by scale, they have become completely lunar-plated.   Ah ! how sad they are when the end of that happy time has come."

" And what happens to them after that ? " asked the Sphinx.

" One night when the moon is hidden their mother comes to them with treacherous wile, and suggests that they should go off on a holiday again to seek the moon—the moon that for a moment seems captured by the pearl-fishers of the sky.   And so off they go merrily, but, alas, no moon appears, and presently they are aware of unwieldly bumping presences upon the surface of the sea, presences as of huge dolphins, and rough voices call across the water, till, scared, the little whitebaits turn home in flight—to find themselves somehow meshed in an invisible prison, a net as fine and

strong

strong as air, into which, O agony, they are presently hauled, lovely banks of silver, shining like opened coffers beneath the coarse and ragged flares of yellow torches.   The rest is silence."

"What sad little lives! and what a cruel world it is!" said the Sphinx—as she crunched with her knife through the body of a lark, that but yesterday had been singing in the blue sky.   Its spirit sang just above our heads as she ate, and the air was thick with the grey ghosts of all the whitebait she had eaten that night.

But there were no longer any tears in her eyes.

II—About the Securities

WHEN I say that my friend Matthew lay dying, I want you so far as possible to dissociate the statement from any conventional, and certainly from any pictorial, conceptions of death which you may have acquired.   Death sometimes shows himself one of those impersonal artists who conceal their art, and, unless you had been told, you could hardly have guessed that Matthew was dying, dying indeed sixty miles an hour, dying of consumption, dying because some one else had died four years before, dying too of debt.

Connoisseurs, of course, would have understood; at a glance, would have named the sculptor who was silently chiselling those noble hollows in the finely modelled face,—that Pygmalion who turns all flesh to stone,—at a glance would have named the painter who was cunningly weighting the brows with darkness that the eyes might shine the more with an unaccustomed light.   Matthew and I had long been students of the strange wandering artist, had begun by hating his art (it is ever so with an art unfamiliar to us!) and had ended by loving it.

"Let

"Let us see what the artist has added to the picture since yesterday," said Matthew, signing to me to hand him the mirror.

"H'm," he murmured, "he's had one of his lazy days, I'm afraid. He's hardly added a touch—just a little heightened the chiaroscuro, sharpened the nose a trifle, deepened some little the shadows round the eyes . . . ."

"O why," he presently sighed, "does he not work a little overtime and get it done? He's been paid handsomely enough . . . ."

"Paid," he continued, "by a life that is so much undeveloped gold-mine, paid by all my uncashed hopes and dreams . . . ."

"He works fast enough for me, old fellow," I interrupted, "there was a time, was there not, when he worked too fast for you and me?"

There are moments, for certain people, when such fantastic unreality as this is the truest realism. Matthew and I talked like this with our brains, because we hadn't the courage to allow our hearts to break in upon the conversation. Had I dared to say some real emotional thing, what effect would it have had but to set poor tired Matthew a-coughing? and it was our aim that he should die with as little to-do as practicable. The emotional in such situations is merely the obvious. There was no need for either of us to state the elementary feelings of our love. I knew that Matthew was going to die, and he knew that—I was going to live; and we pitied each other accordingly, though I confess my feeling for him was rather one of envy,—when it was not congratulation.

Thus, to tell the truth, we never mentioned "the hereafter." I don't believe it even occurred to us. Indeed, we spent the few hours that remained of our friendship in retailing the latest gathered of those good stories with which we had been accustomed to salt our intercourse.

One

One of Matthew's anecdotes was, no doubt, somewhat suggested by the occasion, and I should add that he had always somewhat of an ecclesiastical bias, would, I believe, have ended some day as a Monsignor, a notable " Bishop Blougram."

His story was of an evangelistic preacher who desired to impress his congregation with the unmistakable reality of hell-fire. " You know the Black Country, my friends," he had declaimed, " you have seen it, at night, flaring with a thousand furnaces, in the lurid incandescence of which, myriads of unhappy beings, our fellow-creatures (God forbid!) snatch a precarious existence, you have seen them silhouetted against the yellow glare, running hither and thither as it seemed from afar, in the very jaws of the awful fire. Have you realised that the burdens with which they thus run hither and thither are molten iron, iron to which such a stupendous heat has been applied that it has melted, melted as though it had been sugar in the sun—well! returning to hell-fire, let me tell you this, that in hell they eat this fiery molten metal for ice-cream, yes! and are glad to get anthing so cool."

It was thus we talked while Matthew lay dying, for why should we not talk as we had lived ? We both laughed long and heartily over this story, perhaps it would have amused us less had Matthew not been dying; and then his kind old nurse brought in our lunch. We had both excellent appetites, and were far from indifferent to the dainty little meal which was to be our last but one together. I brought my table as close to Matthew's pillow as was possible, and he stroked my hand with tenderness in which there was a touch of gratitude.

" You are not frightened of the bacteria! " he laughed sadly, and then he told me, with huge amusement, how a friend (and a true dear friend for all that) had come to see him a day or two before, and had hung over the end of the bed to say farewell, daring

to

to approach no nearer, mopping his fear-perspiring brows with a handkerchief soaked in " Eucalyptus "!

" He had brought an anticipatory elegy too," said my friend, " written against my burial.   I wish you'd read it for me," and he fidgetted for it in the nervous manner of the dying, and, finding it among his pillows, handed it to me saying, " you needn't be frightened of it.   It is well dosed with Eucalyptus."

We laughed even more over this poem than over our stories, and then we discussed the terms of three cremation societies to which, at the express request of my friend, I had written a day or two before.

Then having smoked a cigar and drunk a glass of port together (for the assured dying are allowed to " live well "), Matthew grew sleepy, and tucking him beneath the counterpane, I left him, for after all, he was not to die that day.

Circumstances prevented my seeing him again for a week. When I did so, entering the room poignantly redolent of the strange sweet odour of antiseptics, I saw that the great artist had been busy in my absence.   Indeed, his work was nearly at end. Yet to one unfamiliar with his methods, there was still little to alarm in Matthew's face.   In fact, with the exception of his brain and his ice-cold feet, he was alive as ever.   And even to his brain had come a certain unnatural activity, a life as of the grave, a sort of vampire vitality, which would assuredly have deceived any one who had not know him.   He still told his stories, laughed and talked with the same unconquerable humour, was in every way alert and practical, with this difference that he had forgotten he was going to die, and that the world in which he exercised his various faculties was another world to that in which, in spite of his delirium, we ate our last boiled fowl, drank our last wine, smoked our last cigar together.   His talk was so convincingly rational,

dealt

dealt with such unreal matters in so every day a fashion that you
were ready to think that surely it was you and not he whose mind
was wandering.

"You might reach that pocket-book, and ring for Mrs. Davies,"
he would say in so casual a way that of course you would ring.
On Mrs. Davies's appearance he would be fumbling about among
the papers in his pocket-book, and presently he would say, with
a look of frustration that went to one's heart—"I've got a ten
pound note somewhere here for you, Mrs. Davies, to pay you up
till Saturday, but somehow I seem to have lost it. Yet it must be
somewhere about. Perhaps you'll find it as you make the bed in
the morning. I'm so sorry to have troubled you. . . ."

And then he would grow tired and doze a little on his pillow.

Suddenly he would be alert again and with a startling vividness
tell me strange stories from the dreamland into which he was
now passing.

I had promised to see him on the Monday, but had been prevented, and had wired to him accordingly. This was Tuesday.

"You needn't have troubled to wire," he said. "Didn't you
know I was in London from Saturday to Monday?"

"The doctor and Mrs. Davies didn't know," he continued
with the creepy cunning of the dying, "I managed to slip away
to look at a house I think of taking—in fact I've taken it. It's in
—in—now, where is it? Now isn't that silly? I can see it as
plain as anything—yet I cannot, for the life of me, remember
where it is, or the number. . . . . It was somewhere St. John's
Wood way . . . never mind, you must come and see me there
when we get in. . . ."

I said that he was dying in debt, and thus the heaven that lay
about his deathbed was one of fantastic Eldorados, sudden colossal
legacies, and miraculous windfalls.

"I

" I haven't told you," he said presently, " of the piece of good
luck that has befallen me.   You are not the only person in luck.
I can hardly expect you to believe me, it sounds so like the
Arabian nights.   However, it's true for all that.   Well, one of
the little sisters was playing in the garden a few afternoons ago,
making mud-pies or something of that sort, and she suddenly
scraped up a sovereign.   Presently she found two or three more,
and our curiosity becoming aroused, a turn or two with the spade
revealed quite a bed of gold, and the end of it was that on further
excavating, the whole garden proved to be one mass of sovereigns.
Sixty thousand pounds we counted . . . . and then what do you
think—it suddenly melted away . . . ."

He paused for a moment, and continued more in amusement
than regret:

" Yes—the government got wind of it, and claimed the whole
lot as treasure-trove! "

" But not," he added slyly, " before I'd paid off two or three
of my biggest bills.   Yes—and—you'll keep it quiet, of course,
there's another lot been discovered in the garden, but we shall
take good care the government doesn't get hold of it this time, you
may bet."

He told this wild story with such an air of simple conviction
that, odd as it may seem, one believed every word of it.   But the
tale of his sudden good fortune was not ended.

" You've heard of old Lord Osterley," he presently began again.
" Well, congratulate me, old man, he has just died and left everything to me.   You know what a splendid library he had—to think
that that will all be mine—and that grand old park through which
we've so often wandered, you and I.   Well, we shall need fear no
gamekeeper now, and of course, dear old fellow, you'll come and
live with me—like a prince—and just write your own books and

say

say farewell to journalism for ever.   Of course I can hardly believe
it's true yet.   It seems too much of a dream, and yet there's no
doubt about it.   I had a letter from my solicitors this morning,
saying that they were engaged in going through the securities
and—and—but the letter's somewhere over there, you might read
it.   No? can't you find it?   It's there somewhere about I know.
Never mind, you can see it again . . . ." he finished wearily.

"Yes!" he presently said, half to himself, "it will be a wonderful change! a wonderful change!"

At length the time came to say good-bye, a good-bye I knew
must be the last, for my affairs were taking me so far away from
him that I could not hope to see him for some days.

"I'm afraid, old man," I said, "that I mayn't be able to see
you for another week."

"O never mind, old fellow, don't worry about me.   I'm much
better now—and by the time you come again we shall know all
about the securities."

The securities!   My heart had seemed like a stone, incapable
of feeling, all those last unreal hours together, but the pathos of
that sad phrase, so curiously symbolic, suddenly smote it with over-
whelming pity, and the tears sprang to my eyes for the first time.

As I bent over him to kiss his poor damp forehead, and press
his hand for the last farewell, I murmured:

"Yes—dear, dear old friend.   We shall know all about the
securities . . . ."

The Blessed

By W. B. Yeats

CUMHAL the king, being angry and sad,
   Came by the woody way
To the cave, where Dathi the Blessed had gone,
   To hide from the troubled day.

Cumhal called out, bowing his head,
   Till Dathi came and stood,
With blinking eyes, at the cave's edge,
   Between the wind and the wood.

And Cumhal said, bending his knees,
   " I come by the windy way
To gather the half of your blessedness
   And learn the prayers that you say.

" I can bring you salmon out of the streams
   And heron out of the skies."
But Dathi folded his hands and smiled
   With the secrets of God in his eyes.

And Cumhal saw like a drifting smoke
   All manner of blessedest souls,
Children and women and tonsured young men,
   And old men with croziers and stoles.

                           " Praise

" Praise God and God's Mother," Dathi said,
  " For God and God's Mother have sent
The blessedest souls that walk in the world
  To fill your heart with content."

" And who is the blessedest," Cumhal said,
  " Where all are comely and good ?
Is it those that with golden thuribles
  Are singing about the wood ? "

" My eyes are blinking," Dathi said,
  " With the secrets of God half blind.
But I have found where the wind goes
  And follow the way of the wind;

" And blessedness goes where the wind goes
  And when it is gone we die;
And have seen the blessedest soul in the world,
  By a spilled wine-cup lie.

" O blessedness comes in the night and the day,
  And whither the wise heart knows;
And one has seen, in the redness of wine,
  The Incorruptible Rose:

" The Rose that must drop, out of sweet leaves,
  The heaviness of desire,
Until Time and the World have ebbed away
  In twilights of dew and fire! "

The Quest of Sorrow

By Mrs. Ernest Leverson

I

IT is rather strange, in a man of my temperament, that I did not discover the void in my life until I was eighteen years old. And then I found out that I had missed a beautiful and wonderful experience.

I had never known grief. Sadness had shunned me, pain had left me untouched; I could hardly imagine the sensation of being unhappy. And the desire arose in me to have this experience; without which, it seemed to me, that I was not complete. I wanted to be miserable, despairing: a Pessimist! I craved to feel that gnawing fox, Anxiety, at my heart; I wanted my friends (most of whom had been, at some time or other, more or less heartbroken) to press my hand with sympathetic looks, to avoid the subject of my trouble, from delicacy; or, better still, to have long, hopeless talks with me about it, at midnight. I thirsted for salt tears; I longed to clasp Sorrow in my arms and press her pale lips to mine.

Now this wish was not so easily fulfilled as might be supposed, for I was born with those natural and accidental advantages that militate most against failure and depression. There was my appearance

appearance.   I have a face that rarely passes unnoticed (I suppose a man may admit, without conceit, that he is not repulsive), and the exclamation, "What a beautiful boy !" is one that I have been accustomed to hear from my earliest childhood to the present time.

I might, indeed, have known the sordid and wearing cares connected with financial matters, for my father was morbidly economical with regard to me.   But, when I was only seventeen, my uncle died, leaving me all his property, when I instantly left my father's house (I am bound to say, in justice to him, that he made not the smallest objection) and took the rooms I now occupy, which I was able to arrange in harmony with my temperament.   In their resolute effort to be neither uninterestingly commonplace nor conventionally bizarre (I detest—do not you ?—the ready-made exotic) but at once simple and elaborate, severe and florid, they are an interesting result of my complex aspirations, and the astonishing patience of a bewildered decorator.   (I think everything in a room should not be entirely correct ; and I had some trouble to get a marble mantel-piece of a sufficiently debased design.)   Here I was able to lead that life of leisure and contemplation for which I was formed and had those successes—social and artistic—that now began to pall upon me.

The religious doubts, from which I am told the youth of the middle classes often suffers, were, again, denied me.   I might have had some mental conflicts, have revelled in the sense of rebellion, have shed bitter tears when my faiths crumbled to ashes.   But I can never be insensible to incense ; and there must, I feel, be something organically wrong about the man who is not impressed by the organ.   I love religious rites and ceremonies, and on the other hand, I was an agnostic at five years old.   Also, I don't think it matters.   So here there is no chance for me.

To

To be miserable one must desire the unattainable. And of the fair women who, from time to time, have appealed to my heart, my imagination, etc., every one, *without a single exception*, has been kindness itself to me. Many others, indeed, for whom I have no time, or perhaps no inclination, write me those letters which are so difficult to answer. How can one sit down and write, " My dear lady—I am so sorry, but I am really too busy ?"

And with, perhaps, two appointments in one day—a light comedy one, say, in the Park, and serious sentiment coming to see one at one's rooms—to say nothing of the thread of a flirtation to be taken up at dinner and having perhaps to make a jealous scene of reproaches to some one of whom one has grown tired, in the evening—you must admit I had a sufficiently occupied life.

I had heard much of the pangs of disappointed ambition, and I now turned my thoughts in that direction. A failure in literature would be excellent. I had no time to write a play bad enough to be refused by every manager in London, or to be hissed off the stage ; but I sometimes wrote verses. If I arranged to have a poem rejected I might get a glimpse of the feelings of the unsuccessful. So I wrote a poem. It was beautiful, but that I couldn't help, and I carefully refrained from sending it to any of the more literary reviews or magazines, for there it would have stood no chance of rejection. I therefore sent it to a commonplace, barbarous periodical, that appealed only to the masses ; feeling sure it would not be understood, and that I should taste the bitterness of Philistine scorn.

Here is the little poem—if you care to look at it. I called it

FOAM-

FOAM-FLOWERS

Among the blue of Hyacinth's golden bells
(Sad is the Spring, more sad the new-mown hay),
Thou art most surely less than least divine,
Like a white Poppy, or a Sea-shell grey.
I dream in joy that thou art nearly mine;
Love's gift and grace, pale as this golden day,
Outlasting Hollyhocks, and Heliotrope
(Sad is the Spring, bitter the new-mown hay).
The wandering wild west wind, in salt-sweet hope,
With glad red roses, gems the woodland way.

Envoi

A bird sings, twittering in the dim air's shine,
Amid the mad Mimosa's scented spray,
Among the Asphodel, and Eglantine,
" Sad is the Spring, but sweet the new-mown hay."

I had not heard from the editor, and was anticipating the
return of my poem, accompanied by some expressions of ignorant
contempt that would harrow my feelings, when it happened that
I took up the frivolous periodical. Fancy my surprise when
there, on the front page, was my poem—signed, as my things are
always signed, " *Lys de la Vallée*." Of course I could not repress
the immediate exhilaration produced by seeing oneself in print ;
and when I went home I found a letter, thanking me for the
amusing parody on a certain modern school of verse—and enclosing
ten-and-six !

A parody ! And I had written it in all seriousness !

Evidently literary failure was not for me. After all, what I
wanted most was an affair of the heart, a disappointment in love,

an

an unrequited affection. And these, for some reason or other, never seemed to come my way.

One morning I was engaged with Collins, my servant, in putting some slight final touches to my toilette, when my two friends, Freddy Thompson and Claude de Verney, walked into my room.

They were at school with me, and I am fond of them both, for different reasons. Freddy is in the Army; he is two-and-twenty, brusque, slangy, tender-hearted, and devoted to me. De Verney has nothing to do with this story at all, but I may mention that he was noted for his rosy cheeks, his collection of jewels, his reputation for having formerly taken morphia, his epicurism, his passion for private theatricals, and his extraordinary touchiness. One never knew what he would take offence at. He was always being hurt, and writing letters beginning: " Dear Mr. Carington " or " Dear Sir "—(he usually called me Cecil), " I believe it is customary when a gentleman dines at your table," etc.

I never took the slightest notice, and then he would apologise. He was always begging my pardon and always thanking me, though I never did anything at all to deserve either his anger or gratitude.

" Hallo, old chap," Freddy exclaimed, " you look rather down in the mouth. What's the row ? "

" I am enamoured of Sorrow," I said, with a sigh.

" Got the hump—eh ? Poor old boy. Well, I can't help being cheery, all the same. I've got some ripping news to tell you."

" Collins," I said, " take away this eau-de-cologne. It's corked. Now, Freddy," as the servant left the room, " your news."

" I'm

"I'm engaged to Miss Sinclair. Her governor has given in at last. What price that? . . . I'm tremendously pleased, don't you know, because it's been going on for some time, and I'm awfully mashed, and all that."

Miss Sinclair! I remembered her—a romantic, fluffy blonde, improbably pretty, with dreamy eyes and golden hair, all poetry and idealism.

Such a contrast to Freddy! One associated her with pink chiffon, Chopin's nocturnes, and photographs by Mendelssohn.

"I congratulate you, my dear child," I was just saying, when an idea occurred to me. Why shouldn't I fall in love with Miss Sinclair? What could be more tragic than a hopeless attachment to the woman who was engaged to my dearest friend? It seemed the very thing I had been waiting for.

"I have met her. You must take me to see her, to offer my congratulations," I said.

Freddy accepted with enthusiasm.

A day or two after, we called. Alice Sinclair was looking perfectly charming, and it seemed no difficult task that I had set myself. She was sweet to me as Freddy's great friend—and we spoke of him while Freddy talked to her mother.

"How fortunate some men are !" I said, with a deep sigh.

"Why do you say that?"

"Because you're so beautiful," I answered, in a low voice, and in my *earlier manner*—that is to say, as though the exclamation had broken from me involuntarily.

She laughed, blushed, I think, and turned to Freddy. The rest of the visit I sat silent and as though abstracted, gazing at her. Her mother tried, with well-meaning platitudes, to rouse me from what she supposed to be my boyish shyness. . . .

What

II

What happened in the next few weeks is rather difficult to describe. I saw Miss Sinclair again and again, and lost no opportunity of expressing my admiration; for I have a theory that if you make love to a woman long enough, and ardently enough, you are sure to get rather fond of her at last. I was progressing splendidly; I often felt almost sad, and very nearly succeeded at times in being a little jealous of Freddy.

On one occasion—it was a warm day at the end of the season, I remember—we had gone to skate at that absurd modern place where the ice is as artificial as the people, and much more polished. Freddy, who was an excellent skater, had undertaken to teach Alice's little sister, and I was guiding her own graceful movements. She had just remarked that I seemed very fond of skating, and I had answered that I was—on thin ice—when she stumbled and fell. . . . She hurt her ankle a little—a very little, she said.

"Oh, Miss Sinclair—'Alice'—I am sure you are hurt!" I cried, with tears of anxiety in my voice. "You ought to rest—I am sure you ought to go home and rest."

Freddy came up, there was some discussion, some demur, and finally it was decided that, as the injury was indeed very slight, Freddy should remain and finish his lesson. And I was allowed to take her home.

We were in a little brougham; delightfully near together. She leaned her pretty head, I thought, a little on one side—*my* side. I was wearing violets in my button-hole. Perhaps she was tired, or faint.

"How are you feeling now, dear Miss Sinclair?"

"Much better—thanks!"

"I am

"I am afraid you are suffering. . . . I shall never forgot what I felt when you fell !—My heart ceased beating !"

"It's very sweet of you. But, it's really nothing."

"How precious these few moments with you are ! I should like to drive with you for ever ! Through life—to eternity !"

"Really ! What a funny boy you are !" she said softly.

"Ah, if you only knew, Miss Sinclair, how—how I envy Freddy."

"Oh, Mr. Carington !"

"Don't call me Mr. Carington. It's so cold—so ceremonious. Call me Cecil. Won't you ?"

"Very well, Cecil."

"Do you think it treacherous to Freddy for me to envy him—to tell you so ?"

"Yes, I am afraid it is ; a little."

"Oh no. I don't think it is.—How are you feeling now, Alice ?"

"Much better, thanks very much." . . .

Suddenly, to my own surprise and entirely without pre-meditation, I kissed her—as it were, accidentally. It seemed so shocking, that we both pretended I hadn't, and entirely ignored the fact : continuing to argue as to whether or not it was treacherous to say I envied Freddy. . . . I insisted on treating her as an invalid, and lifted her out of the carriage, while she laughed nervously. It struck me that I was not unhappy yet. But that would come.

The next evening we met at a dance. She was wearing flowers that Freddy had sent her ; but among them she had fastened one or two of the violets I had worn in my button-hole. I smiled, amused at the coquetry. No doubt she would laugh at me when she thought she had completely turned my head. She fancied me
a child !

a child! Perhaps, on her wedding-day, I should be miserable at last.

. . . "How tragic, how terrible it is to long for the impossible!"

We were sitting out, on the balcony. Freddy was in the ballroom, dancing. He was an excellent dancer.

"*Impossible!*" she said; and I thought she looked at me rather strangely. "But you don't really, really——"

"Love you?" I exclaimed, lyrically. "But with all my soul! My life is blighted for ever, but don't think of me. It doesn't matter in the least. It may kill me, of course; but never mind. Sometimes, I believe, people *do* live on with a broken heart, and——"

"My dance, I think," and a tiresome partner claimed her.

Even that night, I couldn't believe, try as I would, that life held for me no further possibilities of joy. . . .

About half-past one the next day, just as I was getting up, I received a thunderbolt in the form of a letter from Alice.

Would it be believed that this absurd, romantic, literal, beautiful person wrote to say she had actually broken off her engagement with Freddy? She could not bear to blight my young life; she returned my affection; she was waiting to hear from me.

Much agitated, I hid my face in my hands. What! was I never to get away from success—never to know the luxury of an unrequited attachment? Of course, I realised, now, that I had been deceiving myself; that I had only liked her enough to wish to make her care for me; that I had striven, unconsciously, to that end. The instant I knew she loved me all my interest was gone. My passion had been entirely imaginary. I cared nothing,
absolutely

absolutely nothing, for her.   It was impossible to exceed my indifference.   And Freddy !   Because *I* yearned for sorrow, was that a reason that I should plunge others into it ?   Because I wished to weep, were my friends not to rejoice ?   How terrible to have wrecked Freddy's life, by taking away from him something that I didn't want myself !

The only course was to tell her the whole truth, and implore her to make it up with poor Freddy.   It was extremely complicated.   How was I to make her see that I had been *trying* for a broken heart ; that I *wanted* my life blighted ?

I wrote, endeavouring to explain, and be frank.   It was a most touching letter, but the inevitable, uncontrollable desire for the *beau rôle* crept, I fear, into it and I fancy I represented myself, in my firm resolve not to marry her whatever happened—as rather generous and self-denying.   It was a heart-breaking letter, and moved me to tears when I read it.

This is how it ended :

. . . . "You have my fervent prayers for your happiness, and it may be that some day you and Freddy, walking in the daisied fields together, under God's beautiful sunlight, may speak not unkindly of the lonely exile.

"Yes, exile.   For to-morrow I leave England.   To-morrow I go to bury myself in some remote spot—perhaps to Trouville—where I can hide my heart and pray unceasingly for your welfare and that of the dear, dear friend of my youth and manhood.

"Yours and his, devotedly, till death and after,

"CECIL CARINGTON."

It was not a bit like my style.   But how difficult it is not to
fall

fall into the tone that accords best with the temperament of the person to whom one is writing !

I was rather dreading an interview with poor Freddy. To be misunderstood by him would have been really rather tragic. But even here, good fortune pursued me. Alice's letter breaking off the engagement had been written in such mysterious terms, that it was quite impossible for the simple Freddy to make head or tail of it. So that when he appeared, just after my letter (which had infuriated her)—Alice threw herself into his arms, begging him to forgive her ; pretending—women have these subtleties—that it had been a *boutade* about some trifle.

But I think Freddy had a suspicion that I had been "mashed," as he would say, on his *fiancée*, and thought vaguely that I had done something rather splendid in going away.

If he had only stopped to think, he would have realised that there was nothing very extraordinary in "leaving England" in the beginning of August ; and he knew I had arranged to spend the summer holidays in France with De Verney. Still, he fancies I acted nobly. Alice doesn't.

And so I resigned myself, seeing, indeed, that Grief was the one thing life meant to deny me. And on the golden sands, with the gay striped bathers of Trouville, I was content to linger with laughter on my lips, seeking for Sorrow no more.

Stories Toto Told Me

By Baron Corvo

About Beata Beatrice and the Mamma of San Pietro

"Ah, sir, don't be angry with me, because I really do love her so! What else can I do when she is as pretty as that, and always good and cheerful and patient? And when I met her last evening by the boat-house I took her into my arms asking her to kiss me, and, sir, she did. And then I told her that I loved her dearly, and she said she loved me too. And I said that when I grew up I would marry her, and when I looked into her eyes they were full of tears so I know she loves me; but she is ashamed because she is so poor and her mamma such a hag. But do I mind her being poor—the little pigeon? Ma che! for when I feel her soft arms round me and her breath in my hair, then I kiss her on the lips and neck and bosom, and I know it is Beatrice, her body and her soul, that I want and that I care for, not her ragged clothes."

Toto jumped off the tree trunk and stood before me, with all his lithe young figure tense and strung up as he went on with his declamatory notices.

"Has not your Excellency said that I am strong like an ox, and will it not be my joy to work hard to make my girl happy and rich and grand as the sun? Do you think that I spend what you give me at the wine-shop or the tombola? You know that I don't.

don't. Yes, I have always saved, and now I shall save more, and in a year or two I shall ask your permission to marry her. No, I don't want to go away, or to leave you. May the devil fly away with me to the pit of hell and burn me for ever with his hottest fire if I do! Nor will Beatrice make any difference to your Excellency; you need never see her, you need never even know that there is such a flower of Paradise, such an angel, living near you if you don't wish to know it. And I can assure you that Beatrice has the greatest respect for you, and if you will only be so good and so kind as to let us make each other happy she will be quite proud and glad to serve you as well as I do, and to help me to serve you too. And, sir, you know how fond you are of a fritto? Ah well, Beatrice can make a *rigaglie* so beautiful that you will say it must have come straight from Heaven; and this I know because I have tried it myself."

He flung himself down on the ground and kissed my hands, and kissed my feet, and wept, and made me an awful scene.

I told him to get up and not be a young fool. I said that I didn't care what he did, and asked if I had ever been a brute to him, or denied him anything that was reasonable.

He swore that I was a saint, a saint from Heaven, that I always had been and always should be, because I could not help myself; and was going down on his knees again, when I stopped that, and said he had better bring me the girl and not make me hotter than I was with his noise.

" To tell you the truth, sir," he replied, " I was always quite sure that you would have pity upon us when you knew how very much we loved each other. And when you caught us last night I told Beatrice that now I must let you know everything, because I was certain that as long as I did not deceive you (and you know that I have never done so) there was nothing to be afraid of; and
                                                              I told

I told her you would without doubt like to see her to give her good counsel, because she was my friend; and she said she would call that too much honour. Then I felt her trembling against my heart, so I kissed her for a long time and said she must be brave like I am; and, sir, as you are so gracious as to want to see her, I have taken the liberty of bringing her and she is here."

I had always admired the cleverness of this lad, and was not much surprised at his last announcement.

"Where?" I said.

"I put her behind that tree, sir," and he pointed to a big oak about twenty yards away. I could not help laughing at his deepness; and he took courage, I suppose, from my auspicious aspect. All sorts of clouds of hesitation, uncertainty and doubt moved out of his clear brown eyes, while his face set in a smile absurd and complacently expectant. "Shall I fetch her, sir?"

I nodded. I had had some experience of his amours before; but this was a new phase, and I thought I might as well be prepared for *anything*. He went a few paces away, and disappeared behind the oak tree. There was a little rustle of the underwood, and some kissing for a minute or two. Then he came out again, leading his companion by the hand. I said I was prepared for anything, but I confess to a little gasp at what I saw. It was not a boy and girl who approached me, but a couple of boys—apparently, at least. They came and stood beside the hammock in which I was lying. Toto, you know, was sixteen years old, a splendid, wild (*discolo*) creature, from the Abruzzi, a figure like Cellini's Perseus; skin brown, with real red blood under it; smooth as a peach, and noble as a god. He had a weakness for sticking a dead-white rose in the black waves of hair over his left ear, and the colour of that rose against his cheeks, flushed as they were now, was something to be truly thankful for. I used

to

to make him wear white clothes on these hot summer days down by the lake—a silk shirt with all the buttons undone and the sleeves rolled up, showing his broad brown chest and supple arms, and short breeches of the same, convenient for rowing. (He had half-a-dozen creatures like himself under his command, and their business was to carry my photographic and insect-hunting apparatus, and to wait upon me while I loafed the summers away in the Alban hills or along the eastern coast.) The seeming boy, whom he had called Beatrice, looked about fourteen years old, and far more delicately dainty even than he was. The bold magnificent independence of his carriage was replaced in her by one of tenderness and softness, quite as striking in its way as the other. She wore her hair in a short silky mop like Toto, and her shirt was buttoned up to the spring of her pretty throat. She was about as high as her boy's shoulder, and stood waiting before me with her poor little knees trembling, and a rosy blush coming and going over her face. They were so exquisitely lovely, in that sun-flecked shade with the blue lake for a background, that I could not help keeping them waiting a few minutes. Such pictures as this are not to be seen every day. Presently he put his arm round her neck, and she put hers round his waist, and leaned against him a little. But he never took his eyes off mine.

" Go on, Toto," I said, " what were you going to say ? "

" Ah, well, sir, you see I thought if Beatrice came to live with us—with me, I mean—it would be more convenient for you if she looked like the rest of us, because then she would be able to do things for you as well as we can, and people will not talk."

It struck me immediately that Toto was right again as usual; for, upon my word, this girl of his would pass anywhere for a very pretty boy, with just the plump roundness of the Florentine Apollino, and no more.

" So

" So I got some clean clothes of Guido's, and brought them here early this morning, and then I fetched Beatrice and put them on her, and hid her behind the trees, because I knew you would scold me about her when you came down to read your newspapers; and I determined to tell you everything, and to let you know that the happiness of both of us was in your hands. And I only wanted you to see her like this, in order that you might know that you will not be put to any discomfort or inconvenience if you are so kind as to allow us to love each other."

This looked right enough; but, whether or not, there was no good in being nasty-tempered just then, so I told them to be as happy as they liked, and that I would not interfere with them as long as they did not interfere with me. They both kissed my hands, and I kissed Beatrice on the forehead, and cheeks and lips, Toto looking on as proud as a peacock. And then I told him to take her away and send her home properly dressed, and return to me in half an hour.

I could see very well that all these happenings were natural enough, and that it was not a part I cared to play to be harsh or ridiculous, or to spoil an idyll so full of charm and newness. Besides, I have reason to know jolly well the futility of interfering between the male animal and his mate.

So when Toto came back I said nothing discouraging or *ennuyant* beyond reminding him that he ought to make quite sure of possessing an enduring love for this girl, a love which would make him proud to spend his life with and for her, and her only. I told him he was very young, which was no fault of his, and that if he would take my advice he would not be in a hurry about anything. He said that my words were the words of wisdom, and that he would obey me just as he would the Madonna del Portone in her crown of glory if she came down and told him things then

and

and there; that he had known Beatrice since they had been babies
together, and had always loved her far better than his sisters, and in
a different way too, if I could only understand.   Last night when
he had held her in his arms he told her that he knew she wished
him well, and felt himself so strong and she so weak, looking so
tender and so tempting, that all of a minute he desired her for his
own, and to give somebody a *bastonata* of the finest for her, and
to take her out of the clutches of that dirty mean old witch-cat of
a mamma of hers who never gave her any pleasure, kept her shut
up whenever there was a festa, and, Saints of Heaven! sometimes
beat her simply because she envied her for being beautiful and
delicate, and bright as a young primrose.   "What a hag of a
mamma it was to be cursed with, and what could the Madonna
be thinking about to give such a *donnicciuola* of a mamma to his
own *bellacuccia*!   Not but what the Madonnina was sometimes
inattentive, but then, of course, she had so many people to look
after or she could not have given such a mamma to San Pietro as
she did."

Here I saw a chance of changing the subject, and remarked that
it would be nice to know what sort of a mamma the Madonna
had given to San Pietro.

"Ah, well, sir, you must know that the mamma of San Pietro
was the meanest woman that ever lived—scraping and saving all
the days of her life, and keeping San Pietro and his two sisters
(the nun and the other one, of whom I will tell you another time)
for days together with nothing to eat except perhaps a few potato
peelings and a cheese rind.   As for acts of kindness and charity
to her neighbours, I don't believe she knew what they were,
though of course I am not certain; and whatever good San Pietro
had in him he must have picked up somewhere else.   As soon as
he was old enough to work he became a fisherman, as you know,
                                                          because

because when the Santissimo Salvatore wanted a Pope to govern the Church, He went down to the seaside and chose San Pietro, because He knew that as San Pietro was a fisherman he would be just the man to bear all kinds of hardships, and to catch people's souls and take them to Paradise, just as he had been used to catch fish and take them to the market. And so San Pietro went to Rome, and reigned there for many years. And at last the Pagans settled that all the Catholics had to be killed. And the Catholics thought that though they had no objection to being killed themselves it would be a pity to waste a good Pope like San Pietro, who had been chosen and given to them by the Lord God Himself. Therefore they persuaded San Pietro to run away on a night of the darkest, and to hide himself for a time in a lonely place outside the gates of the city. After he had gone a little way along the Via Appia—and the night was very dark—he saw a grey light on the road in front of him, and in the light there was the Santissimo Himself; and San Pietro was astonished, for His Majesty was walking towards Rome. And San Pietro said: 'O Master, where do you go?' And the Face of the Santissimo became very sad, and He said: 'I am going to Rome to be crucified again.' And then San Pietro knew it was not a noble thing that he was doing to run away on the sly like this, because a shepherd doesn't leave his sheep when wolves come—at least, no shepherd worth a *baiocco*.

"Then San Pietro turned round and went back himself to Rome, and was crucified with much joy between two posts in the Circus of Nero; but he would not be crucified like the Santissimo, because he wished to make amends for his weakness in trying to run away, and he begged and prayed to be crucified with his head where his feet ought to be. The Pagans said most certainly if he liked it that way, it was all the same to them. And

so

so San Pietro made no more ado but simply went straight to Heaven. And, of course, when he got there his angel gave him a new cope and a tiara and his keys, and the Padre Eterno put him to look after the gate, which is a very great honour, but only his due, because he had been of such high rank when he lived in the world. Now after he had been there a little while his mamma also left the world, and was not allowed to come into Paradise, but because of her meanness she was sent to hell. San Pietro did not like this at all, and when some of the other saints chaffed him about it he used to grow angry. At last he went to the Padre Eterno, saying that it was by no means suitable that a man of his quality should be disgraced in this way; and the Padre Eterno, Who is so good, so full of pity, and of mercy that He would do anything to oblige you if it is for the health of your soul, said He was sorry for San Pietro and He quite understood his position. He suggested that perhaps the case of San Pietro's mamma had been decided hurriedly, and He ordered her Angel Guardian to bring the book in which had been written down all the deeds of her life, good or bad.

" ' Now,' said the Padre Eterno, ' We will go carefully through this book and if We can find only one good deed that she has done We will add to that the merits of Our Son and of hers so that she may be delivered from eternal torments.'

" Then the Angel read out of the book, and it was found that in the whole of her life she had only done one good deed; for a poor starving beggar-woman had once asked her, for the love of God, to give her some food, and she had thrown her the top of an onion which she was peeling for her own supper.

" And the Padre Eterno instructed the Angel Guardian of San Pietro's mamma to take that onion-top and to go and hold it over the pit of hell, so that if by chance she should boil up with the

other

other damned souls to the top of that stew, she might grasp the
onion-top and by it be dragged up to Heaven.

"The Angel did as he was commanded and hovered in the air
over the pit of hell holding out the onion-top in his hand, and the
furnace flamed, and the burning souls boiled and writhed like *pasta*
in a copper pot, and presently San Pietro's mamma came up
thrusting out her hands in anguish, and when she saw the onion-
top she gripped it, for she was a very covetous woman, and the
Angel began to rise into the air carrying her up towards Heaven.

"Now when the other damned souls saw that San Pietro's
mamma was leaving them, they also desired to escape and they
hung on to the skirts of her gown hoping to be delivered from their
pain, and still the Angel rose, and San Pietro's mamma held the
onion-top, and many tortured souls hung on to her skirts, and
others to the feet of those, and again others on to them, and you
would surely have thought that hell was going to be emptied
straight away. And still the Angel rose higher and the long
stream of people all hanging to the onion-top rose too, nor was the
onion-top too weak to bear the strain. But when San Pietro's
mamma became aware of what was going on and of the numbers
who were escaping from hell along with her, she didn't like it:
and, because she was a nasty selfish and cantankerous woman, she
kicked and struggled, and took the onion-top in her teeth so that
she might use her hands to beat off those who were hanging to
her skirts. And she fought so violently that she bit through the
onion-top, and tumbled back for always into hell flame.

"So you see, sir, that it is sure to be to your own advantage if
you are kind to other people and let them have their own way so
long as they don't interfere with you."

I chuckled at Toto's moral reflections.

Two Sonnets

By Maurice Baring

I

Because she listened to the quiring spheres
  We thought she did not hear our homely strings;
Stars diademed her hair in misty rings,
Too late we understood those stars were tears.

Without she was a temple pure as snow,
Within were piteous flames of sacrifice;
And underneath the dazzling mask of ice
A heart of swiftest fire was dying slow.

She in herself, as lonely lilies fold
Stiff silver petals over secret gold,
Shielded her passion, and remained afar
From pity :—Cast red roses on the pyre !
She that was snow shall rise to Heaven as fire
In the still glory of the morning star.

You

II

You were the Queen of evening, and the skies
Were soft above you, knowing you were fair,
With Sunset's dewy gold about your hair,
And Twilight in the stillness of your eyes.

You did not know your dear divinity,
And, childlike, all unconscious that you walked
In a high, mystic space, you smiled and talked,
And stooped to pluck a rose and give it me.

As at the gate of Heaven an angel-child
Might wonder at an outcast's pleading gaze,
An outcast kneeling at the golden bars,
And say : " Come be my playmate, here the days
Are longer and the ways outside are wild,
And you shall play with suns and silver stars."

A Letter Home

By Enoch Arnold Bennett

I

R AIN was falling—it had fallen steadily through the night—but
the sky showed promise of fairer weather. As the first
streaks of dawn appeared, the wind died away, and the young
leaves on the trees were almost silent. The birds were insistently
clamorous, vociferating times without number that it was a healthy
spring morning and good to be alive.

A little, bedraggled crowd stood before the park gates, awaiting
the hour named on the notice board when they would be admitted
to such lodging and shelter as iron seats and overspreading
branches might afford. A weary, patient-eyed, dogged crowd—a
dozen men, a boy of thirteen, and a couple of women, both past
middle age—which had been gathering slowly since five o'clock.
The boy appeared to be the least uncomfortable. His feet were
bare, but he had slept well in an area in Grosvenor Place, and was
not very damp yet. The women had nodded on many doorsteps,
and were soaked. They stood apart from the men, who seemed
unconscious of their existence. The men were exactly such as
one would have expected to find there—beery and restless as to
the eyes, quaintly shod, and with nondescript greenish clothes which
for

for the most part bore traces of the yoke of the sandwich board.
Only one amongst them was different.

He was young, and his cap, and manner of wearing it, gave sign
of the sea. His face showed the rough outlines of his history.
Yet it was a transparently honest face, very pale, but still boyish
and fresh enough to make one wonder by what rapid descent he
had reached his present level. Perhaps the receding chin, the
heavy, pouting lower lip, and the ceaselessly twitching mouth
offered a key to the problem.

"Say, Darkey," he said.

"Well ? "

"How much longer ? "

"Can't ye see the clock ?   It's staring ye in the face."

"No. Something queer's come over my eyes."

Darky was a short, sturdy man, who kept his head down and
his hands deep in his pockets. The rain-drops clinging to the
rim of an ancient hat fell every now and then into his grey
beard, which presented a drowned appearance. He was a person
of long and varied experiences ; he knew that queer feeling in the
eyes, and his heart softened.

"Come, lean against the pillar," he said, " if you don't want to
tumble. Three of brandy's what you want. There's four minutes
to wait yet."

With body flattened to the masonry, legs apart, and head
thrown back, Darkey's companion felt more secure, and his
mercurial spirits began to revive. He took off his cap, and
brushing back his light brown curly hair with the hand which
held it, he looked down at Darkey through half-closed eyes, the
play of his features divided between a smile and a yawn. He had
a lively sense of humour, and the irony of his situation was not
lost on him. He took a grim, ferocious delight in calling up the
might-have-beens

might-have-beens and the "fatuous ineffectual yesterdays" of life.
There is a certain sardonic satisfaction to be gleaned from a
frank recognition of the fact that you are the architect of your
own misfortune. He felt that satisfaction, and laughed at Darkey,
who was one of those who bleat about "ill-luck" and "victims of
circumstance."

"No doubt," he would say, "you're a very deserving fellow,
Darkey, who's been treated badly. I'm not." To have attained
such wisdom at twenty-five is not to have lived altogether in
vain.

A park-keeper presently arrived to unlock the gates, and the
band of outcasts straggled indolently towards the nearest sheltered
seats. Some went to sleep at once, in a sitting posture. Darkey
produced a clay pipe, and, charging it with a few shreds of tobacco
laboriously gathered from his waistcoat pocket, began to smoke.
He was accustomed to this sort of thing, and with a pipe in his
mouth could contrive to be moderately philosophical upon occasion.
He looked curiously at his companion, who lay stretched at full
length on another bench.

"I say, pal," he remarked, "I've known ye two days ; ye've
never told me yer name, and I don't ask ye to. But I see ye've
not slep' in a park before."

"You hit it, Darkey ; but how ?"

"Well, if the keeper catches ye lying down he'll be on to ye.
Lying down's not allowed."

The man raised himself on his elbow.

"Really now," he said, "that's interesting. But I think I'll
give the keeper the opportunity of moving me. Why, it's quite
fine, the sun's coming out and the sparrows are hopping round—
cheeky little devils ! I'm not sure that I don't feel jolly."

"I wish I'd got the price of a pint about me," sighed Darkey,
and

and the other man dropped his head and appeared to sleep. Then Darkey dozed a little and heard in his waking sleep the heavy, crunching tread of an approaching park-keeper; he started up to warn his companion, but thought better of it, and closed his eyes again.

"Now then, there," the park-keeper shouted to the man with the sailor hat, "get up! This ain't a fourpenny doss, you know. No lying down." A rough shake accompanied the words, and the man sat up.

"All right, my friend." The keeper, who was a good-humoured man, passed on without further objurgation.

The face of the younger man had grown whiter.

"Look here, Darkey," he said, "I believe I'm done for."

"Never say die."

"No, just die without speaking." His head fell forward and his eyes closed.

"At any rate, this is better than some deaths I've seen," he began again with a strange accession of liveliness. "Darkey, did I tell you the story of the five Japanese girls?"

"What, in Suez Bay?" said Darkey, who had heard many sea stories during the last two days, and recollected them but hazily.

"No, man. This was at Nagasaki. We were taking in a cargo of coal for Hong Kong. Hundreds of little Jap girls pass the coal from hand to hand over the ship's side in tiny baskets that hold about a plateful. In that way you can get 3000 tons aboard in two days."

"Talking of platefuls reminds me of sausage and mash," said Darkey.

"Don't interrupt. Well, five of these gay little dolls wanted to go to Hong Kong, and they arranged with the Chinese sailors to stow away; I believe their friends paid those cold-blooded
fiends

By Enoch Arnold Bennett 233

fiends something to pass them down food on the voyage and give
them an airing at nights. We had a particularly lively trip,
battened everything down tight, and scarcely uncovered till we got
into port. Then I and another man found those five girls among
the coal."

" Dead, eh ? "

" They'd simply torn themselves to pieces. Their bits of frock
things were in strips, and they were scratched deep from top to
toe. The Chinese had never troubled their heads about them at
all, although they must have known it meant death. You may
bet there was a row. The Japanese authorities make you search
ship before sailing, now."

" Well ? "

" Well, I sha'n't die like that. That's all."

He stretched himself out once more, and for ten minutes
neither spoke. The park-keeper strolled up again.

" Get up, there ! " he said shortly and gruffly.

" Up ye get, mate," added Darkey, but the man on the bench
did not stir. One look at his face sufficed to startle the keeper,
and presently two policemen were wheeling an ambulance cart to
the hospital. Darkey followed, gave such information as he could,
and then went his own ways.

II

In the afternoon the patient regained full consciousness. His
eyes wandered vacantly about the illimitable ward, with its rows of
beds stretching away on either side of him. A woman with a
white cap, a white apron, and white wristbands bent over him,
and he felt something gratefully warm passing down his throat.

For

For just one second he was happy. Then his memory returned, and the nurse saw that he was crying. When he caught the nurse's eye he ceased, and looked steadily at the distant ceiling.

" You're better ? "

" Yes." He tried to speak boldly, decisively, nonchalantly. He was filled with a sense of physical shame, the shame which bodily helplessness always experiences in the presence of arrogant, patronising health. He would have got up and walked briskly away if he could. He hated to be waited on, to be humoured, to be examined and theorised about. This woman would be wanting to feel his pulse. She should not ; he would turn cantankerous. No doubt they had been saying to each other, " And so young, too ! How sad ! " Confound them.

" Have you any friends that you would like to send for ? "

" No, none."

The girl (she was only a girl) looked at him, and there was that in her eye which overcame him.

" None at all ? "

" Not that I want to see."

" Are your parents alive ? "

" My mother is, but she lives away in the North."

" You've not seen her lately, perhaps ? "

He did not reply, and the nurse spoke again, but her voice sounded indistinct and far off.

When he awoke it was night. At the other end of the ward was a long table covered with a white cloth, and on this table a lamp.

In the ring of light under the lamp was an open book, an ink-stand and a pen. A nurse (not *his* nurse) was standing by the table, her fingers idly drumming the cloth, and near her a man in evening dress. Perhaps a doctor. They were conversing in low

tones.

tones. In the middle of the ward was an open stove, and the restless flames were reflected in all the brass knobs of the bedsteads and in some shining metal balls which hung from an unlighted chandelier. His part of the ward was almost in darkness. A confused, subdued murmur of little coughs, breathings, rustlings, was continually audible, and sometimes it rose above the conversation at the table. He noticed all these things. He became conscious, too, of a strangely familiar smell. What was it? Ah, yes! Acetic acid—his mother used it for her rheumatics.

Suddenly, magically, a great longing came over him. He must see his mother, or his brothers, or his little sister—some one who knew him, same one who *belonged* to him. He could have cried out in his desire. This one thought consumed all his faculties. If his mother could but walk in just now through that doorway! If only old Spot, even, could amble up to him, tongue out and tail furiously wagging! He tried to sit up, and he could not move! Then despair settled on him, and weighed him down. He closed his eyes.

The doctor and the nurse came slowly up the ward, pausing here and there. They stopped before his bed, and he held his breath.

"Not roused up again, I suppose?"

"No."

"Hm! He may flicker on for forty-eight hours. Not more." They went on, and with a sigh of relief he opened his eyes again. The doctor shook hands with the nurse, who returned to the table and sat down.

Death! The end of all this! Yes, it was coming. He felt it. His had been one of those wasted lives of which he used to read in books. How strange! Almost amusing! He was one of those sons who bring sorrow and shame into a family. Again,

how

how strange ! What a coincidence that he, just *he* and not the man in the next bed, should be one of those rare, legendary good-for-nothings who go recklessly to ruin. And yet, he was sure that he was not such a bad fellow after all. Only somehow he had been careless. Yes, careless, that was the word . . . . nothing worse. . . . . As to death, he was indifferent. Remembering his father's death, he reflected that it was probably less disturbing to die oneself than to watch another pass.

He smelt the acetic acid once more, and his thoughts reverted to his mother. Poor mother ! No, great mother ! The grandeur of her life's struggle filled him with a sense of awe. Strange that until that moment he had never seen the heroic side of her humdrum, commonplace existence ! He must write to her, now, at once, before it was too late. His letter would trouble her, add another wrinkle to her face, but he must write ; she must know that he had been thinking of her.

"Nurse," he cried out, in a thin, weak voice.

"Ssh !" She was by his side directly, but not before he had lost consciousness again.

The following morning he managed with infinite labour to scrawl a few lines :

"Dear Mamma,

"You will be surprised but not glad to get this letter. I'm done for, and you will never see me again. I'm sorry for what I've done, and how I've treated you, but it's no use saying anything now. If Pater had only lived he might have kept me in order. But you were too kind, you know. You've had a hard struggle these last six years, and I hope Arthur and

Dick

Dick will stand by you better than I did, now they are growing up. Give them my love, and kiss little Fannie for me.

"WILLIE."

"Mrs. Hancock——"
He got no further with the address.

III

By some strange turn of the wheel, Darkey gathered several shillings during the next day or two, and feeling both elated and benevolent, he called one afternoon at the hospital, "just to inquire like." They told him the man was dead.

"By the way, he left a letter without an address. Mrs. Hancock—here it is."

"That'll be his mother; he did tell me about her—lived at Endon, Staffordshire, he said. I'll see to it."

They gave Darkey the letter.

"So his name's Hancock," he soliloquised, when he got into the street. "I knew a girl of that name—once. I'll go and have a pint of four half."

At nine o'clock that night Darkey was still consuming four half, and relating certain adventures by sea which, he averred, had happened to himself. He was very drunk.

"Yes," he said, "and them five lil' gals was lying there without a stitch on 'em, dead as meat; 's'true as I'm 'ere. I've seen a thing or two in my time, I can tell ye."

"Talking about these Anarchists——" said a man who appeared anxious to change the subject.

"An—kists," Darkey interrupted. "I tell ye what I'd do
with

with that muck." He stopped to light his pipe, looked in vain for a match, felt in his pockets, and pulled out a piece of paper—the letter.

"I tell you what I'd do. I'd——" He slowly and meditatively tore the letter in two, dropped one piece on the floor, thrust the other into a convenient gas jet, and applied it to the tobacco.

"I'd get 'em 'gether in a heap and I'd—— Damn this pipe." He picked up the other half of the letter, and relighted the pipe.

"After you, mate," said a man sitting near, who was just biting the end from a cigar.

Books

A Letter to the Editor
and an Offer of a Prize

From "The Yellow Dwarf"

Sir: In London, if one is placed sufficiently low in the social heirarchy—or, if high placed, one is sufficiently fond of low life—to frequent houses in which Literature as a subject of conversation is not inhibited, one may occasionally hear it said of this or that recently published book that it has just been " reviewed " in the *Athenæum* or " noticed " in the *Academy*, " praised " by the *Spectator* or " slated " by the *Saturday Review*. I don't know whether you will agree with me in deeming it significant that one almost never hears of a book nowadays that it has been *criticised*. People who run as they talk are not commonly precisians in their choice of words, but the fact that the verb *to criticise*, as governing the accusative case of the substantive *book*, has virtually dropped out of use, seems to me a happy example of right instinct. Books (books in *belles lettres*, at any rate, novels, poems, essays, what you will, not to include scientific, historical, or technical works), books in *belles lettres* are almost never criticised in the professedly critical journals of our period in England. They are reviewed, noticed, praised, slated, but almost never criticised.

I hasten

239

I hasten to exempt from my indictment those journals that are
not professedly critical; to exempt trade journals, for instance,
medical journals, journals of sport and fashion, and the daily newspapers. The most one can fairly require of one's daily newspaper
is that it should give one the news of the day. I'm not denying
that a craving for the news of the day is a morbid craving, but it
is to gratify it that the daily newspapers are daily born, daily to
die. We can't with any sort of justice ask our penny daily for a
considered criticism of books. That were to ask for more than
our pennyworth; and besides, the editor might reasonably retort
upon us, " You have come to the wrong shop." We don't go to
the ironmonger's for a leg of mutton, nor to the stationer's to get
our hair cut. Wherefore I in no wise reproach the penny dailies
(nor even the formidable threepenny daily) for sedulously
eschewing anything remotely in the nature of considered literary
criticism.* Let me add, at once, that I don't reproach them, on
the other hand, for their habits of printing long columns of idio-
matic Journalese, and heading the same NEW BOOKS. They
thereby give employment to the necessitous; they encourage
publishers (poor dears !) to publish—and to advertise; they deceive
nobody within the four-mile radius; they furnish the suburbs with
an article the suburbs could probably not distinguish from the real
thing if they saw the two together; and (to crown all) it is the
inalienable privilege of the British reader to skip. I buy my
Morning Post, that I may follow, from my humble home in
Mayfair, the doings of the Great in Bayswater; my *Daily
News*, that I may be informed of the fluctuations of Mr. Glad-
stone's health; my *Telegraph*, that I may learn what is happening

* But surely, in the *Daily Chronicle*, we have at least, one notable
exception.—ED. Y. B.

in

in Balham, watch the progress of the shilling testimonial to Dr. Grace, savour the English of Mr. Clement Scott, and keep up my Italian by studying the leaders of Mr. Sala; my *Pall Mall Gazette* . . . I really can't think why, unless it be to enjoy the prankful cubsomeness (not to mention the classical attainments) of Mr. W. E. Henley's truculent fifth form; but it is certain that I buy not one of these unexpensive sheets to the end of getting a considered criticism of books.

The case of the professedly critical periodicals, however, is a different and a graver case. They are professedly critical, and they do not criticise. They review, they notice, they extol, they scold; but criticise, but weigh, discriminate, analyse, perceive, appreciate —who will pretend that they do that? They wield the bludgeon and the butter-knife, they employ the copying-press and the garbling-press; but those fine instruments of precision which are the indispensable tools of the true critic's craft, they would appear never to have heard of. For the sake of a modern instance, examine for a moment the methods of the *Saturday Review*. There was a time, and that not so long ago, when the *Saturday Review*, though never critical, was at least diverting; it was supercilious, it was impertinent, it was crabbed and cross-grained, but it was witty, it was diverting. I am speaking, however, of the present *Saturday Review*, which is another matter. From week to week I take it in, and read (or make some sort of an endeavour to read) its " literary " columns. And what do I find? I find articles with such felicitous headings as " Mr. So-and-So—Minor Poet ; " I find perennial allusions to the length of another poet's hair; but— criticism? I find that where once the *Saturday Review* was supercilious and diverting, it is now violent and provincial; but —criticism? I find that where once it spoke to me with the voice of a soured but well-bred and rather witty academic don, it

now

now bellows at me in the tones of a bull of Bashan; but—
criticism? I find—I find anything you like but criticism. Yet,
surely, the *Saturday Review* is amongst the most notorious of
the professedly critical journals of Great Britain. The *Spectator*,
the *Academy*, the *Athenæum*, are different, very different—with a
likeness. The likeness, I would submit, consists in the rigorous
exclusion of considered literary criticism from their columns.*

I am more concerned for the moment to mention and to deplore
this state of things than to inquire into its causes. But certain of
its causes invite no inquiry; they are obvious, they " spring at our
eyes." Foreigners, to be sure, pretend that our trouble is radical
and ineradicable; that the British mind is essentially and hopelessly
uncritical; that directly we attempt to criticise we begin to com-
pare. (" They can only communicate their opinion of Oranges
by translating it in terms of Onions," says Varjine; and he adds,
" The most critical Englishman I ever met was a clown in a circus
at Marseilles.") That is a question I won't go into here. What
is obvious and indisputable is this: that with the dissemination of
ignorance through the length and breadth of our island, by means
of the Board School, a mighty and terrible change has been
wrought in the characters both of the majority of readers and of
the majority of writers. The " gentleman and scholar " who still
flourished when I was young, has sunken into unimportance both
as a reader and as a writer. The bagman and the stockbroker's clerk
(and their lady wives and daughters) 'ave usurped his plyce and his
influence as readers; and the pressman has picked up his fallen pen,
—the pressman, sir, or the presswoman! Well, what, by the
operation of the law of cause and effect, what should we naturally

* THE YELLOW BOOK must note its dissent from the Yellow Dwarf's
observations, in so far, at least, as they affect the *Spectator.*—ED.

expect?

expect? With an illiterate reading mob howling at our doors, and a tribe of pressman scribbling at our tables, what, in the name of the universe, should we expect? What we get; not so? And the poor " gentleman and scholar," where he survives, is exposed to full many risks and full many sorrows. If he reads his penny daily in the morning, he is in danger of seeing his own critical vision obscured or distorted for the rest of the day, as his palate would be blunted should he breakfast off raw red herring. If he wants to write a book, he knows that there is no public to buy or read or understand it : and what's the use of casting pearls before animals that prefer acorns? If he wants to read a book, he knows that the entire output of decent literature in England during a year he might easily learn by heart in a fortnight. So he must read a foreign book or an old book, or else fall back, for fiction, upon our Stanley Weymans and our J. M. Barries; for poetry, upon our Sir Lewis Morrises or our Sir Edwin Arnolds; and for criticism . . . shall I say upon our Mr. Harry Quilters?

The critical periodicals of Great Britain make it a practice to review, notice, praise, or slate almost everything in the guise of a book or booklet, which, by hook or crooklet, contrives to get itself put forth in print. They manage these affairs better in furrin' parts. In furrin' parts, your critical periodical silently ignores ninety-and-nine in every hundred of the books that are printed, and then—*criticises* the hundreth.

The fact is, Mr. Editor, that in order to criticise you must have certain endowments—you must have a certain equipment. You must have eyes and ears, you must have taste; you must have the analytic faculty and the knack of nice expression; you must have the habit of getting at close quarters with your thought and your emotion—you must be able to explain *why*, for what qualities, for what defects, you cherish Mr. Henry James (for

                                                    instance),

instance), regard Mr. Marriott Watson with expectant pleasure,
dread Mr. Anthony Hope, and flee from Miss Marie Corelli
as from the German measles. You must have knowledge—a
University education, indeed, would do you no harm, nor an acquaintance with the literature of France and Russia. You must
have a *tradition of culture*. And, above all, you must have leisure,
—for any sort of considered writing you must have leisure.

Well, how many of these endowments, how much of this
equipment is your Pressman, your Saturday Reviewer, likely to
have? Taste? The analytic faculty? The instinct for the
just word? Knowledge? A University education? An acquaintance with the writings of de la Clos and Frontin, of Poush-
kine and Karamanzine? A tradition of culture? And leisure?
Leisure. He is paid at the rate of so many shillings a column.
And he has his bread to earn; and bread, my dear, is costly. One
does what one can. One glances hurriedly through the book that
has been sent one " for review," and then (provided one is honest,
and has no private spite to wreak upon the author, no private envy
to assuage, no private log to roll) one dashes off one's " thousand
words," more or less, of unconsidered praise or unconsidered abuse,
as the case may be. One says the book is " good," the book is
" bad." Good—bad : with the variations upon them to be found
in his Dictionary of Synonyms : there are your Pressman-Critic's
alternative criticisms. Good—with greater or smaller emphasis ;
bad—with greater or smaller virulence, and more or less frequent
references to the length of the author's hair. There is your
Pressman-Critic's " terminology." A novel by Mr. George
Meredith is—good; a novel by Mr. Conan Doyle is—good. You
would hardly call that manner of criticism searching, enlighten-
ing, exhaustive ; you would hardly call it *nuancé*, I fancy, sir.

But you are wondering why I should take the matter so griev-
ously

ously to heart. I will tell you. It is not, I confess, for patriotic reasons; not that I weep to see England the least among nations in this particular. It is for reasons purely personal and selfish. I love to read criticism. And to deprive me of the chance to do so is to deprive me of a pleasure. I love to discover my own thoughts and feelings about a book accurately expressed in elegant and original sentences by another fellow. When I happen upon such criticism I experience a glow of delight and a glow of pride, almost as great as if I had written it myself; and yet I have had no trouble. Monsieur Anatole France has kindly taken the trouble for me. Well, sir, we have no Monsieur Anatole France in these islands; or, if we have one, he doesn't write for our professedly critical journals. I ransack the serried columns of the *Saturday Review*, and its contemporaries and rivals, in vain, from week to week, to discover my own thoughts and feelings about books accurately expressed in elegant and original sentences. I discover pretty nearly everything except the thing I pine for. I discover plenty of pedantry and plenty of ignorance, plenty of feebleness and plenty of good stodgy " ability," plenty of glitter and plenty of dullness, plenty of fulsomeness and more than a plenty of envy, hatred, malice, and all uncharitableness; but the thing I seek is the one thing I never find.

When I went abroad for my holiday, in August, I took with me a bagful of comparatively recent books, all of which I read, or tried to read, while I was drinking the waters and being douched and swindled at Aix-les-Bains. I yearn, sir, to see my thoughts and feelings about these books set forth in elegant and original phrases by another fellow. And herewith I offer a prize. I will indicate very cursorily in a few rough paragraphs what my thoughts and feelings about the books in question are ; and then I will offer a prize of—well, of fifty shillings—say, £2 10s. od.—to any one,

man

man or woman, who will, on or before the 31st day of December
in the present year, put into my hands a typewritten manuscript
containing what I shall admit to be a polished, a considered—in
one word, a satisfactory expression of my views. I make no
reservation as to the length of the manuscript. It may run to as
many thousand words as its writer wishes.

The first book I opened was not, after all, exactly a recent
book. It was Mr. Hall Caine's *Manxman*. I confess I didn't
open it with much hope of being able to read it, for past experience had taught me that to read a book by Mr. Hall Caine to
the far-glimmering end was apt to be an enterprise beyond my
powers of endurance. In early life I had begun his *Shadow of a
Crime*, and had broken down at the eightieth page; when I was
older, I had begun *The Deemster*, and had broken down at the
eighth—the fearless energy of youth was mine no longer. However, I had been the owner of an uncut copy of the *Manxman* for
well-nigh a twelvemonth; and I was in a Spartan temper; and I
said—with some outward show of resolution, but with a secret
presentiment of failure—I said, " We'll have a try."

Alas, at page 41, where the curtain falls—I beg Mr. Hall
Caine's pardon—where the curtain descends upon the seventh
scene, I saw myself beaten. " The moon had come up in her
whiteness behind, and all was quiet and solemn around. Philip fell
back and turned away his face." All was quiet and solemn *araound !*
It was the final, the crushing, blow. I too fell back and turned
away my face. I closed the *Manxman*, and gave it to my valet,
who, it may please Mr. Hall Caine to learn, said, " Thenk you,
sir ; " and, a week afterwards, the honest fellow told me he had
enjoyed it.

A talent for reading the works of Mr. Hall Caine is a talent
                                                          that

that Heaven has denied me : one can't expect everything here
below.   Their artificial simplicity, their clumsiness, their heaviness, their dreary counterfeit of a kind of common humour, their
laborious strivings for a kind of shoddy pathos, their ignorance,
their vulgarity, their pretentiousness, and withal their unmitigated
insipidity—these are the qualities, no doubt, that make them
popular with the middle classes, that endear them to the Great
Heart of the People, but they are too much for the likes o' me.   I
don't mind vulgarity when I can get it with a dash of spice,
as in the writings of Mr. Ally Sloper, or with a swagger, as
in the writings of Mr. Frank Harris.   I don't mind insipidity
when I can get it with a touch of cosmopolitan culture, as in the
writings of Mr. Karl Bædeker.   But vulgarity and insipidity
mingled, as in the writings of Mr. Hall Caine, are more than my
weak flesh can bear.   On the title-page of *The Manxman* Mr. Caine
prints this modest motto : " What shall it profit a man if he gain
the whole world and lose his own soul ? "   On page 6 he observes :
" In spite of everything he loved her.   That was where the
bitterness of the evil lay."   On page 7, " A man cannot fight
against himself for long.   That deadly enemy is certain to slay."
On page 11, " His first memory of Philip was of sleeping with
him, snuggled up by his side in the dark, hushed and still in a
narrow bed with iron ends to it, and of leaping up in the morning
and laughing."   And then, on page 41, " The moon had come
up in her whiteness behind, and all was quiet and solemn around."
Note the subtle perceptions, the profound insight, the dainty
verbiage, the fresh images, the musical rhythm of these excerpts.
" That was where the bitterness of the evil lay ! "   " A man
cannot fight against himself ! "   " The moon had come up in
her whiteness behind ! " . . . . Faugh, sir, the gentleman writes
with his mouth full.   Let us haste to an apothecary's, and buy an
                                                                    ounce

ounce of civet, to sweeten our imagination. And all was quiet
and solemn *araound !* *

At the forty-first page I closed the *Manxman,* and gave it to
my valet. It was as if for forty-one leaden minutes I had been
listening to the speech of Emptiness incarnate ; but a pompous
Emptiness, a rhetorical Emptiness, an Emptiness with the manner
of an Oracle and the accent of an Auctioneer : an Emptiness that
would have lulled me to slumber if it hadn't sickened me. I
wonder how Mr. Hall Caine keeps awake as he writes.

Nature abhors a vacuum, but the British Public, it would
appear, loves an Emptiness. The Public, however, doesn't matter.
The Great Heart of the People has warmed to bad literature in
all ages and in all countries. The disgraceful thing is that in
England bad literature is taken seriously by persons who profess to
be Critics. The critics of France don't take Monsieur Georges
Ohnet seriously ; the critics of Russia don't take Alexis Gorloff
seriously ; but the critics of England do take Mr. Hall Caine
seriously. Well, it only shows what a little pretentiousness in
this ingenuous land will accomplish.

The value of pretentiousness can scarcely be too highly commended to young authors. If you are more desirous of impressing
the ignorant than of doing good work, if you would rather make
the multitude stare than make the remnant gaze—Be pretentious,
and let who will be clever. A young author who appears to have

* A friend assures me that if I had pursued my wanderings a little
further in Mr. Hall Caine's garden of prose, I might have culled still
fairer blossoms ; and gives as a specimen this, from page 141 : " She
met him on the hill slope with a cry of joy, and kissed him   It came
into his mind to draw away, but he could not, and he kissed her back."
How quaint Manx customs are. In London he would almost certainly
have kissed her lips.

taken

taken this excellent maxim to heart is Mr. John Oliver Hobbes. His was the next book I directed an attack upon, after I had beaten my retreat from the impenetrable *Manxman*. But I found myself confronted with Pretentiousness at the very drawbridge. There fluttered a flag—I daresay, on my unsupported testimony, you could scarce believe it; but I can refer you to the book itself, or (it has been advertised like a patent medicine) to its publishers' advertisements, for corroboration—there fluttered a flag bearing this device—

THE GODS
SOME MORTALS
AND
LORD WICKENHAM
BY
JOHN OLIVER
HOBBES

This, in Christian England! And above it and below it were wonderful drawings, drawings of gods and goddesses and mortals; and, at one side of it, another wonderful drawing, a drawing of an Owl.

When I recovered my breath I turned to Chapter I., *An Aristocratic Household*, and before I had reached the bottom of that short first page, here is the sort of sentence I had to face and vanquish: "The young girl who came forward seemed to have been whipped up into a fragile existence from the very cream of tenderness, love, and folly." It is doubtless very pretty, but do you know what it means? Anyhow, it has the great merit of being Pretentious. I can see the Pressman-Critic, as his eye lights upon it. I can see him "sit up." I can hear him gasp,
and

and murmur to himself, " Ah ! *This* is a book to be treated with respect. This is *written*." Thus, by a discreet appreciation of the value of Pretentiousness, Mr. Hobbes breaks his Pressman-Critic's spirit with his title-page, and has him entirely subjugated about half-way down page 1.

But do you imagine that the author's pretentiousness begins and ends here, at the threshold ? Far from it. His book is pretentious in every line; I might almost say in every dash and comma. It is linked pretentiousness long drawn out. It is packed with aphorisms, with reflections : it is diversified with little essays, little shrieks, and philosophic sighs : all pretentious. On page 135, for instance : " The weak mind is never weary of recounting its failures." *On dirait* the late Mr. Martin Tupper—not? On page 23 : " O Science ! art thou not also sometimes in error ? " *On dirait* the late Mr. Thomas Carlyle. On page 13 : " Men should be careful how they wish." *On dirait* Monsieur de la Palisse. . . . And then, what shall we say of this ? In Chapter IV. Dr. Simon Warre writes a letter; and the author heads the chapter : *In which Warre displays a forgotten talent !* Oddsfish, the letter one is justified in expecting, after that ! What one gets is a quite ordinary, gossipy, rather vulgar, rather snobbish, very pretentious letter; and the only talent Warre displays is the talent of the Reporter, the Reporter for a Society paper; and that talent is unfortunately not forgotten.

Intending competitors for my prize will observe, furthermore, that the story, the plot, of *The Gods, Some Mortals, and Lord Wickenham*, is exactly the same dear old story that used to delight our nursery governesses when we were children. A good husband —oh, so good !—married to a horrid, wicked wife; a lord; a villain; an elopement. The same dear old conventional story,

the

the same dear old conventional personages. I can't say *characters*, for there isn't a character, there isn't an individual, there isn't the ghost of a human creature, in the book. Simon Warre, his wife, his friend, his wife's lover, Allegra—not one is a man or a woman of flesh and blood, whom we can recognize, whom we can think of as of people we have known : each is a formula, a shadow, a conventional type. And then—Allegra! Allegra carried me back an appalling number of years into the past, to the time when I was young and foolish. Everybody, when he was young and foolish (and generally in the flush of enthusiasm that follows his first visit to Italy—for a fortnight, at Easter, say), everybody has written a novel whereof the heroine was a pale mysterious Italian girl, the daughter of a nobleman ; and wasn't she almost always named Allegra ? And then everybody who was prudent has burned his manuscript. I burned mine, thank mercy ; but Mr. John Oliver Hobbes has published his. Ah, weel, bairn, ye maun just live and lurrun.

"Ah, but the style ! The style's the thing ! " cries the Pressman. Quite so ; the style. Mr. Hobbes seems to be perpetually straining in his style for the quality vaguely called distinction (which, I lately read, in the *Saturday Review*, of all places, is as easy as minor poetry), but, easy as it is, he never succeeds in achieving it. What he does achieve is—sometimes a feeble echo of Mr. George Meredith ; sometimes a flimsy imitation of Miss Austen ; sometimes a bit that is Carlylean or Tupperesque ; and, more often, gems of pure Journalese, so that one might wonder, " Is Mr. Hobbes, too, a Pressman ? " But *style* is personal, style is the man. Here there is no style ; there is only a mechanical mixture of the washings of many styles.

From the leaden pretentiousness of Mr. Hall Caine and the glassy pretentiousness of Mr. John Oliver Hobbes, it was restorative

storative to turn to the naturalness, the honesty, and the simplicity of Miss Ménie Muriel Dowie's *Gallia*, Miss Ella D'Arcy's *Monochromes*, and Mr. Kenneth Grahame's *Golden Age*.

Of Miss D'Arcy's book I will leave the would-be winners of my prize full liberty to say what they like; only, they must say this: that the book gives its author at once a place among the three masters (indulge the gender), the three masters of the short-story form at present working in the English tongue; and they must add that Miss D'Arcy is by no means the smallest of the three, and that she does not in the least resemble either of the other two.

Again, of Mr. Grahame's book, say what you will; but be careful also to say that a more melodious or mellow book you have seldom read. Dwell upon the sweetness of the book's *voice*, the tenderness of its humour; dwell upon its pathos, its sympathy, its imagination; upon the rich golden glow it has, which is like a second justification of its title.

In *Gallia*, I own, I suffered one disappointment—nay, I suffered two. First, I was all along haunted by a suspicion that the book had a moral, that it had a purpose, that it was intended, in some measure, as a tract for the times, and not as a mere frank effort in the art of fiction. And secondly, I missed that brilliant personal note, that vibration of the author's living voice, which had delighted me in the *Girl in the Karpathians*, and (still more) in the marvellously clever and vivid little drama, *Wladislaw's Advent*, which you, sir, published some time back in the YELLOW BOOK. But, all the same, though I could have wished Miss Dowie to come nearer to the front in proper person, I enjoyed reading *Gallia* as I have rarely enjoyed reading a latter-day English novel. The style, if severely impersonal, is sincere, direct, effective; the story is new and interesting, the central idea, the motive, being

very

very daring and original indeed; and the characters are distinctly individualised. They are characters, they are human people, they are persons, they aren't mere personages, mere types. Had *Gallia* been a *roman-à-clef*, I think I could have named Dark Essex; I think I could have named Gurdon, too; I'm sure I could have named Miss Essex. As for Bobbie Leighton, little as we see of him, he is a creature of the warmest flesh and the reddest blood; and I, for my part, shall always remember him as a charming fellow whom I met once or twice, but all too infrequently, in Paris, in London, and whose present address I am very sorry not to possess. But Gallia herself I could not have named, though she is as real to me now as she could have been if I had actually known her half my life. If Miss Dowie had, in this book, accomplished nothing more than her full-length portrait of Gallia, she would have accomplished much, for a more difficult model than Gallia a portraitist could hardly have selected. Gallia—so terribly modern, so excessively unusual—a prophecy, rather than a present fact—a girl, an English girl, who *declares her love to a man*, and yet never ceases to be a fresh, innocent, modest, attractive girl, never for an instant becomes masculine, and never loses her hold upon the reader's sympathy!

A writer of fiction could scarcely propose to himself a riskier adventure than that which awaited Miss Dowie when she set out to write the chapter in which Gallia roundly informs Dark Essex that she loves him. Failure was almost a certainty; yet, so far from failing, Miss Dowie has succeeded with apparent ease. The chapter begins with a very fine and delicate observation in psychology. The blankness, the vague pain, rhythmically recurring, but for the specific cause of which Gallia has to pause a little and seek—that is very finely and delicately observed. " ' I remember; there was something that has made me unhappy: what

what was it ? ' Thus her mind would go to work; then suddenly
the sharpness of remembrance would lay hold of her nerves, and a
little inarticulate cry would escape her; her hands would go up to
hide her face, and a shiver, not in her limbs, but in her body,
would shake and sicken her." Presently Dark Essex is shown
into the room, and presently Gallia tells him that she loves him.
The chapter is restrained, the chapter is dignified, the chapter is
convincing, the chapter is moving;—or, rather, the chapters (for
the scene is broken into two chapters, and so to break it was a
prudent measure; little conventional breaks like this doing wonders
to relieve the tension of the reader's emotion). It must have been
difficult enough, in this crisis of the story, to make Gallia herself
move and speak convincingly; it must have been a hundred times
more difficult to contrive the action and the speeches of the
man,—the man who found himself in so unprecedented a situation !

Gallia is a remarkable book, and Gallia is a remarkable young
lady. I have no prejudices in favour of the New Woman; I
proclaim myself quite brazenly an Old Male. But I respect
Gallia, I admire her, I like her, and I am heartily sorry she made
the mistake of marrying Gurdon. It was a mistake, I am persuaded, though an inevitable mistake. But I shall owe a grudge
to Miss Ménie Muriel Dowie if she doesn't by-and-by write
another volume about Gallia, and let me know exactly, in detail,
how her mistaken, inevitable marriage turned out. I shall look
for a volume entitled *Lady Gurdon*—for Mark will of course by
this time have been created a baronet, at the lowest. And, meanwhile, I will ask competitors for my prize to be extremely careful
and exhaustive in their criticisms of *Gallia*.

Two more books I will ask the same young gentlemen and
ladies to consider, and then I will let them off. One is Mr.
Hubert

Hubert Crackanthorpe's *Sentimental Studies*, the other Mr. George Moore's *Celibates*.

In dealing with Mr. Crackanthorpe's book, my prize-critics will kindly give attention to the actuality of his subjects, the clearness of his psychological insight, the intensity of his realisation, the convincingness of his presentation, and the sincerity and dignity of his manner. At the same time, they will point out that Mr. Crackanthorpe often says too much, that he is reluctant to leave anything to his reader's imagination, his reader's experience. He doesn't make enough allowance for his reader's native intelligence. He forgets that the golden rule in writing is simply a paraphrase of the other Golden Rule : *Write as you would be written to.* Mr. Crackanthorpe strains a little too hard, a little too visibly, for the *mot juste.* But the *mot juste* is sometimes not the best word to use. One must know what the *mot juste* is, but sometimes one should erase it and substitute the *demi-mot.* And then isn't Mr. Crackanthorpe handicapped as an artist by a trifle too much moral earnestness ? Moral earnestness in life, I daresay, does more good than harm ; but in Art, if present at all, it should be concealed like a vice. Mr. Crackanthorpe hardly takes pains enough to conceal his. If he won't abandon it—if he won't leave it to such writers as the author of *Trilby* and Miss Annie S. Swann—he should at least hide it under mountains of artistry.

And now for *Celibates. Celibates* is an important book; I'm not quite sure that *Celibates* isn't a great book, but *Celibates* is assuredly a most perplexing, a most exasperating book. How one and the same man can write as ill and as well, as execrably and as effectively, as Mr. George Moore writes, passes my comprehension. His style, for instance. His style is atrocious, and his style is almost classical. His style is like chopped straw, and his style is like architecture. In its material, in its words, phrases, sentences,

tences, his style is as bad as a Christian's style can be. It is harsh, it is slovenly, it is uncouth; fluency, melody, distinction, charm it lacks utterly; it is sometimes downright ungrammatical; it is very often common, banale, pressmanish; and yet . . . . Structurally, in its masses, it could scarcely be better. It has (as Mr. Moore would say) *line ;* its drawing, its perspective, its values are the drawing, the perspective, the values of a master. It is a symmetrical temple built of soiled and broken bricks.

How could a writer who knows his Flaubert as Mr. Moore knows *his* Flaubert, speak of " sleep pressing upon Mildred's eyelids," as Mr. Moore does on page 8? What of *la phrase toute faite ?* How could any one but a pressman say of his heroine that there was " a little pathetic won't-you-care-for-me expression " in her face? On page 33, Mildred Lawson looked at Ralph Hoskin " in glad surprise." On page 49 we have an epigram, a paradox: something or other " is as insignificant as life." On page 51 Ralph says, " I had to make my living ever since I was sixteen." On page 56 Mr. Moore says, " In the park they could talk without fear of being overheard, and they took interest in the changes that spring was effecting in this beautiful friendly nature." Shade of Stevenson, shade of Maupassant, what prose! On page 75: " The roadway was full of *fiacres* plying for hire, or were drawn up in lines three deep." Shade of Lindley Murray, what grammar! And on the same page: " Elsie wished that Walter would present her with a fan." It is almost enough to make one agree with the old fogey who remarked, anent *Esther Waters,* " Mr. Moore writes *about* servants, and should be read *by* them."

But no, the old fogey was wrong. Bad as Mr. Moore's style is in its materials, it is very nearly perfect in its structure; and, what's more, it's *personal.* You feel that it is a living voice, an individual's voice, that it is Mr. George Moore's voice, which is

addressing

addressing you. And surely a style ought to be personal, or else style's not the man.

The question of style apart, however, what makes *Celibates* an impressive book, very nearly a great book, is its insight, its sincerity, its vividness, its sympathy. If *Mildred Lawson* were only decently written—if only some kind soul would do us a decent rendering of it into English—*Mildred Lawson* would be a story that one could speak of in the same breath with *Madame Bovary.* Yes. The assertion is startling, but the assertion is an assertion my prize-critic must boldly hazard and proceed to justify. Mildred Lawson is one of the most interesting and one of the most complex women I have ever met in fiction. Her selfishness, her weakness, her strength, her vanity, her coldness, her hundred and one qualities, traits, moods, are analysed with a minuteness that is scientific, but synthesised with a vividness that is entirely artistic, and therefore convincing, moving, memorable. *John Norton,* structurally, is not quite so faultless as *Mildred Lawson,* but it is still a very notable achievement, a very important contribution to the English fiction of our day; and I don't know whether, on the whole, *Agnes Lahens* isn't the best piece of work in the volume.

However, these are questions for my prize-critics to discuss at length—Mr. Moore's execrable, excellent style; how, as it were, one would imagine he wrote with his boot, not with his pen; his subtle lack of grace, of humour; his deep, true, sympathetic insight; his sincerity, his impressiveness; and what his place is among the four or five considerable writers of fiction now living in England.—I, sir, have already too far trespassed upon your valuable space.

I have the honour to be,
Your obedient servant,
The Yellow Dwarf.

Pierrot

By Olive Custance

PIERROT .... Pierrot .... at first they said you slept,
   And then they told me you would never wake ....
     I dared not think .... I watched the white day break,
The yellow lamps go out .... I have not wept.

But now I kiss your dear cold hands and weep;
   Shaken with sobs I cower beside the bed ....
     At last I realise that you are dead ....
Drawn suddenly into the arms of sleep . .   .

Love! . . . you will never look at me again
   With those rain-coloured, heavy-lidded eyes,
     Closed now for ever .... Pierrot, was it wise
To love so madly since we loved in vain?

In vain! in vain! . . . but Pierrot, it was sweet
   To stem the stealthy hours with wine and song! . . .
     Though death stood up between us stern and strong,
And fate twined nets to trip our dancing feet ....
                    . . . . Too

. . . . Too soon, alas! too soon our summer swooned
    To bitter winter . . . . and against the lace
    Of tossed white pillows lay a reckless face,
With feverish parched mouth like a red wound. . . .

Yet still was our brave love not overthrown,
    And I would nestle at your side and see
    Your large sad eyes grow passionate for me. . .
Love! wake and speak . . .   I cannot live alone. . . .

Blue as blue flame is the great sky above . . . .
    The earth is wonderful and glad and green;
    But shut the sunlight out . . . . for I have seen
Forgetfulness upon the face of love.

The Actor

By Stanley V. Makower

THE dominoes clattered upon the marble tables of the Café Royal, and the steady brilliance of the lights shed a glow over the cloud-girt goddesses that grinned and beckoned in bewildering deshabille from the ceiling. The long, gilded room was crowded with people and with the images of people reflected in its numerous glass panels.

My companion and I sat without speaking, satisfied to rest; for the day had been tiring, and outside the wind was cold, and the rain had beat upon our faces like little cold pellets of lead.

Directly behind us sat a young man who was swaying his body to and fro in so strange a manner that I shuddered, as if in a nightmare, when we are oppressed with the continuous fear that a calamity must happen . . . in a moment, . . . at this moment . . . now . . . and that calamity never happens. Finally the young man lay half across the velvet-cushioned seat, motionless. A glass of coffee stood before him on the table, untasted, with the spoon in it.

Suddenly the head waiter came up, shook him roughly by the shoulders, and said :

" You

" You mustn't do that."

" Do what ? " he asked, wearily.

" Lie about the seats here," replied the other gruffly, and he moved away, perplexed by the sobriety of the speaker's voice, and the strangeness of his conduct. I heard the young man grumble something, and then he put his arms on the table, and his head fell into his hands. So he remained motionless throughout the evening, while the steam rose quickly from the coffee before him, almost as if it were in a hurry to leave the glass.

Satisfied that this was not the moment for the arrival of the catastrophe with which the air seemed pregnant, I dismissed the young man from my thoughts with the meditation that he might either have shot himself, or had a death struggle with the head waiter, but that as he had done neither he was there, just as they so often are in nightmares, to put me off the scent. When you have dreamed much you become wary, and acquire skill in detecting the sham bogies with which a nightmare is peopled, until the figure-head appears, unmistakable, indomitable, malignant, insolent, because clothed with the irresistible power to terrify. You are swiftly conscious that *this* is the director and controller of catastrophes, and that the time for contemptuous ridicule and laughter is over. You break into a low propitiatory prayer. The figure raises a gigantic arm, . . . and then, if Heaven is merciful, you wake in a cold perspiration.

The young man, then, was a sham bogey, and I looked round me to detect the figure-head among the assembled company.

Opposite us sat a middle-aged man with a sandy moustache, who was eating ravenously, fiercely. He chased the pieces over his plate with his fork, and swallowed without masticating. Occasionally he glanced round, and pulled the salt or mustard towards his plate with a brusque, almost angry gesture. At the
table

table next to him sat an older man, with grey head and beard, and thick eyebrows under which were handsome grey eyes. He was glancing casually at a newspaper.

I began to marvel at the contrast between the two men, to picture to myself a thousand scenes to illustrate the calm, placid temperament of the one, the nervous irritability of the other. I let the two figures wander down the vistas of my imagination, and stared blankly in front of me, till the whole scene of the crowded room with its glare of light faded away, and I saw the grey-headed man seated in an armchair in a comfortable, ugly house, telling a fairy tale to three or four little children, whose mother was knitting by the fireside. She was rather pretty, but very frail, and there were light silken curls over her pale forehead. And just when the grey-headed man had reached the climax of his story, I thought, Heaven knows why, that he stopped short, and fixed his eyes upon one of the children, and, amidst cries of " Go on, daddy, do go on," said: " The good fairy never goes on telling stories to little boys whose finger-nails are dirty," and I saw a little boy look sheepishly at his little hands; but before I could go on constructing my picture I was seized with a doubt as to what had made the grey-headed man suddenly so severe, and I came to the conclusion that it was probably because he did not know how the story ended that he suddenly noticed the little boy's dirty finger-nails. And the thought of this amused me so much, that my fancy stopped, and I found myself looking again at the two men before me in the long, bright café, and the smoke of a cigarette, which the grey-headed man was smoking, floated under my nostrils, and the dominoes clattered again in various parts of the room, and I heard the babble of innumerable voices.

By this time the nightmare had passed from me, and I felt much surprise and curiosity when I observed that the two men
were

were talking to each other.   The grey-haired man was holding
the newspaper a little way from him as he listened to the other,
who, while diligently pursuing his food across his plate, threw out
a sentence here and there with the same irregular brusquerie as he
had displayed when he pulled the salt or mustard towards him.
When he had ejaculated a few words he seemed to return to his
food with greater voracity than ever, and cut it about savagely.

" I never read a newspaper," he said; " it's such a damn waste
of time.   One might be eating or drinking all the while."

The other murmured a feeble protest.   He looked as if he were
absolutely incapable of understanding that sort of man.   His face
expressed a disapproval which was at once polite, tolerant, and
perplexed.

" Waste of time," repeated the fierce man; and then rather
louder, " Waste of time!" and he subsided into his plate, which
clinked with the blows of his knife and fork.   When he had swept
it absolutely bare he threw them both into it, pushed it from him,
and said : " The food's beastly."

The old man smiled pleasantly.

" You can get a good dinner at about two places in London,
and I'm sick of both of them.   Here it's beastly, I tell you."

" Why come here ? " asked the other mildly.

" Why come here ? " he retorted quickly.   " Why?   Ha! ha!
Why, indeed!   A very good question."

But he made no attempt to answer it.

" You can't get a decent La Rose here," he went on, and there
was an almost piteous ring in his voice.   " Their wines taste as if
they'd been bottled in a sewer.   I had a wine last week at the
Café Rouge.   That was a queenly wine, sir, queenly," he said,
as if you could not find a more beautifully appropriate epithet.
" I say it was queenly, and I think I know a good wine.   I was
once

once wine-taster to our club, the Corsican, sir—and they had a devilish good cook, I may tell you. Well, sir, I tasted twenty-two glasses of champagne in the dark, and they didn't stump me over a single vintage. What's more, just before they turned up the gas Tommy Webster gave me a mixed glass, sir, and I told him the three different years of which it was made up," and he thumped the table so that the plates and glasses jumped and shivered. Then he looked defiantly at his neighbour, who, somewhat confused, murmured: "Dear, dear, you surprise me."

"When I was acting in Hull, sir," he went on, suddenly, "there was a devilish pretty girl in our company. Her name was Tremaine, sir—Kitty Tremaine. We used to act together twenty years ago." He passed his hand over his face. "Do you know the Golden Mermaid?" he continued. "No, I suppose you don't. It's the oldest hotel in Hull. We all went there one summer afternoon after we'd given a morning performance of Hamlet, and in the garden of that hotel, sir, I drank the finest champagne I ever tasted in my life. We sat round a table under a large tree. We were all very tired. I had been playing Polonius, a Captain, and most of the Prince of Denmark; and Kitty Tremaine was Ophelia, sir. I'm spinning you no yarn. I remember how many of us there were; just eight. And the Queen kept on her stage dress, as it was cooler for her, and we had to play again in the evening. Ophelia had left some flowers in her hair, too," and his voice grew thick with emotion.

"Well, we drank four bottles of that champagne, sir," he added, with the air of a man who has been led into a pleasing digression and returns to his subject with a wrench. "And in between the bottles we danced round the tree. We got a fiddler to fiddle for us, and we brought out the hostess, and we sang a chorus."

He

He was growing more and more excited, and, as he spoke, waved his arms in imitation of a dance.

"And I made it up with the Queen, sir, over a glass of that champagne. She said she knew I never meant badly all the time. No more did I. I never could see what there was against the Queen. And so we kissed while we were dancing and made friends, although in a couple of hours we had to begin quarrelling again to please the people. And when the others were tired I did my great speech at the end of the second act, and everybody clapped, and said I was sure to make a fortune. Sure to make a fortune," he repeated, contemptuously, piteously, with a little laugh at himself.

The grey-headed man sat listening now without venturing to interrupt the speaker with any remarks of his own.

"What a beautiful Ophelia she was, sir. You never saw a finer arm. It reminded one of Siddons'. Only it was finer, sir, I say finer," he went on, as if fearing a protest. "Ophelia, I did love you once," he added, more calmly, as he made a mock gesture of devotion to his neighbour.

"I always considered the conduct of the Prince most reprehensible. Perhaps you won't believe me when I tell you that it was with great difficulty, very great difficulty, that I could ever be persuaded to act that part."

He pronounced the word "very" impressively, and as if it were spelt vai-ree.

"You have no idea what unfeeling people managers are, and my nature has always been a sensitive one. Redmayne, our manager, was as cold as a stone, sir. No more humanity than a rock, sir, or—or the leg of this table," he added, trying to enforce the truth of his statement by the use of an illustration close to hand from which the other could not escape.

"I was

"I was nearly turned out of that company, sir, because I refused to spout some lines that were brutal, and that no gentleman could allow himself to use. I never could play a villain. It cut me to the quick, sir."

The actor was growing tired with his own loquacity, and the grey-headed man was drawing more and more into his shell. He was attempting, ineffectually, to slip the newspaper between himself and the speaker without attracting his notice. But every time that he made an advance of a few inches in lifting the paper from the table the other gave a fresh emphasis to what he was saying, and fixed the offender with his sharp, restless eyes.

In the middle of a long speech about a play called "Vendetta," in which he had acted the part of the King of Naples for fourteen hundred nights until he "really felt the part so much, sir, that it was a struggle for me to leave my palace on the stage, and climb up five flights of stairs to my humble lodging in the town——" He broke off abruptly, and then, waving his hand theatrically, began to declaim with an abundance of false emphasis:

"Indeed this counsellor
Is now most still, most secret, and most grave,
Who always was a foolish prating knave.
Come sir, to draw toward an end with you."

I had risen to go, but stood irresolutely watching the stagey magnificence of his address to the grey-headed man, and enjoying the grand ineptitude with which he delivered the last line, with its absurd pause on the word "end," which he almost shouted across the table.

He turned aside to wave his hand in parting salutation to the Queen, and closed the scene with the words "Good-night, mother," in the accents of which lingered the tone of false tragedy

in

in which he had recited the lines. But before the last syllable had fallen from his lips a change came over his face, one of those changes that reveal the intrusion of an unexpected emotion into the mind of the speaker, an emotion that sweeps everything before it.

The wave of the hand died away, and the arm fell a little helplessly to his side. All the fierceness fled from his face, and into his eyes came an almost despairing look mingled with one of fear, as if a shadow had suddenly risen by his side. With the articulation of those two words some undercurrent of his life rose to the top and drowned his self-assurance so that he sat there broken, transfigured, silent. And whereas before he had seemed only sordid, tawdry, fugitive, he was now exalted, inexplicable, eternal, touched to beauty by the stroke of humanity which had felled him.

As we made our way to the street I could scarcely believe that this was the same man. Behind the seat which we had left sat the young man, motionless as before, with his head in his hands, conspicuous amid the bustle and movement that was round him. In the corner of the room two Spaniards were quarrelling over a game of chess.

Who shall guess what chained the youth's head to his hands? Shall a man presume to explain what made the Spaniards to quarrel, or why that garrulous actor was struck dumb? And how came it that for many days and nights I was haunted by this fragment of the actor's rambling speech, " Ophelia had left some flowers in her hair too " ?

Passion

By Richard Garnett, LL.D., C.B.

THIS flame of Passion that so high in air,
By spice and balsam of the spirit fed,
With fire and fume vast Heaven hath overspread,
And blots the stars with smoke, or dims with glare :
Soon shall it droop, and radiance pure and fair
Again from azure altitudes be shed ;
And we the murky grime and embers red
Shall sift, if haply dust of Love be there.
Gather his ashes from the torrid mould,
And, quenched with drops of Bacchic revelry,
Yield to the Stygian powers to have and hold :
And urn Etrurian let his coffin be ;
For this was made to store the dead and cold,
And is a thing of much fragility.

A Journey of Little Profit

By John Buchan

> " The Devil he sang, the Devil he played
> High and fast and free.
> And this was ever the song he made,
> As it was told to me.
> ' Oh, I am the king of the air and the ground,
> And lord of the seasons' roll,
> And I will give you a hundred pound,
> If you will give me your soul.' "
>
> *The Ballad of Grey Weather.*

THE cattle market of Inverforth is, as all men know north of the Tweed, the greatest market of the kind in the land. For days in the late Autumn there is the lowing of oxen and the bleating of sheep among its high wooden pens, and in the rickety sale-rings the loud clamour of auctioneers and the talk of farmers. In the open yard where are the drovers and the butchers, a race always ungodly and law-despising, there is such a Babel of cries and curses as might wake the Seven Sleepers. From twenty different adjacent eating-houses comes the clatter of knives, where the country folk eat their dinner of beef and potatoes, with beer for sauce, and the collies grovel on the ground for stray morsels. Hither come a hundred types of men from the Highland cateran

with

with scarce a word of English, and the shentleman-farmer of Inverness and Ross, to lowland graziers and city tradesmen, not to speak of blackguards of many nationalities and more professions.

It was there I first met Duncan Stewart of Clachamharstan, in the Moor of Rannoch, and there I heard this story. He was an old man when I knew him, grizzled and wind-beaten; a prosperous man, too, with many herds like Jacob and much pasture. He had come down from the North with kyloes, and as he waited on the Englishmen with whom he had trysted, he sat with me through the long day and beguiled the time with many stories. He had been a drover in his youth, and had travelled on foot the length and breadth of Scotland; and his memory went back hale and vigorous to times which are now all but historical. This tale I heard among many others as we sat on a pen amid the smell of beasts and the jabber of Gaelic :

" When I was just turned of twenty-five I was a wild young lad as ever was heard of. I had taken to the droving for the love of a wild ife, and a wild life I led. My father's heart would be broken long syne with my doings, and well for my mother that she was in her grave since I was six years old. I paid no heed to the ministrations of godly Mr. Macdougall of the Isles, who bade me turn from the error of my ways, but went on my own evil course, making siller, for I was a braw lad at the work and a trusted, and knowing the inside of every public from the pier of Cromarty to the streets of York. I was a wild drinker, caring in my cups for neither God nor man, a great hand with the cards, and fond of the lassies past all telling. It makes me shameful to this day to think on my evil life when I was twenty-five.

" Well, it chanced that in the back of the month of September I found myself in the city of Edinburgh with a flock of fifty sheep
which

which I had bought as a venture from a drunken bonnet-laird and was thinking of selling somewhere wast the country. They were braw beasts, Leicester every one of them, well-fed and dirt-cheap at the price I gave. So it was with a light heart that I drove them out of the town by the Merchiston Road along by the face of the Pentlands. Two or three friends came with me, all like myself for folly, but maybe a little bit poorer. Indeed, I cared little for them, and they valued me only for the whisky which I gave them to drink my health in at the parting. They left me on the near side of Colinton, and I went on my way alone.

"Now, if you'll be remembering the road, you will mind that at the place called Kirk Newton, just afore the road begins to twine over the Big Muir and almost at the head of the Water o' Leith, there is a verra fine public. Indeed, it would be no lee to call it the best public between Embro' and Glesca. The good wife, Lucky Craik by name, was an old friend of mine, for many a good gill of her prandy have I bought; so what would I be doing but just turning aside for refreshment? She met me at the door, verra pleased-like to see me, and soon I had my legs aneath her table and a basin of toddy on the board before me. And whom did I find in the same place but my old comrade Toshie Maclean from the backside of Glen-Lyon. Toshie and I were acquaintances so old that it did not behoove us to be parting quick. Forbye the day was chill without; and within the fire was grand and the crack of the best.

"Then Toshie and I got on quarrelling about the price of Lachlan Farawa's beasts that he sold at Falkirk; and, the drink having aye a bad effect on my temper, I was for giving him the lie and coming off in a great rage. It was about six o'clock in the evening and an hour to nightfall, so Mistress Craik comes in to try and keep me. 'Losh, Duncan,' says she, 'ye'll never try

and

and win ower the muir the nicht. It's mae than ten mile to
Carnwath, and there's nocht atween it and this but whaups and
heathery braes.' But when I am roused I will be more obstinate
than ten mules, so I would be going, though I knew not under
Heaven where I was going till. I was too full of good liquor and
good meat to be much worth at thinking, so I got my sheep on
the road an a big bottle in my pouch and set off into the heather.
I knew not what my purpose was, whether I thought to reach
the shieling of Carnwath, or whether I expected some house of
entertainment to spring up by the wayside. But my fool's mind
was set on my purpose of getting some miles further in my
journey ere the coming of darkness.

" For some time I jogged happily on, with my sheep running
well before me and my dogs trotting at my heels. We left the
trees behind and struck out on the broad grassy path which bands
the moor like the waist-strap of a sword. It was most dreary and
lonesome with never a house in view, only bogs and grey hillsides
and ill-looking waters. It was stony, too, and this more than
aught else caused my Dutch courage to fail me, for I soon fell
wearied, since much whisky is bad travelling fare, and began to
curse my folly. Had my pride no kept me back, I would have
returned to Lucky Craik's ; but I was like the devil for stiff-
neckedness and thought of nothing but to push on.

" I own that I was verra well tired and quite spiritless when I
first saw the House. I had scarce been an hour on the way, and
the light was not quite gone ; but still it was geyan dark, and the
place sprang somewhat suddenly on my sight. For, looking a
little to the left, I saw over a little strip of grass a big square
dwelling with many outhouses, half farm and half pleasure-house.
This, I thought, is the verra place I have been seeking and made sure
of finding ; so whistling a gay tune, I drove my flock toward it.

" When

" When I came to the gate of the court, I saw better of what sort was the building I had arrived at. There was a square yard with monstrous high walls, at the left of which was the main block of the house, and on the right what I took to be the byres and stables. The place looked ancient, and the stone in many places was crumbling away ; but the style was of yesterday and in no way differing from that of a hundred steadings in the land. There were some kind of arms above the gateway, and a bit of an iron stanchion ; and when I had my sheep inside of it, I saw that the court was all grown up with green grass. And what seemed queer in that dusky half-light was the want of sound. There was no neichering of horses, nor routing of kye, nor clack of hens, but all as still as the top of Ben Cruachan. It was warm and pleasant, too, though the night was chill without.

" I had no sooner entered the place than a row of sheep-pens caught my eye, fixed against the wall in front. This I thought mighty convenient, so I made all haste to put my beasts into them ; and finding that there was a good supply of hay within, I leff them easy in my mind, and turned about to look for the door of the house.

" To my wonder, when I found it, it was open wide to the wall ; so, being confident with much whisky, I never took thought to knock, but walked boldly in. There's some careless folk here, thinks I to myself, and I much misdoubt if the man knows aught about farming. He'll maybe just be a town's body taking the air on the muirs.

" The place I entered upon was a hall, not like a muirland farm-house, but more fine than I had ever seen. It was laid with a verra fine carpet, all red and blue and gay colours, and in the corner in a fireplace a great fire crackled. There were chairs, too, and a walth of old rusty arms on the walls, and all manner of
whigmaleeries

whigmaleeries that folk think ornamental. But nobody was
there, so I made for the staircase which was at the further side,
and went up it stoutly. I made scarce any noise so thickly was
it carpeted, and I will own it kind of terrified me to be walking
in such a place. But when a man has drunk well he is troubled
not overmuckle with modesty or fear, so I e'en stepped out and
soon came to a landing where was a door.

" Now, thinks I, at last I have won to the habitable parts of
the house ; so laying my finger on the sneck I lifted it and
entered. And there before me was the finest room in all the world;
indeed I abate not a jot of the phrase, for I cannot think of anything finer. It was hung with braw pictures and lined with big
bookcases of oak well-filled with books in fine bindings. The
furnishing seemed carved by a skilled hand, and the cushions and
curtains were soft velvet. But the best thing was the table, which
was covered with a clean white cloth and set with all kind of good
meat and drink. The dishes were of silver and as bright as Loch
Awe water in an April sun. Eh, but it was a braw braw sight
for a drover ! And there at the far end, with a great pottle of
wine before him, sat the master.

" He rose as I entered, and I saw him to be dressed in the pink
of town fashion, a man of maybe fifty years, but hale and well-
looking, with a peaked beard and trimmed moustache and thick
eyebrows. His eyes were slanted a thought, which is a thing I
hate in any man, but his whole appearance was pleasing.

" ' Mr. Stewart ? ' says he courteously, looking at me. ' Is it
Mr. Duncan Stewart that I will be indebted to for the honour of
this visit ? '

" I stared at him blankly, for how did he ken my name ?

" ' That is my name,' I said, ' but who the tevil tell't you
about it ? '

" ' Oh

"'Oh, my name is Stewart myself,' says he, 'and all Stewarts should be well acquaint.'

"'True,' said I, 'though I don't mind your face before. But now I am here, I think you have a most gallant place, Mr. Stewart.'

"'Well enough. But how have you come to't? We've few visitors.'

"So I told him where I had come from, and where I was going, and why I was forwandered at this time of night among the muirs. He listened keenly, and when I had finished, he says verra friendly-like, 'Then you'll bide all night and take supper with me. It would never be doing to let one of the clan go away without breaking bread. Sit ye down, Mr. Duncan.'

"I sat down gladly enough, though I own that at first I did not half-like the whole business. There was something unchristian about the place, and for certain it was not seemly that the man's name should be the same as my own, and that he should be so well posted in my doings. But he seemed so well-disposed that my misgivings soon vanished.

"So I seated myself at the table opposite my entertainer. There was a place laid ready for me, and beside the knife and fork a long horn-handled spoon. I had never seen a spoon so long and queer, and I asked the man what it meant. 'Oh,' says he, 'the broth in this house is very often hot, so we need a long spoon to sup it. It is a common enough thing, is it not?'

"I could answer nothing to this, though it did not seem to me sense, and I had an inkling of something I had heard about long spoons which I thought was not good; but my wits were not clear, as I have told you already. A serving man brought me a great bowl of soup and set it before me. I had hardly plunged spoon intil it, when Mr. Stewart cries out from the other end:
'Now,

'Now, Mr. Duncan, I call you to witness that you sit down to supper of your own accord. I've an ill name in these parts for compelling folk to take meat with me when they dinna want it. But you'll bear me witness that you're willing.'

" ' Yes, by God, I am that,' I said, for the savoury smell of the broth was rising to my nostrils. The other smiled at this as if well-pleased.

" I have tasted many soups, but I swear there never was one like that. It was as if all the good things in the world were mixed thegether—whisky and kale and shortbread and cocky-leeky and honey and salmon. The taste of it was enough to make a body's heart loup with fair gratitude. The smell of it was like the spicy winds of Arabia, that you read about in the Bible, and when you had taken a spoonful you felt as happy as if you had sellt a hundred yowes at twice their reasonable worth. Oh, it was grand soup!

" ' What Stewarts did you say you comed from,' I asked my entertainer.

" ' Oh,' he says, ' I'm connected with them all, Athole Stewarts, Appin Stewarts, Rannoch Stewarts ; and a' I've a heap o' land thereaways.'

" ' Whereabouts ?' says I, wondering. ' Is't at the Blair o' Athole, or along by Tummel side, or wast the Loch o' Rannoch, or on the Muir, or in Mamore ? '

" ' In all the places you name,' says he.

" ' Got damn,' says I, ' then what for do you not bide there instead of in these stinking lawlands ? '

" At this he laughed softly to himself. ' Why, for maybe the same reason as yoursel, Mr. Duncan. You know the proverb, " A' Stewarts are sib to the Deil." '

" I laughed loudly ; ' Oh, you've been a wild one, too, have you ? Then you're not worse than mysel. I ken the inside of every
public

public in the Cowgate and Cannongate, and there's not another
drover on the road my match at fechting and drinking and dicing.'
And I started on a long shameless catalogue of my misdeeds. Mr.
Stewart meantime listened with a satisfied smirk on his face.

" ' Yes, I've heard tell of you, Mr. Duncan,' he says. ' But
here's something more, and you'll doubtless be hungry.'

" And now there was set on the table a round of beef garnished
with pot-herbs, all most delicately fine to the taste. From a
great cupboard were brought many bottles of wine, and in a
massive silver bowl at the table's head were put whisky and lemons
and sugar. I do not know well what I drank, but whatever it
might be it was the best ever brewed. It made you scarce feel
the earth round about you, and you were so happy you could
scarce keep from singing. I wad give much siller to this day for
the receipt.

" Now, the wine made me talk, and I began to boast of my own
great qualities, the things I had done and the things I was going
to do. I was a drover just now, but it was not long that I would
be being a drover. I had bought a flock of my own, and would
sell it for a hundred pounds, no less ; with that I would buy a
bigger one till I had made money enough to stock a farm ; and
then I would leave the road and spend my days in peace, seeing
to my land and living in good company. Was not my father, I
cried, own cousin, thrice removed, to the Macleans o' Duart, and
my mother's uncle's wife a Rory of Balnacrory ? And I am a
scholar too, said I, for I was a matter of two years at Embro'
College, and might have been roaring in the pulpit, if I hadna
liked the drink and the lassies too well.

" ' See,' said I, ' I will prove it to you ; ' and I rose from the
table and went to one of the bookcases. There were all manner
of books, Latin and Greek, poets and philosophers, but in the main,
                                                      divinity.

divinity. For there I saw Richard Baxter's 'Call to the Un-converted,' and Thomas Boston of Ettrick's 'Fourfold State,' not to speak of the *Sermons* of half a hundred auld ministers, and the 'Hind let Loose,' and many books of the covenanting folk.

" 'Faith,' I says, 'you've a fine collection, Mr. What's-your-name,' for the wine had made me free in my talk. 'There is many a minister and professor in the Kirk, I'll warrant, who has a less godly library. I begin to suspect you of piety, sir.'

" 'Does it not behoove us,' he answered in an unctuous voice, 'to mind the words of Holy Writ that evil communications cor-rupt good manners, and have an eye to our company ? These are all the company I have, except when some stranger such as you honours me with a visit.'

" I had meantime been opening a book of plays, I think by the famous William Shakespeare, and I here proke into a loud laugh. 'Ha, ha, Mr. Stewart,' I says, 'here's a sentence I've lighted on which is hard on you. Listen ! "The Devil can quote Scripture to advantage."

" The other laughed long. 'He who wrote that was a shrewd man,' he said, 'but I'll warrant if you'll open another volume, you'll find some quip on yourself.'

" I did as I was bidden, and picked up a white-backed book, and opening it at random, read : 'There be many who spend their days in evil and wine-bibbing, in lusting and cheating, who think to mend while yet there is time ; but the opportunity is to them for ever awanting, and they go down open-mouthed to the great fire.'

" 'Psa,' I cried, 'some wretched preaching book, I will have none of them. Good wine will be better than bad theology.' So I sat down once more at the table.

" 'You're a clever man, Mr. Duncan,' he says, 'and a well-
read

By John Buchan

read one. I commend your spirit in breaking away from the bands of the kirk and the college, though your father was so thrawn against you.'

"'Enough of that,' I said, 'though I don't know who telled you;' I was angry to hear my father spoken of, as though the grieving him was a thing to be proud of.

"'Oh, as you please,' he says; 'I was just going to say that I commended your spirit in sticking the knife into the man in the Pleasaunce, the time you had to hide for a month about the backs o' Leith.'

"'How do you ken that,' I asked hotly, 'you've heard more about me than ought to be repeated, let me tell you.'

"'Don't be angry,' he said sweetly; 'I like you well for these things, and you mind the lassie in Athole that was so fond of you. You treated her well, did you not?'

"I made no answer, being too much surprised at his knowledge of things which I thought none knew but myself.

"'Oh yes, Mr. Duncan. I could tell you what you were doing to-day, how you cheated Jock Gallowa out of six pounds, and sold a horse to the farmer of Haypath that was scarce fit to carry him home. And I know what you are meaning to do the morn at Glesca, and I wish you well of it.'

"'I think you must be the Devil,' I said blankly.

"'The same, at your service,' said he, still smiling.

"I looked at him in terror, and even as I looked I kenned by something in his eyes and the twitch of his lips that he was speaking the truth.

"'And what place is this, you . . . .' I stammered.

"'Call me Mr. S.,' he says gently, 'and enjoy your stay while you are here and don't concern yourself about the lawing.'

"'The

" ' The lawing ! ' I cried in astonishment, ' and is this a house of public entertainment ? '

" ' To be sure, else how is a poor man to live ? '

" ' Name it,' said I, ' and I will pay and be gone.'

" ' Well,' said he, ' I make it a habit to give a man his choice. In your case it will be your wealth or your chances hereafter, in plain English your flock or your —— '

" ' My immortal soul,' I gasped.

" ' Your soul,' said Mr. S., bowing, ' though I think you call it by too flattering an adjective.'

" ' You damned thief,' I roared, ' you would entice a man into your accursed house and then strip him bare.'

" ' Hold hard,' said he, ' don't let us spoil our good fellowship by incivilities. And, mind you, I took you to witness to begin with that you sat down of your own accord.'

" ' So you did,' said I, and could say no more.

" ' Come, come,' he says, ' don't take it so bad. You may keep all your gear and yet part from here in safety. You've but to sign your name, which is no hard task to a college-bred man, and go on living as you live just now to the end. And let me tell you, Mr. Duncan Stewart, that you should take it as a great obligement that I am willing to take your bit soul instead of fifty sheep. There's no many would value it so high.'

" ' Maybe no, maybe no,' I said sadly, ' but it's all I have. D'ye no see that if I gave it up, there would be no chance left of mending ? And I'm sure I do not want your company to all eternity.'

" ' Faith, that's uncivil,' he says ; ' I was just about to say that we had had a very pleasant evening.'

" I sat back in my chair very down-hearted. I must leave this place as poor as a kirk-mouse, and begin again with little but the

clothes

clothes on my back. I was strongly tempted to sign the bit paper thing and have done with it all, but somehow I could not bring myself to do it. So at last I says to him : 'Well, I've made up my mind. I'll give you my sheep, sorry though I be to lose them, and I hope I may never come near this place again as long as I live.'

" ' On the contrary,' he said, ' I hope often to have the pleasure of your company. And seeing that you've paid well for your lodging, I hope you'll make the best of it. Don't be sparing on the drink.'

" I looked hard at him for a second. 'You've an ill name, and an ill trade, but you're no a bad sort yoursel, and, do you ken, I like you.'

" ' I'm much obliged to you for the character,' says he, 'and I'll take your hand on't.'

" So I filled up my glass and we set to, and such an evening I never mind of. We never got fou, but just in a fine good temper and very entertaining. The stories we told and the jokes we cracked are still a kind of memory with me, though I could not come over one of them. And then, when I got sleepy, I was shown to the brawest bedroom, all hung with pictures and looking-glasses, and with bed-clothes of the finest linen and a coverlet of silk. I bade Mr. S. good-night, and my head was scarce on the pillow ere I was sound asleep.

    *   *   *   *   *

" When I awoke the sun was just newly risen, and the frost of a September morning was on my clothes. I was lying among green braes with nothing near me but crying whaups and heathery hills, and my two dogs running round about and howling as they were mad."

A Fire

By Stephen Phillips

DAZZLED with watching how the swift fire fled
    Along the dribbling roof, I turned my head;
When lo, upraised beneath the lighted cloud
The illumed unconscious faces of the crowd!
Beautiful souls I knew and spirits dire,
A moment naked, and betrayed by fire;
An old grey face in lovely bloom upturned,
The ancient rapture and the dream returned;
A cautious face, now brilliant and rash,
The scheming eyes hither and thither flash;
The experienced face, with all emotion crushed,
Now, as at some great wrong indignant, flushed;
The hungering tramp with indolent gloating stare,
The beggar in glory and devoid of care:
That grey and trivial face, made up of needs,
Now pale and recent from triumphant deeds!
A mother slowly burning with bare breast,
Yet her consuming babe close to her prest;
That prosperous citizen in anguish dire,
Beseeching heaven from purgatorial fire,
Souls unaware by sudden flame betrayed
I saw; then through the darkness stole, afraid.

Chapelle Dissidente
(London)

VÉNÉRABLE temple
    Et digne pasteur !
Sa redingote ample
A l'air de rigueur.

Protestante et raide
Est son âme aussi ;
Le mal n'est pas si
Laid que le remède.

Mains sans onction,
Visage revêche..,
Vite ! qu'on nous prêche
    La tentation !

Mieux vaut, bonne ou male,
    La mort à Paris
    Que la vie au prix
De cette morale !

(Pour Mr. Aubrey Beardsley.)

Wladislaw's Advent

By Ménie Muriel Dowie

I

WHEN I first saw Wladislaw he was sitting on a high tabouret near a hot iron sheet that partially surrounded the tall coke stove; the arches of his feet were curved over the top bar, toes and heels both bent down, suggestive of a bird clasping its perch. This position brought the shiny knees of his old blue serge trousers close up to his chest—for he was bending far forward towards his easel—and the charcoal dust on the knee over which he occasionally sharpened his *fusain* was making a dull smear upon the grey flannel shirt which his half-opened waistcoat exposed.

He wore no coat: it was hanging on the edge of the iron screen, and his right shirt-sleeve, rolled up for freedom in his work, left a strong, rather smooth arm bare.

He always chose a corner near the stove; the coke fumes never gave him a headache, it seemed. It was supposed that he felt the cold of Paris severely; but this can hardly have been the case, considering the toughening winters of his youth away in Poland there. My observation led me to believe that the proximity was courted on account of the facilities it afforded for lighting his cigarette.

284

cigarette. When he rolled a new one and had returned the flat, shabby, red leather case to a pocket, he would get up, open the stove door and pick up a piece of coke—one whose lower half was scarlet and its upper still black—between his finger and thumb, and, holding it calmly to the cigarette, suck in a light with a single inhalation, tossing the coke to its place and re-seating himself upon his tabouret, completely unaware of the amused pairs of eyes that watched quizzically to see his brow pucker if he burnt himself.

Wladislaw was his first name; naturally he had another by which he was generally known, but it is useless to record a second set of Polish syllables for the reader to struggle with, so I leave it alone.   His first name is pronounced Vladislav as nearly as one may write it; and this is to be remembered, for I prefer to retain the correct spelling.   He had been working quite a fortnight in the studio before the day when I strolled in and noticed him, and I do not think that up till then any one had the excitement of his acquaintance.

One or two sketch-books contained hasty and furtive pencil splashes which essayed the picturesqueness of his features; but he was notably shy, and if he observed any one to be regarding him with the unmistakable measuring eye of the sketcher, he would frown and dip behind the canvas on his easel with the silly sensitiveness of a dabchick.   At the dingy *crèmerie* where he ate herrings *marinés*—chiefly with a knife—the curious glances of other *déjeuneurs* annoyed him extremely; which was absurd, of course, for as a rule no artist objects to being made the victim of a brother's brush.   He would colour—I was going to write, like a girl, but why not like the boy that he was?—when the lively Louise, who changed the plates, or swept the knife and fork of such as did not know the habits of the place back on the crumby
marble

marble table with a " V'lá M'sieu," sent a smile accurately darted into his long eyes. He didn't know how to respond to Louise, or any other glances of the same sort in those days; but if I am encouraged to tell further of him, I can give the history of his initiation, for I am bold to say none knows it better—unless it be Louise herself.

What puzzled me about his face, which was a beautiful one, of the pure and refined Hebrew type so rarely met with—the type that was a little commoner, let us hope, in the days when God singled out His People—what puzzled me about it was that it should seem so familiar to me, for, as I say, the type is seldom found. When I came upon Wladislaw, hurrying down the street to the studio with the swiftness of a polecat—no sort of joke intended—it would flash upon me that surely I knew the face, yet not as one feels when one has met some one in a train or sat near him in a tramcar.

The mystery of this was explained before ever I had analysed to myself exactly how the face affected me and where I could have seen it before. It was at the eleven o'clock rest one morning, when the strife of tongues was let loose and I was moving among the easels and stools, talking to the various students that I knew. One of them, her book open, her eyes gleaming and her pencil avid of sketches, was lending a vague ear to the model, who had once been in England, and was describing his experiences with a Royal Academician. They were standing near the stove, the model, careless of the rapid alteration which the grateful heat was effecting in his skin tones, steadily veering from the transparent purple which had gratified an ardent impressionist all the morning, to a dull, hot scarlet upon the fronts of his thighs. While she was talking to the model, my friend was sketching Wladislaw, who ranged remotely at the cold end of the room. The impressionist

sionist joined the group to remonstrate in ineffectual French with the model, and glanced into the sketch-book in passing.

"Just the church-window type, isn't he?" said this flippant person, alluding to the Pole; "and I have seen him behind the altar too, painted on the wall with a symmetrical arrangement of stars in the background, and his feet on a blue air-balloon."

The sketcher nodded, and swept in a curved line for the coat collar just as a controlling voice announced that the rest was up.

And I wondered how I had been so dull as never to think of it; for it was perfectly true, and, oh, so obvious now I knew it! Wladislaw's beautiful head, with the young light-brown beard, the pure forehead, and the long sorrowful eyes, was an ideal presentment of the Nazarene; without the alteration of either feature or expression, he stood up a gloriously simple realisation of the Christ as all pictures have tried to show Him.

I was so amazed by this illumination, that I sat down beside the disconsolate impressionist, who "couldn't do a thing till that idiot cooled down," and was "losing half the morning—the Professor's morning, too," and talked it over.

"H'm, yes—he is. Hadn't you noticed it? I said it the very day he came in. I wonder if he sees it himself? Do you know, I think I could get rather a good thing of him from here? Yes, you wait; I've nothing to do till that beastly hectic colour fades off the model. I'm not going to bother about the background; I've painted that old green curtain till I'm tired. Get a tabouret and sit down while I design a really good window."

She sketched away rapidly, and I watched her as she worked.

"Funny," she remarked, as she blocked in the figure with admirable freedom; "I've never seen the Christ treated in profile, have you? It's rather new—you watch."

It is my regret that I did not disregard every rule and every

courtesy

courtesy and snatch that sketch from her, half-finished though it was; but of a sudden the door opened and the Professor came in. The impressionist, with a sour look at the model's thighs and a despairing consciousness that she would have to hear that her colour was too cold, shut her book with a snap and resumed her brushes.

I had to manœuvre cautiously a retreat to the stairway—for idlers were publicly discouraged during the Professor's visits—and people who would leave off work at any minute when I dropped in to hear the news on ordinary mornings, looked up and frowned studiously over the creaking of my retreating boots.

It may have been about a week later that my acquaintance with Wladislaw commenced, and again the detailing of that circumstance is to serve another purpose one of these days; at any rate, we came across one another in a manner which is to a friendship what a glass frame is to a cucumber, and soon studio friends came to me for news of him, and my protection of him was an openly admitted fact. At first I had been somewhat burdened by a consciousness of his curious beauty; one is not often in the way of talking to a beautiful man of any kind, but I can imagine that classical beauty or historic beauty might be more easily supported. No particular deep would be touched by a meeting with Apollo or Antinous; neither awe, nor reverence, however discredited and worn-out its tradition, has ever attached to them. The counterpart of Montrose or the bonnie Earl o' Murray, much as one would like to meet either, would arouse only picturesque sentimental reflection; but to walk through the Jardin du Luxembourg on a sunny day eating *gaufres*, with—and I say it without the faintest intention of irreverence—with a figure of the Saviour of mankind beside you, is—is arresting. When the eye reposes unintentionally upon it in the silent

moments

moments of conversation, it gives pause. Distinctly, it gives
pause. I have never held it an excuse for anything in art or
literature that one should turn upon a public about to scoff, to be
offended, to be frightened, and announce that " it is true ": that
the incident in either a picture or a story should be " true " is not
a sufficient excuse for the painting or the telling of it. But when
I insist courteously to readers of certain religious convictions that
I am not " making up " either my scenes, my characters, or what,
for want of a better name, shall be called my story, I am only
desirous that they shall absolve me from any desire to be irreverent
and to shock their feelings. They might remember that what is
reverent to them may not be so to me; but I do not hope to
secure so great a concession by any means. What I would
finally point out is that the irreverence goes back further than the
mere writing down of the story; they must accuse a greater than
I if they object to the facts of the case—they must state their
quarrel to the controlling power which designed poor Wladislaw's
physiognomy: to use some of the phrases beloved of the very
class I am entreating, I would suggest that the boy did not
" make himself "; he was " sent into the world " like that.

I daresay—considering what I am going to relate—I daresay he
wished he had not been; he was so very shy a fellow, and it led
to his being a great deal observed and commented upon. What
encouraged me to feel at home with him in spite of his appearance
was the real youngness of his nature. He was extraordinarily
simple and—well, fluffy. For he really suggested a newly-
hatched chicken to me; bits of the egg-shell were still clinging to
his yellow down, if I may hint at the metaphor.

His cleverness was tremendously in advance of his training and
his executive powers. Some day, one could see, he was *going* to
paint marvellously, if he would wait and survive his failures and

forbear

forbear to cut his throat by the way.   His mind was utterly and
entirely on his work; I never heard him speak of much else;
work and the difficulty of producing oneself, no matter with the
help of what medium, was our everyday topic.   And when
desperate fits overtook us we bewailed the necessity of producing
ourselves at all.   Why was it in us?   We didn't think anything
good that we did; we didn't suppose we were ever going to
compass anything decent, and work was a trouble, a fever of
disappointment and stress, which we did not enjoy in the least.
The pleasure of work, we assured one another again and again,
was a pleasure we had never felt.   By nature, inclination and
habit we were incorrigibly idle; yet inside us was this spirit, this
silly, useless, hammering beast that impelled us to the handling of
pen and pencil, and made us sick and irritable and unhappy, and
prevented us taking any pleasure in our dinner.

That was how we used to talk together when we were striding
through the woods round Versailles or idling among storied tombs
in the cemetery at Montmorency; and, dear me! what a lot of
enjoyment we got out of it, and how good the sandwiches were
when we rested for our luncheon!   Sometimes Wladislaw talked
of his mother, whom I apprehended to be a teak-grained Calvinistic
lady with a certain resemblance to the hen who had reared a
duckling by mistake.   I wish now that I had heard more stories
of that rigorous household of his youth, where the fires in winter
were let out at four in the afternoon because his mother had the
idea that one did not feel the cold so much in bed if inured to it
by a sustained chill of some eight hours' duration.   She was
probably quite right: one only wonders why she did not pursue
the principle further and light no fires in the day, because pro-
portionately, of course—— But no matter.   And, indeed, there
are no proportions in the case.   Once reach the superlative
                                                                        frozen,

frozen, and there is nothing left to feel.   His third subject was the frivolity of Paris, of which we knew everything by hearsay and nothing by experience, so were able to discuss with a " wet sheet and a flowing sea," so to speak.   He hated Paris, and he hated frivolity, even as he hated French.   Our conversations, I ought to say, were carried on in German, which we spoke with almost a common measure of inaccuracy;   and I think that he probably knew as little of the French language as he knew of the frivolity of Paris.

I tried to encourage him to take long walks and long tours on tramways—it should never be forgotten that you can go all over Paris for threepence—and when his work at the studios was sufficiently discouraging he would do so, sometimes coming with me, sometimes going alone.   We explored Montmartre together both by day and gas light;   we fared forth to the Abattoirs, to the Place de la Roquette, to the Boulevard Beaumarchais and the Boulevard Port Royal, the Temple and " les Halles."

But Wladislaw was alone the day he set out to inspect the Bois de Boulogne, the Parc Monceau, the Madeleine, and the *grands Boulevards*.

I remember seeing him start.   If he had been coming with me he would have had on a tie and collar (borrowed from another student) and his other coat;   he would, in fact, have done his best to look ordinary, to rob himself, in his youthful pride and ignorant vanity, of his picturesque appearance.   I am sorry to say it, since he was an artist;   but it is true—he would.

As it was, he sallied out in the grey woollen shirt, with its low collar, the half-buttoned waistcoat, the old, blue, sloppily-hanging coat, with one sleeve obstinately burst at the back, and the close astrakhan cap on one side of his smooth straight hazel hair.   When I ran across him next day in the neighbourhood of

the

the oleander tubs that surrounded with much decorative ability
the doors of the Café Amadou, he agreed to come to my rooms
and have a cup of coffee, in order to narrate the exciting and
mysterious incident of the day before.

Sitting on each side of my stove, which was red-hot and threat-
ening to crack at any minute, Wladislaw, with cautions to me
" not to judge too soon: I should see if it had not been strange,
this that had happened to him," told me this ridiculous story.

He had started up the Bois; he had found the Parc Monceau;
he had come down a big street to the Madeleine; he had looked
in; it had reminded him of a concert-hall, and was not at all
impressive (*gar nicht imponirend*); he had walked along the left-
hand side of the Boulevard des Capucines. It was as poor a
street as he could have imagined in a big town, the shops
wretched; he supposed in London our shops were better? I
assured him that in London the shops were much better; that it
was a standing mystery to me, as to all the other English women
I knew, where the pretty things for which Paris is celebrated
were to be bought. And I implored him to tell me his adventure.

Ah! Well—now the point was reached; now I was to hear!
One minute!—Well, he had come opposite the Café de la Paix;
and he had paused an instant to contemplate the unrelieved
commonplace ugliness of the average Frenchman as there to be
observed—and then he had pursued his way.

It was getting dusk in the winter afternoon, and when he came
through the Place de l'Opéra all the lights were lit, and he was
delighted, as who must not be, by the effect of that particular bit
of Paris? He was just crossing the Place to go down the left-
hand side of the Avenue, when it occurred to him that he was
being followed.

It

It here struck me that the beginning of Wladislaw's first
adventure in Paris was highly unoriginal; but I waited with a
tempered interest to hear how he had dealt with it.   Here are his
own words, but losing much of their quaintness by being rendered
in an English which even I cannot make quite ungrammatical.

"I went on very quickly a little way, then I walked slowly,
slowly—very slow, and turned suddenly sharp round.   Yes, I
was being followed; there he was, a man in a black frock coat,
and——"

" A man ? " I blurted out, having been somehow unprepared
for this development.

" What else ? " said Wladislaw.   " Did you think it was going
to be a cat ? "

Well, more or less, I *had* fancied .... but I wouldn't interrupt him.

" Black coat and grey trousers, black bow tie and one of those
hats, you know ? "   With his cigarette hand he made a rapid
pantomime about his head that outlined sufficiently the flat-
brimmed top hat of the artistic Frenchman, so often distinguished,
but more usually a little ridiculous.

" I went on at an ordinary pace till I came to the Rue de
Rivoli, then at that Café where the omnibus for St. Sulpice stops
I waited "—Wladislaw's eyes were gleaming with an unwonted
mischief, and he had quite lost his Judaic majesty—" to get a
good look.   There he was.   A man not yet forty; dark, interesting, powerful face; a red ribbon in his button-hole."

" A red ribbon ? "   But then I remembered that every second
Frenchman has a red ribbon.

" I thought, ' Shall I take him a nice walk this cold evening ?
Shall I go down and cross the river to Notre Dame, then home
up the Boulevard St. Michel ? '   But no, it was late.   I had had
nothing

nothing to eat; I wanted to get to the Bouillon Robert before dinner would be over. I ran into the Bureau and got a number; then I watched, and the first omnibus that had room I climbed up on the *impériale* and *watched him try for a seat inside!* Ah, I knew he was after me. I felt as if I had stolen something! Then the omnibus started. He had not got a seat. When it is already six you cannot get a seat inside, you know!"

I knew. "He came up with you?" I said.

"On the *impériale* also there was no room. I lost sight of him, but on the Pont du Carrousel I saw a *fiacre!*"

In spite of my earlier feeling I was a little interested; more so when Wladislaw told of his walking into a certain restaurant near the Gare Montparnasse—a restaurant where you dine with *hors d'œuvres* and dessert at a scoured wood table for 80 centimes, sitting down beside several *ouvriers*—and seeing the stranger saunter in and take a seat at a corner table.

I feel quite incapable of rendering in English the cat-and-mouse description of the dinner which Wladislaw gave me; so I come to the time when he paid his *addition*, and turning up his coat collar, made his way out and up the Boulevard Montparnasse in the ill-lighted winter night, the stranger appearing inevitably in his wake at each gas-lamp, till the side street was reached in which Wladislaw lived on the fourth floor of a certain number thirteen. At his door Wladislaw, of course, paused, and looked the street up and down without seeing his pursuer.

"But no doubt," said my sly Pole, "he was hiding inside a courtyard door. And now, what do you make of that?"

I had to own that I made nothing of it; and we sat and speculated foolishly for fully half an hour, till we tired of the effort and returned to our equally vapid haverings about "work" and our common difficulties.

Four

By Ménie Muriel Dowie

Four days later—I had meantime confided the story to no one—
four days later Wladislaw approached me mysteriously from
behind as I was returning one morning from a visit to the Rue
de la Gaieté, with a bunch of onions, half a loaf of black bread,
and two turkey-thighs in a string-bag.

I knew from the set of his cap that something unusual had
happened; and besides, it was the hour at which he should have
been scraping at his *fusain* in the men's studio. He put a letter
in my hand.

" You will say nothing to anybody ? I want you to translate
it. I can't understand it all. But you will tell no one ? "

I responded with an eager denial and the question as to who
there could be for me to tell.

He seemed to overlook the half-hundred of students we both
knew, as readily as I did; and we opened the letter.
This was it:

" Monsieur,—My name may perhaps be a sufficient assurance to you
that my unusual conduct of the other evening in discovering for
myself your residence and profession had no unworthy motive. The
explanation is simple. I am painting a large canvas, to be called
'The Temptation.' I cannot proceed for want of a model for my
Christ. When my eyes fell upon you, I realised instantly that yours
was the only face in the world that could satisfy my aspiration. It
was impossible for me not to follow you, at the risk of any and every
misunderstanding. I beg you to receive my complete apologies.
Will you sit to me ? I appeal to you as a brother of the brush—
permit me to leave behind me the most perfect Christ-face that has
ever been conceived. Times and terms shall be as you will.

" Accept, Monsieur and colleague, the assurance of my most
distinguished sentiments.

" DUFOUR."

I looked

I looked at it, laughing and gasping. I repeated some of the sounding phrases. So this artist—well I knew his name at the Mirlitons—this genius of the small red fleck had pursued Wladislaw for miles on foot and in fiacre, had submitted himself and his digestion to an 80 centime dinner of blatant horse-flesh, had tracked the student to his lodgings, got his style and title from Madame in the *rez-de-chaussée*, and finally written him this letter to ask—to implore, rather, that Wladislaw should be the model for his contemplated picture of the Redeemer! It was really interesting enough; but what struck me as curious was that Dufour of the tulle skirt and tarlatan celebrity—the portraitist of the *filles de joie* —should conceive it possible to add to his reputation by painting the Man of Sorrows.

II

It will have been gathered that Wladislaw was poor; just how poor, I think no one among us ever knew. He would sit all the evening long without a fire, and his habit of keeping a large piece of bread in a coat pocket and breaking bits off to nibble during the morning or afternoon's work very naturally gave rise to a legend that he lived upon bread alone.

I, for one, would sooner believe that to have been the case than have credited for a moment the story of the student who claimed to have noticed a heap of fish heads and tails in a corner of his room, the disagreeable residue of a small barrel of raw dried herring which he had kept by him.

I suppose that he paid his classes and boarding charges out of money sent at intervals from home, like any other student; but the final outward evidence of any shortness in cash was the colour of

of the packet in which he bought his tobacco. A careful observer
might have accurately dated the arrival of his funds by noting the
orange paper which enclosed his " Levant Supérieur." Then, as
it behoved him to be careful, the canary yellow of the cheaper
" Levant "; and finally the sign manual of approaching destitu-
tion in the common brown wrapper of his " Caporal." I am
inclined to say that I noticed his leisurely but inevitable descent
of these pecuniary steps every month.

Further, if moderately affluent, he would indulge in five sous'
worth of roasted chestnuts whenever we went out together, and
only on one occasion did it occur to me to provide him with a
tram fare. Despite this poverty, I am very sure that when he
arranged ultimately, at my instance, to sit to Monsieur Dufour
for his picture of " Christ led up into the Wilderness to be
tempted of the Devil," Wladislaw was very far from thinking of
the remuneration.

The fact was, he had differed rather pointedly with a big
Russian at the evening class, a man preternaturally irritable
because eternally afflicted by the toothache; there had been
words, the Russian had announced his intention of throwing the
Pole from the top of the stairs, and being a taller, more muscular
fellow, had picked him up and carried him to the door, when
Wladislaw wriggled dexterously from his grasp, and jerked him
down no fewer than eleven steps upon his spine. He described to me
afterwards with less truth than artistic sympathy the neat bobbing
sound as each individual vertebra knocked upon the wooden
stairs.

This incident, and the fact that the Russian had taken an oath
in public to pay his defeat a round dozen of times, served to cool
Wladislaw's interest in the evening class. He told me also that
the light tried his eyes; and he would come up in the morning
with

with a fine vermilion point in their corners, the result, as I insisted, of his dipping locks of hair.

With a choice of reasons for his coming, I was yet surprised when he came, late one evening, and having whistled the opening bars of Chopin's " Dirge of Poland " below my seventh-floor window, decoyed me to the roadway, and described his first visit to the studio of Dufour in the Rue de Vaugirard.

Out of mere curiosity we had wandered to the number, one afternoon after the reception of the letter; and I well remembered the living stench of the *impasse*, the dead trails of an enterprising Virginia creeper, the broken mass of plaster casts which sufficiently located a young sculptor near at hand, and the cracked Moorish lamp which lay upon its side in the half-choked drain. All we had seen of the studio's furnishings was the silk-threaded back of a magnificent curtain which blocked an upper square of lights; but I knew that inside all must be on a much greater scale of artistic beauty than the queer, draughty barns of art-student friends, where I often juggled with a cup of tea—tea produced from a corner shrouded modestly in the green canvas covering of a French waggon and the dusty, bellying folds of a brown fishing-net. I was now to hear from Wladislaw what the interior was really like; how the great Dufour appeared when seen from the front instead of the rear, so to say, and upon what terms the negotiations were begun.

A certain indecisiveness in Wladislaw's painting was reflected in his conversation: he never could describe anything. Perhaps this is to do him an injustice; I would rather say that he had no idea of giving a detailed description. By whiles you might get a flash equivalent to one of his illuminative brush strokes, which was very certain to be an unsurpassable apprecation of the fact or the circumstances; but bid him begin at the beginning and go

coolly

coolly to the end, and you had him useless, flurried, monosyllabic and distraught.

I had early learned this; so I stood pretty patiently, although in thin slippers, on our half-made road, a red clay slough by reason of much carting, and listened to half-intelligible fragments of bad German, from which I gleaned quite a good deal that I wanted to know. First of all, it seemed the studio had another door; one we had never seen; you made your way round the back of the sculptor's white powdery habitation, and discovered yourself opposite a little annexe where the artist kept his untidier properties, and the glass and china which served for any little refreshment he might be disposed to take in working hours. The door here had been opened by an untidy, half-dressed French-woman, with her boots unbuttoned and a good deal of cigarette ash upon her high-braced bust; she appeared unaware of Wladislaw's arrival, for she came to the door to empty something, and he nearly received the contents of a small enamelled tin thing in his face.

A moment later, much shaken by the off-hand insolence of her remarks, he penetrated to the presence of Dufour himself, and was agreeably soothed by the painter's reception of him. Of Dufour's manner and remarks, or the appearance of his workshop, I could get no idea. He had a canvas, twelve feet by nine, upon an easel, and it seems he made a rapid *croquis* of his picture upon a smaller upright, and had a few masterly skirmishes with the *fusain* for the position of his Christ's head, begging the model to walk naturally up and down the studio, so as to expose unconsciously various attitudes of face.

During these saunterings Wladislaw should have come by some idea of his surroundings; but he was continually harrassed and distracted by the movements of the woman in the unbuttoned boots, and seemed to have observed very little.

Upon

Upon a high point of an easel was hung a crown of thorns, and beside this leaned a reed; but Dufour explained that he had abandoned that more conventional incident in favour of the Temptation in the Wilderness, and explained at some length the treatment that he contemplated of the said Temptation. Nothing, of course, was to be as it had ever been before; the searching light of modern thought, of modern realism, was to be let in upon this old illustration, from which time had worn the sharpness long ago.

"They must feel it; it must come right down to them—to their lives; they must find it in their path as they walk—irrefutable, terrible—and the experience of any one of them!" Dufour had said. "And for that, contrast! You have here the simplicity of the figure; the man, white, assured, tense, unassailable. Then, here and there, around and above, the thousand soft presentments of temptation. And these, though imaginatively treated, are to be real—real. He was a man; they say He had a man's temptations; but where do we really hear of them? You will see them in my picture; all that has ever come to you or me is to be there. Etherealised, lofty, deified, but . . . our temptations."

"And you see what a subject? The advantages, the opportunities? The melting of the two methods? The *plein air* for the figure, and all that Art has ever known or imagined outside this world—everything a painter's brain has ever seen in dreams—for the surroundings. Is it to be great? Is it to be final? Ah, you shall see! And yours is the face of all the world for it. You are a re-incarnation. One moment so. I must have the head *trois quarts* with the chin raised."

Dufour talked himself to perspiration, so Wladislaw said, and even I at third hand was warmed and elated.

Surely

Surely it was a striking achievement. I don't think it occurred to me then to reflect how large a practice Dufour had had with the "temptations" realistically treated; certainly he had a name for the painting of them which no one could outdo; and if his new departure from the direction of gas and limelight to *plein air* went well there was everything to hope.

"And when are you to go again?" I asked, as I scraped the clay from my slippers on the wide door mat in our draughty *entresol*.

"Not for three days; he goes out of town, to Nancy. On Sunday night I go again, and am to pose in costume. He is to have me after, every night for a week, while he draws only, to choose his exact position; after that, I have to give up some daylight; but it won't matter, for I can join the evening class again for black and white. I have often thought of it, and meant to."

"And you don't think it is going to tire you horribly—standing and not saying anything?"

"Tire? Nothing could tire me. I could pose on one leg for him like a stork, for hours at a time, and never complain."

"I don't think it likely that a position of that kind——" I began; but he struck in:

"But not if that woman is about. She makes me nervous. You should see her hands: they are all white and swollen. When I ran a thorn in my thumb and it swelled, it went like that—all dead and cooked-looking."

"Don't!" I shouted. "Of course she won't be there. It isn't likely he would have a servant about when he worked."

"She isn't a servant; she called him 'Toni,' and she took hold——"

"She was a *model*," I said; and Wladislaw, who was so head-

long

long because so very young, heard the note of finality in my voice, and looking puzzled but complaisant, reserved further comment on the woman in the unbuttoned boots.

*   *   *   *   *

All that follows this, I am unable to tell in Wladislaw's own words; the facts were not given me at one, nor yet at two recitals—they were piled heterogeneously in my mind, just as he told them at odd moments in the months that followed; and that they have arranged themselves with some sort of order is to be accounted for first of all by their dramatic nature, and secondly by the inherent habit of my memory, which often straightens and adjusts, although unbidden, all that is thrown into it, so that I may take things out nearly as I would have them: thus one may pick articles, ordered in one's absence, from the top left-hand drawer in a dressing-table.

At half-past eight upon the Sunday it was a very black night indeed in the Rue de Vaugirard. Wladislaw had well-nigh fallen prone over the broken Moorish lamp, now frozen firmly in the gutter which was the centre of the *impasse*; he had made his way round by the sculptor's studio, found the door unlocked, and being of a simple, unquestioning temperament, had strolled into the untidy, remote little annexe which communicated by a boarded passage with the handsome *atelier*.

A small tin lamp of the kind a concierge usually carries, glassless, flaming at a cotton wick with *alcoöl à brûler*, was withstanding an intermittent buffeting by a wind which knew the best hole in the window to come in at. Wladislaw nearly lost half of his long light-brown moustache by lighting his cigarette at it in a draught.

It was cold, and he had to undress to his skin; the comfort of
a cigarette

a cigarette was not to be denied.   Also he was late for his appointment, and this annoyed him.   He picked up the lamp
when he had taken coat and cap off, and searched for the costume
he was to wear.

A row of pegs upon the wall offered encouragement.   With a
certain awkwardness, which was the result of his shyness of touching unfamiliar garments, he knocked down two hats—women's
hats: one a great scooped thing with red roses below the rim;
the other like a dish, with green locusts, horribly life-like (and no
wonder, since they were the real insects), crawling over it.   He
hastily replaced these, and took up a white thing on another nail,
which might have been the scant robe he was to wear.

It was fine and soft to his hand; it exhaled an ineffable
perfume of a sort of sweetness which belonged to no three-franc
bottle, and had loose lace upon it and ribbons.   He dropped this
upon the ground, thinking shudderingly of the woman in the
unbuttoned boots.   At last he came upon the garment he was to
wear; it seemed to him that he knew it at once when he touched
it; it was of a thick, coarse, resistant woollen fabric, perhaps
mohair, with a dull shine in the rather unwilling folds; there was
very little stuff in it—just a narrow, poor garment, and of course,
white; wool-white.   Wladislaw wondered vaguely where Dufour
could have come by this wonderfully archaic material, ascetic
even to the touch.   Then he sat down upon a small disused stove
and took off his boots and socks.   Still hanging upon the nail was
a rope cord, frayed rather, and of hemp, hand twisted.   That was
the whole costume; the robe and the cord.

He was out of his shirt and ready to put on the Hebrew dress,
when he was arrested again by some half-thought in his mind,
and stood looking at it as it lay thrown across a heap of dusty
toiles.   It seemed so supremely real a thing—just what The Man
must

must have worn; he could imagine the old story more nearly than ever he had done before.

He could see Him, His robes of red or purple laid aside, clothed only in the white under-garment; the beautiful purity, the unimpeachable holiness of Him only the greater to see; young, perfect, without sin or soil; the veritable " Jesus led up of the Spirit into the wilderness to be tempted of the Devil."

And he himself, Wladislaw, was the true image of that grand figure as He has come down through all the histories to the eyes of an indifferent world.

When he lifted his hand to his head, bewildered and held by it, the old blue trousers fell to the ground, and he stood there naked in the cold, taking his mind back along the familiar lines of the wonderful story, entering into the feelings of that Jew-Man who was persecuted; who, whether man or God, lived the noblest life, left the finest example—who walks to-day, as He did then, beside the few who may be called His disciples.

A blast that caught the little lamp full in its foul, yellow flame-tongue, left Wladislaw in the dark. He felt about for matches; perhaps no act could have so certainly restored him to this world, from which his thoughts had wandered. He found none anywhere. His straying hand came upon the garment; he caught it up and slipped it over his head, half horrified to feel that it came below his collar-bone in the neck, and left his arms with only half-a-dozen inches of sleeve.

Matches were lurking in his trousers pocket, and he had the sulphury splutter going in a moment and the lamp re-lit.

Turning to place it in a quieter corner, he faced a dusty square of looking-glass, unframed, such as painters usually have, its edges sunk into the dusty wall; he had quite a surprise to see himself.

More than half fascinated, he made a swift arrangement of his
hair

hair, smoothed the soft flow of his moustache and beard, knotted
the rope cord round his waist, and stood there only a second or
two longer. Then, nerved by the startling simplicity, the convincing faithfulness of his whole appearance, he opened the door
and went down the passage to the studio, frowning and stepping
gingerly on the cold boards.

* * * * *

The curious murmur of sounds that struck his ear; voices, the
music of glasses and silver, the slap, as it might have been a hand
upon a cheek, and the vagrant notes of some untuned musical
instrument—these all he barely noticed, or supposed they came
from the sculptor's adjacent studio.

He opened the door and brushed aside the dark *portière* that
screened out draughts; he stepped into the studio, into a hot, over-
charged air, thick with the flat smell of poured wines and fruit
rind, coloured with smoke, poisoned with scent, ringing harshly to
voices—an air that of itself, and if he had seen nothing, would have
nauseated him.

He saw dimly, confusedly; orange and yellow blobs of light
seemed to be swinging behind grey-blue mists that rolled and eddied
round the heads of people so wild, he did not know if he looked at
a dream picture, a picture in a bad dream. If he made another step
or two and stood, his arms straight at his sides, his head up, his long
eyes glaring beneath drawn perplexed brows, he did not know it.
There was a sudden pause, as though by a chemical process the
air had been purged of sounds. Then a confused yell burst
from among the smoke clouds, mixed with the harsh scrape of
chairs shot back upon the floor; that, too, ceased, and out
of the frozen horror of those halted people, some incoherent,
hysteric whimpering broke out, and a few faint interrupted
exclamations.

At

At a table heaped with the *débris* of a careless feast he saw Dufour, his coat off, his waistcoat and shirt unbuttoned, his head rolled weakly back upon the gilded woodscroll of his Louis Quinze chair: his face flushed and swollen, strangely broadened, coarsened and undone, with sick, loose expressions rolling over it as shallow water rolls above a stone; he had in his hands an old lute, a studio property, from which he had been picking poor detached, discordant notes.

There were other men, with wild arrested merriment in their faces, the merriment of licence. Mixed among them, tangling like the serpents and reptiles in an allegorical picture, were women of whom the drapery or the bareness seemed indifferently lewd.

One had fainted with a glass at her lips, and the splash of spilled liquor was on her neck and dripping from her chin. No one heeded her.

Another had dashed her head upon the table; her hands were clutched in her hair, shaking with a palsy of terror; and from her arose the sobs which were no more than the dull moaning of a beast in labour.

One other, in a dress all Paris would have recognised as being the orange ballet-muslins in which Dufour had painted his celebrated " Coquelicot," was lying with long white arms spread on the back of a chair; above her low black satin bodice the waves of her dead-white breast were heaving convulsively; her red hair blazed from under the live fantastic orange-poppy horns that spread out from her head; her clever, common little face was twitching to recover a vinous courage, the black eyes were blinking, the crooked lines of her mouth—more fascinating than any fancied bow-curve—were moving in irresponsible striving to open on one side, as they had a habit of doing, and let out some daring phrase.

All

All that they saw, these miserable revellers, was the white figure of the Christ standing in the chastened light at the far end of the studio.   There had been a slight rattling sound—a curtain had been drawn, and then the beautiful form had stepped out and stood before them—the very type of manhood Christ had chosen, if pictures may be trusted, when He came to this earth: the pure forehead, the patient sorrowful eyes, reproach in the expression of the eyebrows and the mouth, the young beard and brown soft hair—in a word, the Nazarene.

When Dufour raised a wavering arm, and with a smile of drunken intelligence exclaimed, " Ah, c'est mon Jésus-Christ! Bonsoir, monsieur! " a renewed shiver of apprehension went round among the madly frightened people.   Then he rose, throwing off a cowering woman, staggering a little, holding to his chair, and turned to address to his guests a mock speech of introduction:

" Mesdames et Messieurs, je vous présente mon modèle, l'excellent Ladislas! "

When he had declaimed thus, rising superior to a thickened stammer, " La Coquelicotte," as the orange lady had at once been named, bounded from her chair with a scream.   It was the signal for a lightning change of emotion: the hysterics rose to an abandoned shout of uncontrollable laughter; the moaning woman raised her head; the men banged the table and exclaimed according to their mood.   One caught a handful of green stuff from a vase that had already been knocked over, and dashed them to the ground in front of the rock-still white figure.   The dark-haired woman—Wladislaw had not recognised her, and she wore shoes this time—laid her swollen hand upon Dufour's shoulder and cried harshly, " Va, Toni! Monsieur a besoin d'un âne! "

More screams greeted this pleasantry, and " La Coquelicotte "
flew

flew towards the figure with a *pas de cancan*; one arm tightened round his neck like a lasso.

Then his frozen quiet left him; there was a sort of fight between them.

An oath in his own tongue burst from him, but she twisted her fingers below his arms and dragged him towards the table, meeting every effort at resistance with a kiss. His head swam as he saw her face come close to him, its crooked mouth open, and the blank in her line of even teeth which was supposed to be a charm; her coarse hair seemed to singe his neck as it brushed upon him, and in a moment he was pushed into a chair at the table and received a handful of red rose-petals in his face from a woman opposite.

Dufour was murmuring some apologies about forgetting the appointment. He had been away; had come back in time for this supper, long arranged—a farewell to his old manner and his old loves; but Wladislaw barely listened. When " La Coqueli-cotte," sat upon his knee, he threatened to strike her, and then bethought him with shame that she was a woman.

He took a glass that was pushed to him, and drank to steady himself. It was Chartreuse they had given him—Chartreuse, more deadly and more insidious than pure spirit—and in a very little while his head failed him, and he remembered nothing after. Perhaps it was as well. The wild laughter and indecent jokes surged up hotter than before; every one strove to forget the stun of that terrible moment, when, at the jarring scrape of the curtain-rings upon their rod, the white figure of the Christ had interrupted them; when it had seemed, indeed, that the last day had come, that judgment and retribution, harsher than all hell to those taken in their sinning, had fallen on them as they shrieked and howled like human swine amid the refuse of their feast.

That

That was a moment they never forgot. It carried no lesson, it gave no warning, it altered nothing, and was of no use; but it frightened them, and they were not strong enough to wipe out its cold memory.

There is perhaps a moral in Wladislaw's story; if so, I have had no thought to write it. Certainly the world has turned and made mock, like those men and women, at the Christ-figure; and as I write I find myself wondering about the great promise which is still the Hope of some.

When He comes, if He is to come, will it be upon some such scene that He will choose to enter?

Castle Campbell,
    September, 1891.

A Dream of November

By Edmund Gosse

Far, far away, I know not where, I know not how,
   The skies are grey, the boughs are bare, bare boughs in
   flower:
Long lilac silk is softly drawn from bough to bough,
   With flowers of milk and buds of fawn, a broidered shower.

Beneath that tent an Empress sits, with slanted eyes,
   And wafts of scent from censers flit, a lilac flood;
Around her throne bloom peach and plum in lacquered dyes,
   And many a blown chrysanthemum, and many a bud.

She sits and dreams, while bonzes twain strike some rich bell,
   Whose music seems a metal rain of radiant dye;
In this strange birth of various blooms, I cannot tell
   Which spring from earth, which slipped from looms, which
   sank from sky.

Beneath her wings of lilac dim, in robes of blue,
   The Empress sings a wordless hymn that thrills her bower;
My trance unweaves, and winds, and shreds, and forms anew
   Dark bronze, bright leaves, pure silken threads, in triple flower.

Apple Blossom in Brittany

I

I T was the feast of the Assumption in Ploumariel, at the hottest
part of the afternoon. Benedict Campion, who had just
assisted at vespers, in the little dove-cotted church—like everything else in Ploumariel, even vespers were said earlier than is the
usage in towns—took up his station in the market-place to watch
the procession pass by. The head of it was just then emerging
into the Square : a long file of men from the neighbouring
villages, bare-headed and chaunting, followed the crucifer. They
were all clad in the picturesque garb of the Morbihan peasantry,
and were many of them imposing, quite noble figures with their
clear-cut Breton features, and their austere type of face. After
them a troop of young girls, with white veils over their heads,
carrying banners—children from the convent school of the
Ursulines ; and then, two and two in motley assemblage (peasant
women with their white coifs walking with the wives and
daughters of prosperous *bourgeois* in costumes more civilised but
far less pictorial) half the inhabitants of Ploumariel—all, indeed,
who had not, with Campion, preferred to be spectators, taking
refuge from a broiling sun under the grateful shadow of the chestnuts

311

nuts in the market-place. Last of all a muster of clergy, four or five strong, a small choir of bullet-headed boys, and the Curé of the parish himself, Monsieur Letêtre chaunting from his book, who brought up the rear.

Campion, leaning against his chestnut tree, watched them defile. Once a smile of recognition flashed across his face, which was answered by a girl in the procession. She just glanced from her book, and the smile with which she let her eyes rest upon him for a moment, before she dropped them, did not seem to detract from her devotional air. She was very young and slight—she might have been sixteen—and she had a singularly pretty face; her white dress was very simple, and her little straw hat, but both of these she wore with an air which at once set her apart from her companions, with their provincial finery and their rather common-place charms. Campion's eyes followed the little figure until it was lost in the distance, disappearing with the procession down a by-street on its return journey to the church. And after they had all passed, the singing, the last verse of the "Ave Maris Stella," was borne across to him, through the still air, the voices of children pleasantly predominating. He put on his hat at last, and moved away; every now and then he exchanged a greeting with somebody—the communal doctor, the mayor; while here and there a woman explained him to her gossip in whispers as he passed, " It is the Englishman of Mademoiselle Marie-Ursule—it is M. le Curé's guest." It was to the dwelling of M. le Curé, indeed, that Campion now made his way. Five minutes' walk brought him to it; an unpretentious white house, lying back in its large garden, away from the dusty road. It was an untidy garden, rather useful than ornamental; a very little shade was offered by one incongruous plane-tree, under which a wooden table was placed and some chairs. After *déjeûner*, on those hot August days,
Campion

Campion and the Curé took their coffee here ; and in the evening it was here that they sat and talked while Mademoiselle Hortense, the Curé's sister, knitted, or appeared to knit, an interminable shawl ; the young girl, Marie-Ursule, placidly completing the quartet with her silent, felicitous smile of a convent-bred child, which seemed sometimes, at least to Campion, to be after all a finer mode of conversation. He threw himself down now on the bench, wondering when his hosts would have finished their devotions, and drew a book from his pocket as if he would read. But he did not open it, but sat for a long time holding it idly in his hand, and gazing out at the village, at the expanse of dark pine-covered hills, and at the one trenchant object in the foreground, the white façade of the convent of the Ursuline nuns. Once and again he smiled, as though his thoughts, which had wandered a long way, had fallen upon extraordinarily pleasant things. He was a man of barely forty, though he looked slightly older than his age : his little, peaked beard was grizzled, and a life spent in literature, and very studiously, had given him the scholar's premature stoop. He was not handsome, but, when he smiled, his smile was so pleasant that people credited him with good looks. It brought, moreover, such a light of youth into his eyes, as to suggest that if his avocations had unjustly aged his body, that had not been without its compensations—his soul had remained remarkably young. Altogether, he looked shrewd, kindly and successful, and he was all these things, while if there was also a certain sadness in his eyes—lines of lassitude about his mouth—this was an idiosyncracy of his temperament, and hardly justified by his history, which had always been honourable and smooth. He was sitting in the same calm and presumably agreeable reverie, when the garden gate opened, and a girl—the young girl of the procession, fluttered towards him.

" Are

"Are you quite alone?" she asked brightly, seating herself at his side. "Has not Aunt Hortense come back?"

Campion shook his head, and she continued speaking in English, very correctly, but with a slight accent, which gave to her pretty young voice the last charm.

"I suppose she has gone to see *la mère Guémené*. She will not live another night they say. Ah! what a pity," she cried, clasping her hands; "to die on the Assumption—that is hard."

Campion smiled softly. "Dear child, when one's time comes, when one is old as that, the day does not matter much." Then he went on : "But how is it you are back ; were you not going to your nuns?"

She hesitated a moment. "It is your last day, and I wanted to make tea for you. You have had no tea this year. Do you think I have forgotten how to make it, while you have been away, as I forget my English words?"

"It's I who am forgetting such an English habit," he protested. "But run away and make it, if you like. I am sure it will be very good."

She stood for a moment looking down at him, her fingers smoothing a little bunch of palest blue ribbons on her white dress. In spite of her youth, her brightness, the expression of her face in repose was serious and thoughtful, full of unconscious wistfulness. This, together with her placid manner, the manner of a child who has lived chiefly with old people and quiet nuns, made her beauty to Campion a peculiarly touching thing. Just then her eyes fell upon Campion's wide-awake, lying on the seat at his side, and travelled to his uncovered head. She uttered a protesting cry : "Are you not afraid of a *coup de soleil?* See—you are not fit to be a guardian if you can be so foolish as that. It is I who have to look after you." She took up the great grey hat and

set

set it daintily on his head ; then with a little laugh she disappeared
into the house.

When Campion raised his head again, his eyes were smiling,
and in the light of a sudden flush which just died out of it, his
face looked almost young.

II

This girl, so foreign in her education and traditions, so foreign
in the grace of her movements, in everything except the shade of
her dark blue eyes, was the child of an English father ; and she
was Benedict Campion's ward. This relation, which many
persons found incongruous, had befallen naturally enough. Her
father had been Campion's oldest and most familiar friend ; and
when Richard Heath's romantic marriage had isolated him from so
many others, from his family and from his native land, Campion's
attachment to him had, if possible, only been increased. From
his heart he had approved, had prophesied nothing but good of an
alliance, which certainly, while it lasted, had been an wholly ideal
relation. There had seemed no cloud on the horizon—and yet
less than two years had seen the end of it. The birth of the
child, Marie-Ursule, had been her mother's death ; and six months
later, Richard Heath, dying less from any defined malady than
because he lacked any longer the necessary motive to live,
was laid by the side of his wife. The helpless child remained, in
the guardianship of Hortense, her mother's sister, and elder by
some ten years, who had already composed herself contentedly, as
some women do, to the prospect of perpetual spinsterhood, and the
care of her brother's house—an ecclesiastic just appointed curé of
Ploumariel. And here, ever since, in this quiet corner of Brittany,

in

n the tranquil custody of the priest and his sister, Marie-Ursule had grown up.

Campion's share in her guardianship had not been onerous, although it was necessarily maintained ; for the child had inherited, and what small property would come to her was in England, and in English funds. To Hortense Letêtre and her brother such responsibilities in an alien land were not for a moment to be entertained. And gradually, this connection, at first formal and impersonal, between Campion and the Breton presbytery, had developed into an intimacy, into a friendship singularly satisfying on both sides. Separate as their interests seemed, those of the French country-priest, and of the Englishman of letters, famous already in his own department, they had, nevertheless, much community of feeling apart from their common affection for a child. Now, for many years, he had been established in their good graces, so that it had become an habit with him to spend his holiday—it was often a very extended one—at Ploumariel ; while to the Letêtres, as well as to Marie-Ursule herself, this annual sojourn of Campion's had become the occasion of the year, the one event which pleasantly relieved the monotony of life in this remote village ; though that, too, was a not unpleasant routine. Insensibly Campion had come to find his chief pleasure in con-sideration of this child of an old friend, whose gradual growth beneath influences which seemed to him singularly exquisite and fine, he had watched so long ; whose future, now that her child-hood, her schooldays at the convent had come to an end, threatened to occupy him with an anxiety more intimate than any which hitherto he had known. Marie-Ursule's future ! They had talked much of it that summer, the priest and the Englishman, who accompanied him in his long morning walks, through green lanes, and over white, dusty roads, and past fields perfumed with

the

the pungently pleasant smell of the blood-red *sarrasin*, when he paid visits to the sick who lived on the outskirts of his scattered parish. Campion became aware then of an increasing difficulty in discussing this matter impersonally, in the impartial manner becoming a guardian. Odd thrills of jealousy stirred within him when he was asked to contemplate Marie-Ursule's possible suitors. And yet, it was with a very genuine surprise, at least for the moment, that he met the Curé's sudden pressing home of a more personal contingency—he took this freedom of an old friend with a shrewd twinkle in his eye, which suggested that all along this had been chiefly in his mind. " *Mon bon ami*, why should you not marry her yourself ? That would please all of us so much." And he insisted, with kindly insistence, on the propriety of the thing : dwelling on Campion's established position, their long habit of friendship, his own and his sister's confidence and esteem, taking for granted, with that sure insight which is the gift of many women and of most priests, that on the ground of affection alone the justification was too obvious to be pressed. And he finished with a smile, stopping to take a pinch of snuff with a sigh of relief— the relief of a man who has at least seasonably unburdened himself.

"Surely, *mon ami*, some such possibility must have been in your mind ? "

Campion hesitated for a moment ; then he proffered his hand, which the other warmly grasped. " You read me aright," he said slowly, "only I hardly realised it before. Even now—no, how can I believe it possible—that she should care for me. *Non sum dignus, non sum dignus*. Consider her youth, her inexperience ; the best part of my life is behind me."

But the Curé smiled reassuringly. " The best part is before you, Campion ; you have the heart of a boy. Do we not know
you ?

you ? And for the child—rest tranquil there ! I have the word of
my sister, who is a wise woman, that she is sincerely attached to
you ; not to speak of the evidence of my own eyes. She will be
seventeen shortly, then she can speak for herself. And to whom
else can we trust her ?

The shadow of these confidences hung over Campion when he
next saw Marie-Ursule, and troubled him vaguely during the
remainder of his visit, which this year, indeed, he considerably
curtailed. Inevitably he was thrown much with the young girl,
and if daily the charm which he found in her presence was
sensibly increased, as he studied her from a fresh point of view, he
was none the less disquieted at the part which he might be called
upon to play. Diffident and scrupulous, a shy man, knowing
little of women ; and at least by temperament, a sad man, he
trembled before felicity, as many at the palpable breath of misfortune. And his difficulty was increased by the conviction,
forced upon him irresistibly, little as he could accuse himself or
vanity, that the decision rested with himself. Her liking for him
was genuine and deep, her confidence implicit. He had but to
ask her and she would place her hand in his and go forth with
him, as trustfully as a child. And when they came to celebrate
her *fête*, Marie-Ursule's seventeenth birthday—it occurred a little
before the Assumption—it was almost disinterestedly that he had
determined upon his course. At least it was security which he
could promise her, as a younger man might not ; a constant and
single-minded kindness ; a devotion not the less valuable, because
it was mature and reticent, lacking, perhaps, the jealous ardours of
youth. Nevertheless, he was going back to England without
having revealed himself ; there should be no unseasonable haste in
the matter ; he would give her another year. The Curé smiled
deprecatingly at the procrastination ; but on this point Campion

was

was firm. And on this, his last evening, he spoke only of trivial things to Marie-Ursule, as they sat presently over the tea—a mild and flavourless beverage—which the young girl had prepared. Yet he noticed later, after their early supper, when she strolled up with him to the hill overlooking the village, a certain new shyness in her manner, a shadow, half timid, half expectant in her clear eyes which permitted him to believe that she was partly prepared. When they reached the summit, stood clear of the pine trees by an ancient stone Calvary, Ploumariel lay below them, very fair in the light of the setting sun ; and they stopped to rest themselves, to admire.

"Ploumariel is very beautiful," said Campion after a while. "Ah ! Marie-Ursule, you are fortunate to be here."

"Yes." She accepted his statement simply, then suddenly : "You should not go away." He smiled, his eyes turning from the village in the valley to rest upon her face : after all, she was the daintiest picture, and Ploumariel with its tall slate roofs, its sleeping houses, her appropriate frame.

"I shall come back, I shall come back," he murmured. She had gathered a bunch of ruddy heather as they walked, and her fingers played with it now nervously. Campion stretched out his hand for it. She gave it him without a word.

"I will take it with me to London," he said ; "I will have Morbihan in my rooms."

"It will remind you—make you think of us sometimes ? "

For answer he could only touch her hand lightly with his lips. "Do you think that was necessary ? " And they resumed their homeward way silently, although to both of them the air seemed heavy with unspoken words.

When

III

When he was in London—and it was in London that for nine months out of the twelve Benedict Campion was to be found—he lived in the Temple, at the top of Hare Court, in the very same rooms in which he had installed himself, years ago, when he gave up his Oxford fellowship, electing to follow the profession of letters. Returning there from Ploumariel, he resumed at once, easily, his old avocations. He had always been a secluded man, living chiefly in books and in the past ; but this year he seemed less than ever inclined to knock at the hospitable doors which were open to him. For in spite of his reserve, his diffidence, Campion's success might have been social, had he cared for it, and not purely academic. His had come to be a name in letters, in the higher paths of criticism ; and he had made no enemies. To his success indeed, gradual and quiet as this was, he had never grown quite accustomed, contrasting the little he had actually achieved with all that he had desired to do. His original work was of the slightest, and a book that was in his head he had never found time to write. His name was known in other ways, as a man of ripe knowledge, of impeccable taste ; as a born editor of choice reprints, of inaccessible classics : above all, as an authority—the greatest, upon the literature and the life (its flavour at once courtly, and mystical, had to him an unique charm) of the seventeenth century. His heart was in that age, and from much lingering over it, he had come to view modern life with a curious detachment, a sense of remote hostility : Democracy, the Salvation Army, the novels of M. Zola—he disliked them all impartially. A Catholic by long inheritance, he held his religion for something more than an

heirloom ;

heirloom ; he exhaled it, like an intimate quality ; his mind being essentially of that kind to which a mystical view of things comes easiest.

This year passed with him much as any other of the last ten years had passed ; at least the routine of his daily existence admitted little outward change. And yet inwardly, he was conscious of alteration, of a certain quiet illumination which was a new thing to him.

Although at Ploumariel when the prospect of such a marriage had dawned on him, his first impression had been one of strangeness, he could reflect now that it was some such possibility as this which he had always kept vaguely in view. He had prided himself upon few things more than his patience ; and now it appeared that this was to be rewarded ; he was glad that he had known how to wait. This girl, Marie-Ursule, had an immense personal charm for him, but, beyond that, she was representative—her traditions were exactly those which the ideal girl of Campion's imagination would possess. She was not only personally adorable ; she was also generically of the type which he admired. It was possibly because this type was, after all, so rare, that looking back, Campion in his middle age, could drag out of the recesses of his memory no spectre to compete with her. She was his first love precisely because the conditions, so choice and admirable, which rendered it inevitable for him to love her, had never occurred before. And he could watch the time of his probation gliding away with a pleased expectancy which contained no alloy of impatience. An illumination—a quite tranquil illumination : yes, it was under some such figure, without heart-burning, or adolescent fever, that love as it came to Campion was best expressed. Yet if this love was lucent rather than turbulent, that it was also deep he could remind himself, when a letter from the priest, while the spring was yet young, had sent him to Brittany, a month or two before his accustomed time, with an anxiety that was not solely due to bewilderment.

"*Our child is well, mon bon*," so he wrote. "*Do not alarm yourself. But it will be good for you to come, if it be only because of an idea she has, that you may remove. An idea! Call it rather a fancy—at least your coming will dispel it. Petites entêtées: I have no patience with these mystical little girls.*"

His musings on the phrase, with its interpretation varying to his mood, lengthened his long sea-passage, and the interminable leagues of railway which separated him from Pontivy, whence he had still some twenty miles to travel by the *Courrier*, before he reached his destination. But at Pontivy, the round, ruddy face of M. Letêtre greeting him on the platform dispelled any serious misgiving. Outside the post-office the familiar conveyance awaited them : its yellow inscription "Pontivy-Ploumariel," touched Campion electrically, as did the cheery greeting of the driver, which was that of an old friend. They shared the interior of the rusty trap—a fossil among vehicles—they chanced to be the only travellers, and to the accompaniment of jingling harness, and the clattering hoofs of the brisk little Carhaix horses, M. Letître explained himself.

"A vocation, *mon Dieu!* if all the little girls who fancied themselves with one, were to have their way, to whom would our poor France look for children? They are good women, *nos Ursulines*, ah, yes; but our Marie-Ursule is a good child, and blessed matrimony also is a sacrament. You shall talk to her, my Campion. It is a little fancy, you see, such as will come to young girls; a convent ague, but when she sees you" . . . He took snuff with emphasis, and flipped his broad fingers suggestively. "*Craque!* it is a betrothal, and a *trousseau*, and not the habit of religion, that Mademoiselle is full of. You will talk to her?"

Campion

Campion assented silently, absently, his eyes had wandered away, and looked through the little square of window at the sad-coloured Breton country, at the rows of tall poplars, which guarded the miles of dusty road like sombre sentinels. And the priest with a reassured air pulled out his breviary, and began to say his office in an imperceptible undertone. After a while he crossed himself, shut the book, and pillowing his head against the hot, shiny leather of the carriage, sought repose; very soon his regular, stertorous breathing, assured his companion that he was asleep. Campion closed his eyes also, not indeed in search of slumber, though he was travel weary; rather the better to isolate himself with the perplexity of his own thoughts. An indefinable sadness invaded him, and he could envy the priest's simple logic, which gave such short shrift to obstacles that Campion, with his subtle melancholy, which made life to him almost morbidly an affair of fine shades and nice distinctions, might easily exaggerate.

Of the two, perhaps the priest had really the more secular mind, as it certainly excelled Campion's in that practical wisdom, or common sense, which may be of more avail than subtlety in the mere economy of life. And what to the Curé was a simple matter though, the removal of the idle fancy of a girl, might be to Campion, in his scrupulous temper, and his overweening tender-ness towards just those pieties and renunciations which such a fancy implied, a task to be undertaken hardly with relish, perhaps without any real conviction, deeply as his personal wishes might be implicated in success. And the heart had gone out of his journey long before a turn of the road brought them in sight of Ploumariel.

Up

IV

Up by the great, stone Calvary, where they had climbed nearly a year before, Campion stood, his face deliberately averted, while the young girl uttered her hesitating confidences; hesitating, yet candid, with a candour which seemed to separate him from the child by more than a measurable space of years, to set him with an appealing trustfulness in the seat of judgment—for him, for her. They had wandered there insensibly, through apple-orchards white with the promise of a bountiful harvest, and up the pine-clad hill, talking of little things—trifles to beguile their way—perhaps, in a sort of vain procrastination. Once, Marie-Ursule had plucked a branch of the snowy blossom, and he had playfully chided her that the cider would be less by a *litre* that year in Brittany. "But the blossom is so much prettier," she protested; "and there will be apples and apples—always enough apples. But I like the blossom best—and it is so soon over."

And then, emerging clear of the trees, with Ploumariel lying in its quietude in the serene sunshine below them, a sudden strenuousness had supervened, and the girl had unburdened herself, speaking tremulously, quickly, in an undertone almost passionate; and Campion, perforce, had listened. . . . A fancy? A whim? Yes, he reflected; to the normal, entirely healthy mind, any choice of exceptional conditions, any special self-consecration or withdrawal from the common lot of men and women must draw down upon it some such reproach, seeming the mere pedantry of inexperience. Yet, against his reason, and what he would fain call his better judgment, something in his heart of hearts stirred sympathetically with this notion of the girl. And it was no fixed resolution, no
deliberate

deliberate justification which she pleaded. She was soft, and pliable, and even her plea for renunciation contained pretty, feminine inconsequences; and it touched Campion strangely. Argument he could have met with argument; an ardent conviction he might have assailed with pleading; but that note of appeal in her pathetic young voice, for advice, for sympathy, disarmed him.

"Yet the world," he protested at last, but half-heartedly, with a sense of self-imposture: "the world, Marie-Ursule, it has its disappointments; but there are compensations."

"I am afraid, afraid," she murmured.

Their eyes alike sought instinctively the Convent of the Ursulines, white and sequestered in the valley—a visible symbol of security, of peace, perhaps of happiness.

"Even there they have their bad days: do not doubt it."

"But nothing happens," she said simply; "one day is like another. They can never be very sad, you know."

They were silent for a time: the girl, shading her eyes with one small white hand, continued to regard the convent; and Campion considered her fondly.

"What can I say?" he exclaimed at last. "What would you put on me? Your uncle—he is a priest—surely the most natural adviser—you know his wishes."

She shook her head. "With him it is different—I am one of his family—he is not a priest for me. And he considers me a little girl—and yet I am old enough to marry. Many young girls have had a vocation before my age. Ah, help me, decide for me!" she pleaded; "you are my *tuteur*."

"And a very old friend, Marie-Ursule." He smiled rather sadly. Last year seemed so long ago, and the word, which he had almost spoken then, was no longer seasonable. A note in his
voice,

voice, inexplicable, might have touched her. She took his hand impulsively, but he withdrew it quickly, as though her touch had scalded him.

" You look very tired ; you are not used to our Breton rambles in this sun. See, I will run down to the cottage by the chapel and fetch you some milk. Then you shall tell me."

When he was alone the smile faded from his face and was succeeded by a look of lassitude, as he sat himself beneath the shadow of the Calvary to wrestle with his responsibility. Perhaps it was a vocation : the phrase, sounding strangely on modern ears, to him, at least, was no anachronism. Women of his race, from generation to generation, had heard some such voice and had obeyed it. That it went unheeded now was, perhaps, less a proof that it was silent, than that people had grown hard and deaf, in a world that had deteriorated. Certainly the convent had to him no vulgar, Protestant significance, to be combated for its intrinsic barbarism ; it suggested nothing cold nor narrow nor mean, was veritably a gracious choice, a generous effort after perfection. Then it was for his own sake, on an egoistic impulse, that he should dissuade her ? And it rested with him ; he had no doubt that he could mould her, even yet, to his purpose. The child ! how he loved her. . . . But would it ever be quite the same with them after that morning ? Or must there be henceforth a shadow between them ; the knowledge of something missed, of the lower end pursued, the higher slighted ? Yet, ir she loved him ? He let his head drop on his hands, murmured aloud at the hard chance which made him at once judge and advocate in his own cause. He was not conscious of praying, but his mind fell into that condition of aching blankness which is, perhaps, an extreme prayer. Presently he looked down again at Ploumariel, with its coronal of faint smoke ascending in the
perfectly

perfectly still air, at the white convent of the Dames Ursulines, which seemed to dominate and protect it. How peaceful it was! And his thoughts wandered to London : to its bustle and noise, its squalid streets, to his life there, to its literary coteries, its politics, its society ; vulgar and trivial and sordid they all seemed from this point of vantage. That was the world he had pleaded for, and it was into that he would bring the child. . . . And suddenly, with a strange reaction, he was seized with a sense of the wisdom of her choice, its pictorial fitness, its benefit for both of them. He felt at once and finally, that he acquiesced in it ; that any other ending to his love had been an impossible grossness, and that to lose her in just that fashion was the only way in which he could keep her always. And his acquiescence was without bitterness, and attended only by that indefinable sadness which to a man of his temper was but the last refinement of pleasure. He had renounced, but he had triumphed ; for it seemed to him that his renunciation would be an ægis to him always against the sordid facts of life, a protest against the vulgarity of instinct, the tyranny of institutions. And he thought of the girl's life, as it should be, with a tender appreciation—as of something precious laid away in lavender. He looked up to find her waiting before him with a basin half full of milk, warm still, fresh from the cow ; and she watched him in silence while he drank. Then their eyes met, and she gave a little cry.

"You will help me ? Ah, I see that you will ! And you think I am right ?"

"I think you are right, Marie-Ursule."

"And you will persuade my uncle ? "

"I will persuade him."

She took his hand in silence, and they stood so for a minute, gravely regarding each other. Then they prepared to descend.

The Rose

By Henry W. Nevinson

(A mediæval citizen speaks)

Stephen, clerk of Oxford town,
  Oh, the weary while he lies,
Wrapt in his old college gown,
  Burning, burning till he dies!
    And 'tis very surely said,
    He shall burn when he is dead,
    All aflame from foot to head.

Stephen said he knew a rose—
  One and two, yea, roses three—
Lovelier far than any those
  Which at service-time we see,
    Emblems of atonement done,
    And of Christ's belovèd One,
    And of Mary's mystic Son.

Stephen

Stephen said his roses grew
  All upon a milk-white stem,
Side by side together two,
  One a little up from them,
      Sweeter than the rose's breath,
      Rosy as the sun riseth,
      Warm beside; that was his death.

Stephen swore, as God knows well,
  Just to touch that topmost bud,
He would give his soul to hell—
  Soul and body, bones and blood,
      Hell has come before he dies;
      Burning, burning there he lies,
      But he neither speaks nor cries.

Ah, what might those roses be?
  Once, before the dawn was red,
Did he wander out to see
  If the rose were still a-bed?
      Did he find a rose-tree tall
      Standing by the garden wall?
      Did he touch the rose of all?

Stephen, was it worth the pain,
  Just to touch a breathing rose?
Ah, to think of it again,
  Look, he smiles despite his throes.
      Did he dream that hell would be
      Years hereafter?   Now, you see,
      Hell, is here, and where is she?

At

At my word, through all his face
Flames the infernal fire within,
Mary, Mary, grant me grace,
Still to keep my soul from sin!
    Thanks to God, my rose was grown
    Not so sweet, but all my own,
    Not so fair, but mine alone.

Mr. Stevenson's Forerunner

By James Ashcroft Noble

For a long time—I can hardly give a number to its years—I have been haunted by a spectre of duty. Of late the visitations of the haunter have recurred with increasing frequency and added persistence of appeal ; and though, like Hamlet, I have long dallied with the ghostly behest, like him I am at last compelled to obedience. Ghosts, I believe, have a habit of putting themselves in evidence for the purpose of demanding justice, and my ghost makes no display of originality : in this respect he follows the time-honoured example of his tribe, and if peace of mind is to return to me the exorcism of compliance must needs be uttered.

Emerson in one of his gnomic couplets proclaims his conviction that

> " One accent of the Holy Ghost
> This heedful world hath never lost "—

a saying which, shorn of its imaginative wings and turned into a pedestrian colloquialism, reads something like this—" What deserves to live the world will not let die." It is a comforting belief, yet there are times when Tennyson's vision of the " fifty seeds," out of which Nature " often brings but one to bear," seems nearer to the common truth of things ; and all the world's heedfulness

heedfulness will not exclude Oblivion with her poppies from some spot which should have been sacred to Fame with her amaranth and asphodel. Still there will always be those who will stretch out a hand to repel or evict the intruder—even as in Mr. Watts's noble allegory Love would bar the door against Death—and I would fain play my little part in one not inglorious eviction.

I want to write of a wholly-forgotten prose-man (forgotten, that is, by all save a solitary enthusiast here and there), but I must first speak of a half-forgotten singer. Only people who are on the shady side of middle-age can remember the intense enthusiasm excited by the first work of the young Glasgow poet, Alexander Smith. He had been discovered by that mighty hunter of new poets, the Rev. George Gilfillan ; and in the columns of Mr. Gilfillan's journal *The Critic* had been published a number of verses which whetted the appetite of connoisseurs in the early fifties for the maiden volume of a bard who, it was broadly hinted, might be expected to cast Keats into shadow. The prediction was a daring one ; but the fifties, like the nineties, were a hey-day of new reputations; and when that brilliant though somewhat amorphous work, *A Life Drama*, saw the light, a good many people, not wholly indiscriminating, were more than half inclined to think that it had been fulfilled. The performance of the new poet, taken as a whole, might be emotionally crude and intellectually ineffective, but its affluence in the matter of striking imagery was amazing, and the critical literature of the day was peppered with quotations of Alexander Smith's "fine passages." Very few people open *A Life Drama* now, though much time is spent over books that are a great deal poorer ; but if any reader, curious to know what kind of thing roused the admiration of connoisseurs in the years 1853-4, will spend an hour over the volume, he will come to the conclusion that it is a very remarkable

specimen

specimen of what may be called the decorative style of poetic
architecture.

> "An opulent soul
> Dropt in my path like a great cup of gold,
> All rich and rough with stories of the gods."

> "The sun is dying like a cloven king
> In his own blood ; the while the distant moon,
> Like a pale prophetess that he has wronged,
> Leans eager forward with most hungry eyes
> Watching him bleed to death, and, as he faints,
> She brightens and dilates ; revenge complete
> She walks in lonely triumph through the night."

> "My drooping sails
> Flap idly 'gainst the mast of my intent ;
> I rot upon the waters when my prow
> Should grate the golden isles."

> "The bridegroom sea
> Is toying with the shore, his wedded bride,
> And, in the fulness of his marriage joy,
> He decorates her tawny brow with shells,
> Retires a space to see how fair she looks,
> Then, proud, runs up to kiss her."

These and such things as these were what the admiring critics
loved to quote, and that they were indeed "fine passages" could not
be denied even by people whose tastes were for something a little
less gaudy. What was denied by those who were able to preserve
some calmness of judgment amid the storm of enthusiasm was
that this kind of fineness was the kind that goes to the making
of great poetry. The special fine things were ingenious, striking
and

and sometimes beautiful conceits ; they were notable *tours de force*
of poetic fancy ; but they bore little if any witness to that illuminating revealing imagination of which great poetry is all compact.
The young writer's images were happy discoveries of external and
accidental resemblances ; not revelations of inherent and inter-
pretative affinity.   Howsoever graceful and pretty in its way were
the figure which likened the sea and the shore to a bridegroom
and his bride, it gave no new insight into the daily mystery of the
swelling and ebbing tide—no such hint of a fine correspondence
between the things of sense and of spirit as is given in the really
imaginative utterance of Whitman :

" Surely whoever speaks to me in the right voice, him or her I shall
      follow,
  As the water follows the moon silently with fluid steps anywhere
      around the globe."

What was most characteristic therefore in the verse of Alexander Smith was a winning or arresting quality of fancy ; and, in
poetry, fancy, though not to be despised, exercises a subordinate
sway—" she is the second, not the first."   It may be that Smith
came to see this : it is more probable that he came to feel it, as a
man feels many things which he does not formulate in a clearly
outlined thought : at any rate, after the publication of *Edwin of
Deira*, his third volume of verse, he ceased almost entirely from
song, and chose as his favourite vehicle of expression a literary form
in which his special gift counted for more, and carried greater
weight of value, than it could ever count or carry in the poems
by which he first caught the world's ear.

And yet, curiously enough, while Smith's reputation as a poet
still lingers in a faint after-glow, the essays in which he expressed
                                                           himself

himself with so much more of adequacy and charm cannot be said to have won fame at all. They have had from the first their little circle of ardent admirers, but it has never widened; its circumference has never touched, never even approximated to, the circumference of that larger circle which includes all lovers of letters. To be unacquainted with Lamb or Hunt, Hazlitt or De Quincey, would be recognised as a regrettable limitation of any man's knowledge of English literature : non-acquaintance with Alexander Smith as a writer of prose is felt to be one of those necessary ignorances that can hardly be lamented because they are rendered inevitable by the shortness of life and the multiplicity of contending appeals. The fact that Smith as a poet achieved little more than a *succès d'estime* may have prejudiced his reputation as an essayist ; but whatever theory be constructed to account for it, recent literary history presents no more curious instance of utter refusal to really admirable work of deserved recognition and far-reaching fame.

For it must be noted and insisted upon that the essays of Alexander Smith are no mere caviare literature. They have neither the matter nor the manner of coterie performance—the kind of performance which appeals to an acquired sense, and gives to its admirer a certain pleasing consciousness of aloofness from the herd. He is in the true line of descent from the great predecessors just named ; and as they were his lineal forerunners, so are Mr. Robert Louis Stevenson and Mr. Richard Le Gallienne his lineal descendants. Indeed the name of Mr. Stevenson suggests, or rather re-suggests, a thought which is more or less familiar to most of us—that in the world of letters there are seasons uncongenial to certain growths of fame which in another spring and autumn might have blossomed and borne much fruit. Only by some such consideration is it possible to account for the

curious

curious fact that while *Virginibus Puerisque* and *Men and Books* found their audience at once, *Dreamthorp* and *Last Leaves* are still so largely unknown, and can now only be procured by diligent search of the catalogues of the second-hand booksellers.   The fact is all the more curious because Alexander Smith may be roughly described as a Stevenson born out of due time.   Roughly, of course, for the individuality of thinking and utterance which is so important in all pure literature is, in the essay, not only important but essential—the one thing needful, apart from which all other things are, comparatively speaking, of no account ; and in both Smith's work and Mr. Stevenson's the note of personality always rings clear and true.

Their essays are what the essay in its purest form always tends to be—the prose analogue of the song of self-expression, with its explicit or implicit autobiography, that touches us as we are never touched by external splendours of epic or drama.   In Montaigne, the father of the essay, the personal confession has an almost boyish incontinence of frankness : in Smith, as in all the modern men, it has more of reticence and reserve, but it is there all the time ; and even when the thought seems most abstract and impersonal the manner of its utterance has not the coldness of disquisition, but the warmth of colloquy.   We learn something of the secret of this quality of the work from a few sentences in which Smith discourses of his favourite craft and of his fellow-craftsmen.   Just as two or three of our best sonneteers—Wordsworth and Rossetti to wit—have written admirable sonnets in celebration of the sonnet, so Alexander Smith is seldom seen to greater advantage than in the pages where he magnifies his office and makes himself the essayist of the essay.

"The essay, as a literary form, resembles the lyric, in so far as it

is

is moulded by some central mood—whimsical, serious, or satirical.
Give the mood, and the essay, from the first sentence to the last, grows
around it as the cocoon grows around the silkworm. . . . . The essayist
is a kind of poet in prose, and if harshly questioned as to his uses, he
might be unable to render a better apology for his existence than a
flower might. The essay should be pure literature, as the poem is
pure literature. The essayist wears a lance, but he cares more for the
sharpness of its point than for the pennon that flutters upon it, than
for the banner of the captain under whom he serves. He plays with
death as Hamlet played with Yorick's skull, and he reads the morals—
strangely stern, often, for such fragrant lodging—which are folded up
in the bosoms of roses. He has no pride, and is deficient in a sense
of the congruity and fitness of things. He lifts a pebble from the
ground, and put it aside more carefully than any gem ; and on a nail
in a cottage door he will hang the mantle of his thought, heavily
brocaded with the gold of rhetoric."

It may be remarked in parenthesis that the above sentences
were published in 1863, and they provide what is probably the first
statement by an English writer with any repute of the famous
doctrine "Art for art's sake" to which Smith seems to have
worked his own way without the prompting of Gallican suggestion. Indeed, even in 1869, when Mr. Patrick Proctor
Alexander edited Smith's posthumous volume, *Last Leaves*, he
remarked in his introduction that he had thought of excluding
the essay entitled "Literary Work," in which the same doctrine
was more elaborately advocated, apparently on the ground that it
was a new heresy which might expose Smith to the pains and
penalties of literary excommunication. How curious it seems.
In ten years the essay which Mr. Alexander printed with an
apology became the accepted creed of all or nearly all the younger
men of letters in England, and now it is no longer either a
dangerous

dangerous luxury or an article of orthodox faith, but one of those uninteresting commonplaces which applied in one way is a truism, in another a fatuous absurdity. So does fortune turn her wheel for theories as well as for men and women.

In the passage just quoted Smith deals with the essay mainly as simple literature, but he loves and praises it not as literature only, but as autobiography; not merely as something that is in itself interesting and attractive, but as a window through which he can peer in upon something more interesting still—the master who built the house after his own design and made it an architectural projection of himself.

"You like to walk round peculiar or important men as you like to walk round a building, to view it from different points and in different lights. Of the essayist, when his mood is communicative, you obtain a full picture. You are made his contemporary and familiar friend. You enter into his humours and his seriousness. You are made heir of his whims, prejudices, and playfulness. You walk through the whole nature of him as you walk through the streets of Pompeii, looking into the interior of stately mansions, reading the satirical scribblings on the walls. And the essayist's habit of not only giving you his thoughts, but telling you how he came by them, is interesting, because it shows you by what alchemy the ruder world becomes transmuted into the finer. We like to know the lineage of ideas, just as we like to know the lineage of great earls and swift race-horses. We like to know that the discovery of the law of gravitation was born of the fall of an apple in an English garden on a summer afternoon. Essays written after this fashion are racy of the soil in which they grow, as you taste the lava in the vines grown on the slopes of Etna, they say. There is a healthy Gascon flavour in Montaigne's Essays; and Charles Lamb's are scented with the primroses of Covent Garden."

In

In the first of these passages Alexander Smith speaks of the mantle of the essayist's thought " heavily brocaded with the gold of rhetoric," and he himself was a cunning embroiderer. It was a gift of nature, but he did not learn at once how he could best utilise it. He brocaded his poetry, and on poetry brocade even of gold is an impertinence, just as is paint—*pace* Gibson—on the white marble of the sculptured group or figure. In the essay he found a form which relies less exclusively upon body of imagination and perfectness of pure outline—which is more susceptible to legitimate adornment by the ornamentation of a passing fancy. It is a form in which even the conceit is not unwelcome : to use the language of science the conceit finds in the essay its fit environment. Thus, in Smith's pages Napoleon dies at St. Helena " like an untended watch-fire " ; Ebenezer Elliot, the Corn Law rhymer, is " Apollo, with iron dust upon his face, wandering among the Sheffield knife-grinders " ; the solitary Dreamthorp doctor has a fancy for arguing with the good simple clergyman, but though " he cannot resist the temptation to hurl a fossil at Moses," " he wears his scepticism as a coquette wears her ribbons—to annoy if he cannot subdue—and when his purpose is served, he puts aside his scepticism—as the coquette puts her ribbons." When the black funeral creeps into Dreamthorp from some outlying hamlet, the people reverently doff their hats and stand aside, for, as Smith puts it, " Death does not walk about here often, but when he does, he receives as much respect as the squire himself." There is, in this last sentence, a touch of quiet Addisonian irony ; and, indeed, Smith reminds us at times of almost all his great predecessors in the art of essay-writing—of his prime favourites Montaigne and Bacon (" our earliest essayists and our best " is his own eulogium) ; and also of Addison, Steele, Lamb, Hazlitt, and Leigh Hunt. But it is never a reminder
that

that brings with it a suggestion of imitation. The methods and graces of these distinguished forerunners are to be found in Smith's pages only by patient analysis, and then never in their crude state, for his personality fuses them into a new amalgam and stamps them with a new hall-mark.

Perhaps the most purely individual qualities of Smith's work are given to it partly by his remarkable aptitude for the presentation of his thought in simile and metaphor ; partly by his fine feeling for colour, and, indeed, for all the elements of picturesqueness ; and partly by a native tendency to sombreness of reflection which makes such a theme as that of the essay, " On Death and the Fear of Dying," attractive rather than repellant, or—to speak, perhaps, with greater accuracy—repellant, yet irresistibly fascinating, as is the eye of the rattlesnake to its prey. The image-making endowment makes itself manifest in almost every passage that it would be possible to quote as characteristic ; and it may be noted that the associative habit of mind betrays itself not merely in the sudden simile which transfixes a resemblance on the wing, but in the numerous pages in which Smith showed his love for tracing the links of the chain that connects the near and the far, the present and the past, the seen and the unseen. Thus he writes in his Dreamthorp cottage :

"That winter morning when Charles lost his head in front of the banqueting-hall of his own palace, the icicles hung from the eaves of the houses here, and the clown kicked the snowballs from his clouted shoon, and thought but of his supper when at three o'clock the red sun set in the purple mist. On that Sunday in June, while Waterloo was going on, the gossips, after morning service, stood on the country roads discussing agricultural prospects, without the slightest suspicion that the day passing over their heads would be a famous one in the calendar. . . . The last setting sun that Shakespeare saw reddened the
windows

windows here, and struck warmly on the faces of the hinds coming home from the fields. The mighty storm that raged while Cromwell lay a-dying, made all the oak-woods groan round about here, and tore the thatch from the very roofs that I gaze upon. When I think of this I can almost, so to speak, lay my hand upon Shakespeare and upon Cromwell. These poor walls were contemporaries of both, and I find something affecting in the thought. The mere soil is, of course, full older than either, but *it* does not touch one in the same way. A wall is the creation of a human hand ; the soil is not."

Smith's picturesqueness is fully in evidence here, though the passage was not quoted to illustrate it. Indeed, there are few writers who satisfy so largely the visual sense of the imagination. Even his literary appraisements—witness the essays on Dunbar and Chaucer, and that charming paper "A Shelf in my Book-case "—have a pictorial quality, as if he must *see* something as well as *think* something. Here is Dreamthorp where the essayist, the transfigured Alexander Smith—"Smith's Smith " as the Autocrat of the Breakfast-table would put it—lives his ideal life :

"This place suits my whim, and I like it better year after year. As with everything else, since I began to love it I find it growing beautiful. Dreamthorp—a castle, a chapel, a lake, a straggling strip of grey houses, with a blue film of smoke over all—lies embosomed in emerald. Summer with its daisies runs up to every cottage door. From the little height where I am now sitting I see it beneath me. Nothing could be more peaceful. The wind and the birds fly over it. A passing sunbeam makes brilliant a white gable-end, and brings out the colours of the blossomed apple-tree beyond, and disappears. I see figures in the street, but hear them not. The hands on the church clock seem always pointing to one hour. Time has fallen asleep in the afternoon sunshine. I make a frame of my fingers and look at my

my picture. On the walls of the next Academy's exhibition will
hang nothing half so beautiful."

This is the *tout ensemble*, but every detail has its own pictorial
charm.   There is the canal—a prosaic unpicturesque thing is a
canal; but this particular canal has "a great white water-lily
asleep on its olive-coloured face," while to the picture-making eye
" a barge trailing up through it in the sunset is a pretty sight;
and the heavenly crimsons and purples sleep quite lovingly upon
its glossy ripples.   Nor does the evening star disdain it, for as I
walk along I see it mirrored as clearly as in the waters of the
Mediterranean itself."

The sombreness of reflection noted as one of the characteristic
features of Smith's work as an essayist gives to that work a
recognisable autumnal feeling.   It is often difficult to think of
it as the work of a young man full of the ordinary buoyant life of
youth; though when the difficulty presents itself one may remember
also that the young man was destined to die at thirty-seven—that
fatal age for the children of imagination—and it is, perhaps, not
too fanciful to indulge the thought that some presentiment of early
doom may have given to Smith's meditative moods much of their
pensive seriousness.   However this may be, it is certain that
Alexander Smith, with a constancy which the most careless reader
cannot fail to note, recurred again and again, both when opportunity offered and when opportunity had to be made, to the theme
of death, its mystery, its fear, and its fascination.   In one of his
poems, which I quote from memory, he speaks of his life as a
highway which, at some unknown point, has his grave cut across;
and even in the joyous " Spring Chanson " the poet, addressing the
singing merle, drops suddenly from the major into the minor key,
and ends upon the note by which the key is dominated:

" Men

"Men live and die, the song remains ; and when
   I list the passion of thy vernal breath
   Methinks thou singest best to Love and Death—
To happy Lovers and to dying Men."

Autumn and death must needs be naturally allied in human
thought, though to the joyous-minded even autumn will be
associated with its present fruitage rather than with its presage of
dissolution ; but this intrusion of death into a celebration of the
life and growth of spring seems irrelevant, almost morbid : it may
even seem artificial, as if the poet were deliberately striving after a
strong literary effect by the expedient of an unnatural juxtaposition
of incongruous ideas. To a man of Smith's mind and temperament it has certainly neither irrelevance nor artificiality ; whether
we can rightly call it morbid depends upon the meaning we
attach to a word to which the personal feeling rather than the
common reason gives a definition. Smith's habit was to endeavour
to realise death that he might more fully and richly realise life.
"To denude death of its terrible associations," he writes, "were
a vain attempt, the atmosphere is always cold around an iceberg";
and yet in imagination he loves to draw near the iceberg for some
shivering moments that he may enjoy more exquisitely the warmth
of summer sun or piled-up winter fire. To his constant thought

"There are considerations which rob death of its ghastliness, and
help to reconcile us to it. The thoughtful happiness of a human being
is complex, and in certain moved moments which, after they have gone,
we can recognise to have been our happiest, some subtle thought of
death has been curiously intermixed. And this subtle admixture it is
that gives the happy moment its character—which makes the difference
between the gladness of a child, resident in mere animal health and
impulse, and too volatile to be remembered, and the serious joy of a
                                                            man

man who looks before and after, and takes in both this world and the next. Speaking broadly, it may be said that it is from some obscure recognition of the fact of death that life draws its final sweetness. . . . . This recognition does not always terrify. The spectre has the most cunning disguises, and often when near us, we are unaware of the fact of proximity. Unsuspected, this idea of death lurks in the sweetness of music ; it has something to do with the pleasure with which we behold the vapour of morning ; it comes between the passionate lips of lovers ; it lives in the thrill of kisses. "An inch deeper, and you will find the emperor." Probe joy to its last fibre and you will find death."

To preserve always in the background of the mind some great thought or momentous interest, tends to ensure a certain fine justice in a man's estimate of the relative proportions of smaller things lying in the front of it, and Alexander Smith's essays have a restful quality of measure, balance, and sanity. In the "Essay on an Old Subject," published in *Last Leaves*, the young man who had but recently gone into the thirties writes with imaginative prescience—or possibly from a premature experience—of the joys and gains of middle-age (by which he means the forty-fifth year or thereabouts) ; and there is in most of his essays, especially in the *Dreamthorp* papers which came earliest, a middle-aged maturity which charms and satisfies, and never disturbs. But it is not a middle-age which has ossified into routine and become dead to youth's enthusiasms—witness the fine ardour of the concluding sentence of the essay in which he "memorises" Carlyle's appearance at Edinburgh to deliver his Rectorial address : "When I saw him for the first time stand up amongst us the other day, and heard him speak kindly, brotherly, affectionate words . . . . I am not ashamed to confess that I felt moved towards him as I do not think, in any possible combination of circumstances, I could have felt

felt moved towards any other living man." And yet, though he has
not lost youths ardour, he has freed himself from youth's arrogant
impatience; he can be moved by enthusiasms, but not driven helplessly before them; he can protect himself from himself and survey
his own thought " in the round "; he has learned the lessons of
Clough's pregnant words, " and yet—consider it again." At the
same time his manner is never that tantalising, irritating manner
of explicit guards, reserves, limitations—the manner of the writer
who is always making himself safe by the sudden "but" or
"nevertheless" or "notwithstanding." The due limitation is conveyed implicitly, in the primal statement of the thought—in the
touch of irony or humorous extravagance which hints with
sufficing clearness that this or that is not to be interpreted *au pied
de la lettre.* The delightful essay " On Vagabonds," at the close of
the *Dreamthorp* volume, might be described roughly as a glorifica-
tion of the life of Bohemia, and an impeachment, or at any rate a
depreciation of commonplace Philistine respectability. In dealing
with such a theme with such a bent of mind, the temptation to
force the note, to overcharge the colour, would be to most men—
to all young men, impatient of restricting conventions—well-nigh
irresistible; but Smith resists it with no apparent effort of
resistance. There is no holding of himself in lest he should speak
unadvisedly with his tongue; on the contrary, he lets himself go
with perfect abandonment. The " genuine vagabond," he says,
" takes captive the heart," and he declares it " high time that a
moral game law were passed for the preservation of the wild and
vagrant feelings of human nature "; but just when we expect the
stroke of exaggeration there comes instead the light touch of saving
humour, and we know that the essayist is in less danger even than
we of losing his head, or, as the expressive cant phrase has it,
" giving himself away."

Some

Some of the few (and if I could succeed in increasing their number I should be greatly content) who know Alexander Smith's prose well, and love it even as they know, have probably favourite papers or favourite groups. Some may feel especially drawn to the essays of pure reflection, such as "Death and the fear of Dying" and "The importance of a Man to himself"; others to that delightful group in which the familiar simplicities of nature supply texts for tranquil meditation—"Dreamthorp," "Christmas," and "Books and Gardens," in which last there is also some delightful character-portraiture in the vignettes of the village doctor and clergyman; others to the essays in literary appreciation, such as "Dunbar," "Geoffrey Chaucer," "Scottish Ballads," and "A Shelf in my Bookcase." In the words applied by Charles Lamb, with a certain free unscrupulousness to the whole world of books, I must say with regard to Alexander Smith's essays, "I have no preferences." To me they all have a charm which somewhat dulls the edge of discrimination, for the writer rather than the theme is the centre of interest; he is the hero of the play, and he is never off the stage. Still in some torture chamber of inquiry certain names might be extracted from me, and I think they would be "Dreamthorp," "Books and Gardens," and "A Lark's Flight." This last study, which has not been previously named, is one of the most noteworthy of Smith's essays, and will be grateful to the more lazy readers inasmuch as it tells a story. It is the story of a murder and an execution, the murder vulgar and commonplace enough—a crime of brutal violence, the execution a sombrely picturesque function, with one striking incident which seized and held the imagination of the boy who witnessed it; and the story is told with an arresting vividness to which I know only one parallel in English literature, the narrative appendix to De Quincey's famous essay,
"On

"On Murder, considered as one of the Fine Arts." The execution took place, after the old custom in Scotland, on the spot where the crime had been committed—a lonely stretch of grassland, some distance outside the city of Glasgow. The criminals were Irish navvies, members of a large gang employed in the neighbourhood, and as there were some rumours of a rescue, a detachment of cavalry, supplemented by field-pieces, surrounded the scaffold. Of the scene itself, and the one occurrence round which its latent pathos crystallised, Smith gives the recollections of boyhood. The men were being brought in a cart to the place of execution, and when they reached the turn of the road where they could first see the black cross-beam with its empty halters, the boy noted the eager, fascinated gaze the doomed men cast upon it. At last the place was reached, and Smith writes :

"Around it a wide space was kept clear by the military ; the cannon were placed in position ; out flashed the swords of the dragoons ; beneath and around on every side was the crowd. Between two brass helmets I could see the scaffold clearly enough, and when in a little while the men, bareheaded and with their attendants, appeared upon it, the surging crowd became stiffened with fear and awe. And now it was that the incident, so simple, so natural, so much in the ordinary course of things, and yet so frightful in its tragic suggestions, took place. Be it remembered that the season was early May, that the day was fine, that the wheatfields were clothing themselves in the green of the young crop, and that around the scaffold, standing on a sunny mound, a wide space was kept clear. When the men appeared beneath the beam, each under his own proper halter, there was a dead silence,—every one was gazing too intently to whisper to his neighbour even. Just then, out of the grassy space at the foot of the scaffold, in the dead silence audible to all, a lark rose from the side of its nest, and went singing upward in its happy flight. O heaven ! how did
that

that song translate itself into dying ears? Did it bring, in one wild burning moment, father and mother, and poor Irish cabin, and prayers said at bedtime, and the smell of turf fires, and innocent sweet-hearting, and rising and setting suns? Did it—but the dragoon's horse has become restive, and his helmet bobs up and down and blots everything; and there is a sharp sound, and I feel the great crowd heave and swing, and hear it torn by a sharp shiver of pity, and the men whom I saw so near but a moment ago are at immeasurable distance, and have solved the great enigma,—and the lark has not yet finished his flight: you can see and hear him yonder in the fringe of a white May cloud. . . . . There is a stronger element of terror in this incident of the lark than in any story of a similar kind I can remember.

Gasps of admiration are amateurish, provincial, ineffective, but after reading such a passage as this, the words that come first—at any rate to me—are not in the least critical but simply exclama-tory. It is wonderful writing! Then comes a calmer and more analytical moment in which one discovers something of the secret of the art in what has seemed at first not art at all but sheer nature. Mr. Pater, in one of his most instructive essays, has shown that the "classical" element in art is "the quality of order in beauty," and that "it is that addition of strangeness to beauty that con-stitutes the romantic character," romantic art at its best being moreover distinguished by a fine perfection of workmanship. This surely then is an impressive miniature example of romantic art with its combination of strangeness and beauty, and its flaw-less technique—its absolute saturation of the vehicle of expression with the very essence of the thing, the emotion that is to be expressed. Note the directness and simplicity of the early narrative sentences; they are a mere recital of facts, and their very baldness only mitigated by a single emotional phrase, "the

surging

surging crowd became stiffened with fear and awe," prepares the
mind for what is to follow. And then, the sudden break in the
second sentence beginning "Did it,"—how perfectly natural it
seems, and yet how dexterous it really is; how it renders perfectly
and at a single stroke what the best-chosen words of narrative
would have rendered jumblingly, the brevity of the interval
between the lark's rising and the consummation of doom—the
sharp bewildering suddenness of the end. Then, lastly, the
curious in these things may notice a certain peculiarity in the
construction of the concluding sentence of the story—the penultimate sentence of the quotation. There are in the volume barely
nine lines, and in these lines the word "and" occurs eleven times.
All frequent and close repetitions of a single word are generally
avoided by good writers, and the repetition of an insignificant
conjunction such as "and" is, as a rule, something to be specially
avoided. Smith habitually avoided as carefully as any of us, but
here he had to give the feeling of impetuosity, of eager hurry to
get the ghastly story told, and the "and" which rapidly accumu-
lates detail upon detail recurs as naturally and inevitably as in the
voluble speech of a little child bursting into her mother's room
with some marvellous recital of adventure encountered in her
morning walk. This is the high literary art which instinctively
and perfectly adapts the means of language—of word, sound, pause,
and cadence—to the end of absolute expression.

Alexander Smith himself is never wearisome; and it would ill
become me to weary those whom I would fain interest by sur-
plusage of comment; but I should like to add a word or two concerning those essays in which he appears as a critic of literature.
Mr. Oscar Wilde has said that all good criticism is simply autobiography—that is, I suppose, a statement of personal preferences. I accept the definition if I may enlarge it by saying
that

that criticism is not merely a statement of personal preferences but of justifications for such preferences presented with a view to persuasion. Of course even with this rider the definition still leaves autobiography the main element in criticism, and of such autobiographical appraisement Smith was a master. Whether he formulated the rule never to write of any authors whose work he did not enjoy I cannot say : he certainly acted upon it with the most delightful results. So keen in his gusto, so adequate and appetising his expression of it, that one may dare to say the next best thing to reading Montaigne, Bacon, Chaucer, and the Scottish Ballads, is to read what Alexander Smith has to say about them. His talk about books is always so human that it will delight people whom one would not think of calling literary. He discourses on *The Canterbury Tales* not as a man weighing and measuring a book, but as a wayfarer sitting in the inn-yard of the Tabard at Southwark, watching the crowd of pilgrims with the eye of an acute and good-natured observer, taking notes of their appearance, and drawing from it shrewd inferences as to habit and character. He has certain favourite volumes upon which he expatiates in the essay entitled " A Shelf in my Bookcase "; and the principle of selection is obvious enough. They are books full of a rich humanity ; beneath their paragraphs or stanzas he can feel the beating heart. The literary vesture is *simply* a vesture which half reveals and half conceals the objects of his love—the man or woman who lives and breathes behind. He reveals in the old Scotch ballads and German hymns, for in them the concealing veil is thin, and the thoughts and loves and pains of simple souls in dead centuries are laid open and bare. He prefers Hawthorne's *Twice-told Tales* to his longer and more elaborate works, such as *Transformation* and *The Scarlet Letter*, because he finds more of the man in them, the solitary author who had no public to think of, of, and who wrote because he must. He has a genuine catholicity, but it is not that uninteresting catholicity which lacks defined circumferences ; and his general sensibility to excellence is emphasised by frank confession of his limitations. The author of *Paradise Lost* evidently lies a little outside the reach of Alexander Smith's tentacles of sympathy.

"Reading Milton is like dining off gold plate in a company of kings ; very splendid, very ceremonious, and not a little appalling. Him I read but seldom, and only on high days and festivals of the spirit. Him I never lay down without feeling my appreciation increased for lesser men—never without the same kind of comfort that one returning from the presence feels when he doffs respectful attitude and dress of ceremony, and subsides into old coat, familiar arm-chair, and slippers. After long-continued organ-music the jangle of the Jew's harp is felt as an exquisite relief."

There is a trace of Philistinism here—the Philistinism which is not ashamed but rather complacent ; and it may seem a strange whim on the part of one who loves Smith's work to choose as a final sample of it a passage which, some of the elect may think, does not show him at his best. But Danton's commendation of audacity, though not universally valid, is a word of wisdom to the advocate with a strong case. Alexander Smith's best is good with such a rare and delightful quality of goodness that his appreciator shows no great temerity in abandoning all reserves and concealments. He is not afraid of painting the wart, because it is overpowered by strength of feature and charm of expression. Alexander Smith, as he shows himself in his prose—in *Dreamthorp*, in *Last Leaves*, and in that entrancing book *A Summer in Skye*—is one of those writers concerning whom even a lover may tell not only the truth, but the whole truth. For myself, I read his essays when I was young and
                                                           found

found them full of stimulation; I have read them again since I have become middle-aged, and have found them satisfyingly rest-giving.   At no time have they been found wanting in something of rare and delicate delight.   If criticism be indeed autobiography, no verdict upon the essays of Alexander Smith could well be at, once more critical or more praiseful than this confession.   I love Mr. Stevenson and my later contemporaries; but I think I must confess that I love my early contemporary, Mr. Stevenson's countryman and forerunner, better still.

The Fool's Hour
The First Act of a Comedy

By John Oliver Hobbes
and George Moore

CHARACTERS OF THE COMEDY

Lord Doldrummond
Cyril, *his Son* (Viscount Aprile)
Sir Digby Soame
Charles Mandeville, *a tenor*
Mr. Banish, *a banker*
The Hon. Arthur Featherleigh
Mr. Samuel Benjamin, *a money-lender*
Lady Doldrummond
Julia, *an heiress*
The Hon. Mrs. Howard de Trappe, *her mother,
    a widow*
Sarah Sparrow, *an American prima donna*

Act

Act I

Scene—*The Library in* Lord Doldrummond's *house at Brighton. The scene represents a richly-furnished but somewhat oppressive room. The chairs and tables are all narrow, the lamp-shades stiff, the windows have double glasses.* Lord Doldrummond, *a man of middle-age, handsome, but with a dejected, browbeaten air, sits with a rug over his knees, reading "The Church Times."* The Butler *announces* "Sir Digby Soame." Sir Digby *is thin and elderly; has an easy smile and a sharp eye; dresses well; has two manners—the abrupt with men, the suave with women; smiles into his beard over his own witticisms.*

Lord Dol. Ah, Soame, so you are here at last?

Soame. [*Looking at his watch.*] I am pretty punctual, only a few minutes late.

Lord Dol. I am worried, anxious, irritable, and that has made the time seem long.

Soame. Worried, anxious? And what about? Are you not well? Have you found that regularity of life ruins the constitution?

Lord Dol. No, my dear Soame, no. But I am willing to own that the existence which my wife enjoys, and which I have learnt to endure, would not suit every one.

Soame. I am glad to find you more tolerant. You used to hold the very harshest and most crude opinions. I remember when we were boys, I could never persuade you to accept the admirable doctrine that a reformed rake makes the best husband!

Lord Dol. [*Timidly.*] Repentance does not require so large an income as folly! This may explain that paradox. You know, in
my

my way, I, too, am something of a philosopher! I married very young, whereas you entered the Diplomatic Service and resolved to remain single: you wished to study women. I have lived with one for five-and-twenty years. [*Sighs.*]

Soame. Oh, I admit at once that yours is the greater achievement and was the more daring ambition.

Lord Dol. I know all I wish to know about women, but men puzzle me extremely. So I have sent for you. I want your advice. It is Cyril who is the cause of my uneasiness. I am afraid that he is not happy.

Soame. Cyril not happy? What is he unhappy about? You have never refused him anything?

Lord Dol. Never! No man has had a kinder father! When he is unreasonable I merely say " You are a fool, but please yourself! " No man has had a kinder father!

Soame. Does he complain?

Lord Dol. He has hinted that his home is uncongenial—yet we have an excellent cook! Ah, thank heaven every night and morning, my dear Digby, that you are a bachelor. Praying for sinners and breeding them would seem the whole duty of man. I was no sooner born than my parents were filled with uneasiness lest I should not live to marry and beget an heir of my own. Now I have an heir, his mother will never know peace until she has found him a wife!

Soame. And will you permit Lady Doldrummond to use the same method with Cyril which your mother adopted with such appalling results in your own case?

Lord Dol. It does not seem my place to interfere, and love-affairs are not a fit subject of conversation between father and son!

Soame. But what does Cyril say to the matrimonial prospect?

Lord

Lord Dol. He seems melancholy and eats nothing but oranges. Yes, Cyril is a source of great uneasiness.

Soame. Does Lady Doldrummond share this uneasiness?

Lord Dol. My wife would regard a second thought on any subject as a most dangerous form of temptation. She insists that Cyril has everything which a young man could desire, and when he complains that the house is dull, she takes him for a drive!

Soame. But *you* understand him?

Lord Dol. I think I do. If I were young again——

Soame. Ah, you regret! I always said you would regret it if you did not take your fling! The pleasures we imagine are so much more alluring, so much more dangerous, than those we experience. I suppose you recognise in Cyril the rascal you might have been, and feel that you have missed your vocation?

Lord Dol. [*Meekly.*] I was never unruly, my dear Soame. We all have our moments, I own, yet—well, perhaps Cyril has inherited the tastes which I possessed at his age, but lacked the courage to obey.

Soame. And so you wish me to advise you how to deal with him! Is he in love? I have constantly observed that when young men find their homes unsympathetic, it is because some particular lady does not form a member of the household. It is usually a lady, too, who would not be considered a convenient addition to any mother's visiting-list!

Lord Dol. Lady Doldrummond has taught him that women are the scourges of creation. You, perhaps, do not share that view!

Soame. Certainly not. I would teach him to regard them as the reward, the compensation, the sole delight of this dreariest of all possible worlds.

Lord Dol. [*Uneasily.*] Reward! Compensation! Delight! I
beg

beg you will not go so far as that. What notion would be more upsetting? Pray do not use such extreme terms!

Soame. Ha! ha! But tell me, Doldrummond, is it true that your wife insists on his retiring at eleven and rising at eight? I hear that she allows him nothing stronger than ginger ale and lemon; that she selects his friends, makes his engagements, and superintends his amusements? Should he marry, I am told she will even undertake the office of best man!

Lord Dol. Poor soul! she means well; and if devotion could make the boy a saint he would have been in heaven before he was out of his long clothes. As it is, I fear that nothing can save him.

Soame. Save him? You speak as though you suspected that he was not such a saint as his mother thinks him.

Lord Dol. I suspect nothing. I only know that my boy is unhappy. You might speak to him, and draw him out if occasion should offer—but do not say a word about this to Lady Doldrummond.

[*Enter* Lady Doldrummond.—*She is a tall, slight, but not angular woman. Her hair is brown, and brushed back from her temples in the simplest possible fashion. Self-satisfaction (of a gentle and ladylike sort) and eminent contentment with her lot are the only writings on her smooth, almost girlish countenance. She has a prim tenderness and charm of manner which soften her rather cutting voice.*]

Lady Dol. What! Cyril not here? How do you do, Sir Digby? I am looking for my tiresome boy. I promised to take him to pay some calls this afternoon, and as he may have to talk I must tell him what to say. He has no idea of making himself pleasant to women, and is the shyest creature in the world!

Soame. You have always been so careful to shield him from all responsibility,

responsibility, Lady Doldrummond. Who knows what eloquence, what decision, what energy he might display, if you did not possess these gifts in so pre-eminent a degree as to make any exertion on his part unnecessary, and perhaps disrespectful.

Lady Dol. Ah! mothers are going out of fashion. Even Cyril occasionally shows a certain impatience when I venture to correct him. As if I would hurt any one's feelings unless from a sense of duty! And pray, where is the pleasure of having a son if you may not direct his life ?

Lord Dol. Cyril might ask, where is the pleasure of having parents if you may not disobey them.

Lady Dol. [*To* Soame.] When Herbert is alone with me he never makes flippant remarks of this kind. [*To* Lord Doldrummond.] I wonder that you like to give your friends such a wrong impression of your character. [*Turning to* Sir Digby.] But I think I see your drift, Sir Digby. You wish to remind me that Cyril is now at an age when I must naturally desire to see him established in a home of his own.

Soame. You have caught my meaning. As he is now two-and-twenty, I think he should be allowed more freedom than may have been expedient when he was—say, six months old.

Lady Dol. I quite agree with you, and I trust you will convince Herbert that women understand young men far better than their fathers ever could. I have found the very wife for Cyril, and I hope I may soon have the pleasure of welcoming her as a daughter.

Soame. A wife! Good heavens! I was suggesting that the boy had more liberty. Marriage is the prison of all emotions, and I should be very sorry to ask any young girl to be a man's gaol-keeper.

Lord Dol. Sir Digby is right.

Lady

Lady Dol. The presence of a third person has the strangest effect on Herbert's moral vision.   As I have trained my son with a care and tenderness rarely bestowed nowadays even on a girl, I think I may show some resentment when I am asked to believe him a being with the instincts of a ruffian and the philosophy of a middle-aged bachelor.   No, Sir Digby, Cyril is not *my* child if he does not make his home and his family the happiest in the world!

Soame. Yes?

Lady Dol. He has no taste for cards, horses, brandy, or actresses. We read together, walk together, and drive together.   In the evening, if he is too tired to engage in conversation, I play the piano while he dozes.   Lately he has taken a particular interest in Mozart's classic light opera.   Any interest of that kind is so elevating, and I know of nothing more agreeable than a musical husband.

Lord Dol. You see she is resolved on his marriage, and she has had Julia de Trappe on a visit with us for the last five weeks in the hope of bringing matters to a crisis.

Lady Dol. And why not?   Our marriage was arranged for us, and what idle fancies of our own could have led to such perfect contentment?

[Lord Doldrummond *avoids her eyes.*]

Soame. Julia de Trappe?   She must be the daughter of that Mrs. Howard de Trappe who gives large At Homes in a small house, and who spends her time hunting for old lovers and new servants.

Lady Dol. I own that dear Julia has been allowed to meet men and women who are not fit companions for a young girl, no matter how interesting they may be to the general public.   Only
yesterday

yesterday she told me she was well acquainted with Mr. Mandeville, the tenor. Mrs. de Trappe, it seems, frequently invites him to dinner. Still, Julia herself is very sensible, and the family is of extraordinary antiquity.

Soame. But the mother? If she has not been in the divorce court, it is through no fault of her own.

Lady Dol. [*Biting her lip.*] Mrs. de Trappe is vain and silly, I admit; but as she has at last decided to marry Mr. Banish, the banker, I am hoping she will live in his house at Hampstead, and think a little more about her immortal soul.

Soame. Does Cyril seem at all interested in Miss Julia?

Lady Dol. Cyril has great elegance of mind, and is not very strong in the expression of his feelings one way or the other. But I may say that a deep attachment exists between them.

Soame. A man must have sound wisdom before he can appreciate innocence. But I have no desire to be discouraging, and I hope I may soon have the pleasure of congratulating you all on the wedding. Good-bye.

Lord Dol. What! Must you go?

Soame. Yes. But [*aside to* Lord Dol.] I shall bear in mind what you say. I will do my best. I have an engagement in town to-night. [*Chuckles.*] An amusing one.

Lord Dol. [*With envy.*] Where?

Soame. At the Parnassus.

Lady Dol. [*With a supercilious smile.*] And what is the Parnassus?

Soame. A theatre much favoured by young men who wish to be thought wicked, and by young ladies who *are.* Good-bye, good-bye. [*Shakes hands with* Lord *and* Lady Doldrummond *and goes out.*]

Lady Dol. Thank goodness, he is gone! What a terrible example

example for Cyril. I was on thorns every second lest he should come in. Soame has just those meretricious attractions which appeal to youth and inexperience. That you should encourage such an acquaintance, and even discuss before him such an intimate matter as my hope with regard to Julia, is, perhaps, more painful than astonishing.

Lord Dol. They are both too young to marry. Let them enjoy life while they may.

Lady Dol. Enjoy life? What a degrading suggestion! I have often observed that there is a lurking taste for the vicious in every Doldrummond. [*Picking up* Cyril's *miniature from the table.*] Cyril is pure Bedingfield: my second self!

[*The Butler announces* Mrs. De Trappe, Mr. Arthur Featherleigh, Mr. Banish. Mrs. de Trappe *is a pretty woman with big eyes and a small waist ; she has a trick of biting her under-lip, and looking shocked, as it were, at her own audacity. Her manner is a little effusive, but always well-bred. She does not seem affected, and has something artless, confiding, and pathetic.* Mr. Featherleigh *has a nervous laugh and a gentlemanly appearance ; otherwise inscrutable.* Mr. Banish *is old, well-preserved, rather pompous, and evidently mistakes deportment for dignity.*]

Mrs. de Trappe. [*Kissing* Lady Dol. *on each cheek.*] Dear Edith, I knew we should surprise you. But Mr. Banish and I are house-hunting, and I thought I must run in and see you and Julia, if only for a second. I felt sure you would not mind my bringing Arthur [*indicating* Featherleigh.] He is so lonely at the prospect of my marriage that Mr. Banish and I have promised to keep him always with us. We have known each other so long. How should we spend our evenings without him? James admits they would be tedious, don't you, James. [*Indicating* Banish.]
                                                                    Banish.

Banish. Certainly, my dear.

Lady Dol. [*Stiffly.*] I can well understand that you have learned to regard Mr. Featherleigh as your own son. And as we advance in years, it is so pleasant to have young people about us.

Mrs. de Trappe. [*After a slight pause*] How odd that it should never have struck me in that light before! I have always thought of Arthur as the trustee, as it were, of my poor fatherless Julia. [*To Banish.*] Have I not often said so, James?

Banish. [*Dryly.*] Often. In fact I have always thought that Julia would never lack a father whilst Arthur was alive. But I admit that he is a little young for the responsibility.

Feather. [*Unmoved.*] Do not forget, Violet, that our train leaves in fifty-five minutes.

Lord Dol. [*Catching a desperate glance from* Lady Doldrummond.] Then I shall have time to show you the Russian poodles which the Duke of Camden brought me from Japan.

Mrs. de Trappe. [*Peevishly.*] Yes, please take them away. [*Waving her hand in the direction of* Banish *and* Featherleigh.] Edith and I have many secrets to discuss. Of course she will tell you [*to Lord Dol.*] everything I have said when we are gone, and I shall tell Arthur and James all she has said as we go home. But it is so amusing to think ourselves mysterious for twenty minutes. [*As the men go out laughing, she turns to* Lady Doldrummond *with a sigh.*] Ah, Edith, when I pause in all these gaieties and say to myself, Violet, you are about to marry a second husband, I cannot feel sufficiently thankful that it is not the third.

Lady Dol. The third?

Mrs. de Trappe. To face the possibility of a third honeymoon, a third disappointment, and a third funeral would tax my courage to the utmost! And I am not strong.

Lady

Lady Dol. I am shocked to see you so despondent. Surely you anticipate every happiness with Mr. Banish?

Mrs. de Trappe. Oh, yes. He has money, and Arthur thinks him a very worthy sort of person. He is a little dull, but then middle-class people are always so gross in their air when they attempt to be lively or amusing; so long as they are grave I can bear them well enough, but I know of nothing so unpleasant as the sight of a banker laughing. As Arthur says, City men and butlers should always be serious.

Lady Dol. Do you think that the world will quite understand— Arthur?

Mrs. de Trappe. What do you mean, Edith? A woman must have an adviser. Arthur was my late husband's friend, and he is my future husband's friend. Surely that should be enough to satisfy the most exacting.

Lady Dol. But why marry at all? why not remain as you are?

Mrs. de Trappe. How unreasonable you are, Edith! How often have you urged me to marry Mr. Banish, and now that it is all arranged and Arthur is satisfied, you begin to object.

Lady Dol. I thought that you liked Mr. Banish better.

Mrs. de Trappe. Better than Arthur? No, I am not so unkind as that, nor would James wish it. I am marrying because I am poor. My husband, as you know, left nearly all his money to Julia, and I feel the injustice so acutely that the absurd settlement he made on me is spent upon doctor's bills alone. If it were not for Arthur and one or two other kind friends who send me game and other little things from time to time, I could not exist at all. [*Draws off her gloves, displays a diamond ring on each finger, and wipes her eyes with a point-lace pocket-handkerchief.*] And when I think of all that I endured with De Trappe! How often have I been roused from a sound sleep to see the room illuminated and De

Trappe,

Trappe, rolled up in flannel, sitting by the fire reading " Lead, kindly Light." What an existence! But now tell me about Julia.   I hope she does not give you much trouble.

Lady Dol. I only hope that I may keep her always with me.

Mrs. de Trappe. How she must have improved!   When she is at home I find her so depressing.   And she does not appeal to men in the least.

Lady Dol. I could wish that all young girls were as modest.

Mrs. de Trappe. Oh, I daresay Julia has all the qualities we like to see in some other woman's daughter.   But if you were her mother and had to find her a husband, you would regard her virtues in another light.   Fortunately she has eight thousand a year, so she may be able to find somebody.   Still, even money does not tempt men as it once did.   A girl must have an extraordinary charm.   She is so jealous of me.   I cannot keep her out of the drawing-room when I have got callers, especially when Mr. Mandeville is there.

Lady Dol. I have heard of Mr. Mandeville.   He is an actor, a singer.

Mrs. de Trappe. A lovely tenor voice.   All the women are in love with him, except me.   I would not listen to him.   And now they say he is going to marry Sarah Sparrow—a great mistake.   I should like to know who would care about him or his singing, once he is married.

Lady Dol. And who is Sarah Sparrow ?

Mrs. de Trappe. Don't you know ?   She is the last great success.   She has two notes: B flat and the lower G—the orchestra plays the rest.   You must go to the Parnassus and hear her.   To-night is the dress rehearsal of the new piece.

Lady Dol. And do you receive Miss Sparrow ?

Mrs. de Trappe. No, women take up too much time.   They

say,

say, too, that she is frantically jealous because Mandeville used to come and practise in my boudoir. He says no one can accompany him as I do!

Lady Dol. I hope Cyril does not meet Mr. Mandeville when he goes to your house.

Mrs. de Trappe. Let me see. I believe I introduced them. At any rate, I know I saw them at luncheon together last week.

Lady Dol. At luncheon together! Cyril and this person who sings? What could my boy and Mr. Mandeville have in common?

Mrs. de Trappe. They both appear to admire Sarah Sparrow very much. And I cannot find what men see in her. She is not tall and her figure is most innocent; you would say she was still in pinafores. As for her prettiness, I admit she has fine eyes, but of course she blackens them. I think the great attraction is her atrocious temper. One never knows whom she will stab next.

Lady Dol. [*Half to herself.*] Last week Cyril came in after midnight. He refused to answer my questions.

Mrs. de Trappe. You seem absent-minded, my dear Edith. [*Pause.*] I must be going now. Where are Arthur and James? We have not a moment to lose. We are going to choose wedding presents. James is going to choose Arthur's and Arthur is going to choose James's, so there can be no jealousy. It was I who thought of that way out of the difficulty. One does one's best to be nice to them, and then something happens and upsets all one's plans. Where is Cyril?

Lady Dol. I am afraid Cyril is not at home.

Mrs. de Trappe. Then I shall not see him. Tell him I am angry, and give my love to Julia. I hope she does not disturb you when you are in the drawing-room and have visitors. So difficult to keep a grown-up girl out of the drawing-room. Where can those men be. [*Enter* Lord Doldrummond, Mr. Featherleigh,

leigh, *and* Mr. Banish.] Ah! here they are. Now, come along; we haven't a moment to lose. Good-bye, Edith.

> [*Exeunt (after wishing their adieux)* Mrs. de Trappe, Mr. Featherleigh, *and* Mr. Banish, Lord Doldrummond *following them.*]

Lady Dol. [*Stands alone in the middle of the room, repeating.*] Cyril and—Sarah Sparrow! My son and Sarah Sparrow! And he has met her through the one woman for whom I have been wrong enough to forget my prejudices. What a punishment!

> [Julia *enters cautiously. She is so unusually beautiful that she barely escapes the terrible charge of sublimity. But there is a certain peevishness in her expression which adds a comfortable smack of human nature to her classic features.*]

Julia. I thought mamma would never go. I have been hiding in your boudoir ever since I heard she was here.

Lady Dol. Was Cyril with you?

Julia. Oh, no; he has gone out for a walk.

Lady Dol. Tell me, dearest, have you and Cyril had any disagreement lately? Is there any misunderstanding?

Julia. Oh, no. [*Sighs.*]

Lady Dol. I remember quite well that before I married Herbert he often suffered from the oddest moods of depression. Several times he entreated me to break off the engagement. His affection was so reverential that he feared he was not worthy of me. I assure you I had the greatest difficulty in overcoming his scruples, and persuading him that whatever his faults were I could help him to subdue them.

Julia. But Cyril and I are not engaged. It is all so uncertain, so humiliating.

Lady

Lady Dol. Men take these things for granted. If the truth were known, I daresay he already regards you as his wife.

Julia. [*With an inspired air.*] Perhaps that is why he treats me so unkindly. I have often thought that if he were my husband he could not be more disagreeable! He has not a word for me when I speak to him. He does not hear. Oh, Lady Doldrummond, I know what is the matter. He is in love, but I am not the one. You are all wrong.

Lady Dol. No, no, no. He loves you; I am sure of it. Only be patient with him and it will come all right. Hush! is that his step? Stay here, darling, and I will go into my room and write letters. [*Exit, brushing the tears from her eyes.*]

[Butler *ushers in* Mr. Mandeville. *Neither of them perceive* Julia, *who has gone to the window.*]

Butler. His Lordship will be down in half an hour, sir. He is now having his hair brushed.

Julia. [*In surprise as she looks round.*] Mr. Mandeville! [*Pause.*] I hardly expected to meet you here.

Mandeville. And why, may I ask?

Julia. You know what Lady Doldrummond is. How did you overcome her scruples?

Mandeville. Is my reputation then so very bad?

Julia. You—you are supposed to be rather dangerous. You sing on the stage, and have a tenor voice.

Mandeville. Is that enough to make a man dangerous?

Julia. How can *I* tell? But mamma said you were invincible. You admire mamma, of course. [*Sighs.*]

Mandeville. A charming woman, Mrs. de Trappe. A very interesting woman; so sympathetic.

Julia. But she said she would not listen to you.

Mandeville·

Mandeville. Did she say that? [*A slight pause.*] I hope you will not be angry when I own that I do not especially *admire* your mother. A quarter of a century ago she may have had considerable attractions, but—are you offended?

Julia. Offended? Oh, no. Only it seems strange. I thought that all men admired mamma. [*Pause.*] You have not told me yet how you made Lady Doldrummond's acquaintance.

Mandeville. I am here at Lord Aprile's invitation. He has decided that he feels no further need of Lady Doldrummonds' apron-strings.

Julia. Oh, Mr. Mandeville, are you teaching him to be wicked?

Mandeville. But you will agree with me that a young man cannot make his mother a kind of scribbling diary?

Julia. Still, if he spends his time well, there does not seem to be any reason why he should refuse to say where he dines when he is not at home.

Mandeville. Lady Doldrummond holds such peculiar ideas; she would find immorality in a sofa-cushion. If she were to know that Cyril is coming with me to the dress rehearsal of our new piece!

Julia. It would break her heart. And Lord Doldrummond would be indignant. Mamma says his own morals are so excellent!

Mandeville. Is he an invalid?

Julia. Certainly not. Why do you ask?

Mandeville. Whenever I hear of a charming husband I always think that he *must* be an invalid. But as for morals, there can be no harm in taking Cyril to a dress rehearsal. If you do not wish him to go, however, I can easily say that the manager does not care to have strangers present. [*Pause.*] Afterwards there is to be a ball at Miss Sparrow's.

Julia.

Julia. Is Cyril going there, too?

Mandeville. I believe that he has an invitation, but I will persuade him to refuse it, if you would prefer him to remain at home.

Julia. You are very kind, Mr. Mandeville, but it is a matter of indifference to me where Lord Aprile goes.

Mandeville. Perhaps I ought not to have mentioned this to you?

Julia. [*Annoyed.*] It does not make the least difference. In fact, I am delighted to think that you are taking Cyril out into the world. He is wretched in this house. [*With heroism.*] I am glad to think that he knows any one so interesting and clever and beautiful as Sarah Sparrow. I suppose she would be considered beautiful?

Mandeville. [*With a profound glance.*] One can forget her— sometimes.

Julia. [*Looking down.*] Perhaps—when I am as old as she is— I shall be prettier than I am at present.

Mandeville. You always said you liked my voice. We never see anything of each other now. I once thought that—well— that you might like me better. Are you sure you are not angry with me because I am taking Cyril to this rehearsal?

Julia. Quite sure. Why should I care where Cyril goes? I only wish that I, too, might go to the theatre to-night. What part do you play? And what do you sing? A serenade?

Mandeville. [*Astounded.*] Yes. How on earth did you guess that? The costume is, of course, picturesque, and that is the great thing in an opera. A few men can sing—after a fashion—but to find the right clothes to sing *in*—that shows the true artist.

Julia. And Sarah; does she look *her* part?

Mandeville. Well, I do not like to say anything against her,

but

but she is not quite the person I should cast for la Marquise de la Perdrigonde. Ah! if you were on the stage, Miss de Trappe! You have just the exquisite charm, the grace, the majesty of bearing which, in the opinion of those who have never been to Court, is the peculiar distinction of women accustomed to the highest society.

Julia. Oh, I should like to be an actress!

Mandeville. No! no! I spoke selfishly—if you only acted with *me*, it would be different; but—but I could not bear to see another man making love to you—another man holding your hand and singing into your eyes—and—and Oh——, this is madness. You must not listen to me.

Julia. I am not—angry, but—you must never again say things which you do not mean. If I thought you were untruthful it would make me so—so miserable. Always tell me the truth. [*Holds out her hand.*]

Mandeville. You are very beautiful!

[*She drops her eyes, smiles, and wanders unconsciously to the mirror.*]

[Lady Doldrummond *suddenly enters from the boudoir, and* Cyril *from the middle door.* Cyril *is handsome, but his features have that delicacy and his expression that pensiveness which promise artistic longings and domestic disappointment.*]

Cyril. [*Cordially and in a state of suppressed excitement.*] Oh, mother, this is my friend Mandeville. You have heard me mention him?

Lady Dol. I do not remember, but——

Cyril. When I promised to go out with you this afternoon, I forgot that I had another engagement. Mandeville has been kind enough to call for me.

Lady

Lady Dol. Another engagement, Cyril?

[*Lord Doldrummond enters and comes down, anxiously looking from one to the other.*]

Cyril. Father, this is my friend Mandeville. We have arranged to go up to town this afternoon.

Lady Dol. [*Calmly.*] What time shall I send the carriage to the station for you? The last train usually arrives about——

Cyril. I shall not return to-night. I intend to stay in town. Mandeville will put me up.

Lord Dol. And where are you going?

Mandeville. He is coming to our dress rehearsal of the " Dandy and the Dancer."

Cyril. At the Parnassus. [*Lord and Lady Doldrummond exchange horrified glances.*] I daresay you have never heard of the place, but it amuses me to go there, and I must learn life for myself. I am two-and-twenty, and it is not extraordinary that I should wish to be my own master. I intend to have chambers of my own in town.

Lady Dol. Surely you have every liberty in this house?

Lord Dol. If you leave us, you will leave the rooms in which your mother has spent every hour of her life, since the day you were born, planning and improving. Must all her care and thought go for nothing? The silk hangings in your bedroom she worked with her own hands. There is not so much as a penwiper in your quarter of the house which she did not choose with the idea of giving you one more token of her affection.

Cyril. I am not ungrateful, but I cannot see much of the world through my mother's embroidery. As you say, I have every comfort here. I may gorge at your expense and snore on your pillows and bully your servants. I can do everything, in fact, but
live.

live.   Dear mother, be reasonable. [*Tries to kiss her.   She remains quite frigid.*]

[Footman *enters.*]

Footman. The dog-cart is at the door, my lord.

Cyril. You think it well over and you will see that I am perfectly right.   Come on, Mandeville, we shall miss the train. Make haste: there is no time to be polite.   [*He goes out, dragging* Mandeville *after him, and ignoring* Julia.]

Lord Dol. Was that my son?   I am ashamed of him!   To desert us in this rude, insolent, heartless manner.   If I had whipped him more and loved him less, he would not have been leaving me to lodge with a God knows who.   I disown him! The fool!

Lady Dol. If you have anything to say, blame *me !*   Cyril has the noblest heart in the world; *I* am the fool.

Curtain.

A Study. *Sir Frederick Leighton, P.R.A.*

L'Education Sentimentale. *Aubrey Beardsley*

Portrait of a Gentleman. *Will Rothenstein*

The Reflected Faun. *Laurence Housman*

Portrait of Mrs. Patrick Campbell. *Aubrey Beardsley*

Portrait of a Lady.   *Charles W Furse*

The Renaissance of Venus.   *Walter Crane*

Garçons de Café. *Aubrey Beardsley*

Portrait of Himself.   *P. Wilson Steer*

Portrait of Henry James.   *John S. Sargent, A.R.A.*

The Old Bedford Music Hall. *Walter Sickert*

Portrait of Aubrey Beardsley. *Walter Sickert*

La Dame aux Camélias.   *Aubrey Beardsley*

Charley's Aunt. *Walter Sickert*

Skirt-Dancing. *P. Wilson Steer*

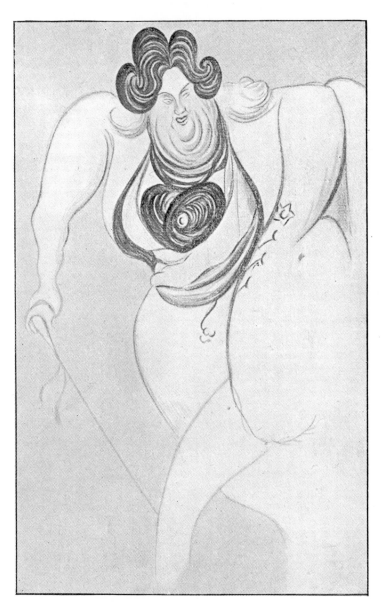

George the Fourth. *Max Beerbohm*

Mr. Richard Le Gallienne. *Walter Sickert*

Portrait of Mr. George Moore. *Walter Sickert*

Mr. John Davidson. *Will Rothenstein*

The Mysterious Rose Garden. *Aubrey Beardsley*

Study of Durham.   *F. G. Cotman*

The Mirror.   *P. Wilson Steer*

Portrait of a Girl. *Robert Halls*

A Sketch. *Constantin Guys*

The Yellow Book. *Gertrude D. Hammond*

Souvenir de Paris. *Charles Conder*

Portrait of Kenneth Grahame.   *E. A. Walton*

A Barb. *John Lavery*

COME UNTO THESE YELLOW SANDS
AND THEN TAKE HANDS.
COURTSIED WHEN YE HAVE & KISS'D
THE WILD WAVES WHIST,
FOOT IT FEATLY HERE & THERE;
& SWEET SPRITES THE BURTHEN BEAR

" Come unto these Yellow Sands." *H. Isabel Adams*

The Dew. *J. Herbert McNair*

The Butterflies.   *D. Y. Cameron*

" So the wind drove us on to the cavern of gloom,
    Where we fell in the toils of the foul sea-snake;
Their scaly folds drew us on to our doom,
    Pray for us, stranger, for Christ's sweet sake."

Patten Wilson.

Portrait of Miss Evelyn Sharp.　*E. A. Walton*

Grief. *A. Szold*

Old Houses off the Dry Gate, Glasgow.   *Muirhead Bone*

A Shepherd Boy. *E. Philip Pimlott*